MATTHEW

The King and His Kingdom

STUDY SET

JEFF CAVINS AND SARAH CHRISTMYER

West Chester, Pennsylvania

Nihil obstat: Rev. Msgr. Joseph G. Prior, S.T.D.
Censor Librorum
June 12, 2007

Imprimatur: +Justin Cardinal Rigali
Archbishop of Philadelphia
June 18, 2007

Matthew: The King and His Kingdom is a resource of *The Great Adventure* Catholic Bible Study Program.

Jeff Cavins, General Editor, *The Great Adventure* Catholic Bible Study Program, and Presenter, *Matthew: The King and His Kingdom*
Sarah Christmyer, Editor, *The Great Adventure* Catholic Bible Study Program, Author, *Matthew: The King and His Kingdom*

Ascension
Post Office Box 1990
West Chester, PA 19380
1-800-376-0520
ascensionpress.com

Cover design: Devin Schadt

Printed in the United States of America

ISBN 978-1-935940-79-1

MATTHEW

The King and His Kingdom

Questions

Responses

Welcome to *The Great Adventure*

"To fall in love with God is the greatest of all romances; to seek him, the greatest adventure."

– St. Augustine

The Bible is at the heart of our Catholic Faith—and our relationship with God. It is the living Word of God, where our Father meets with us and lovingly speaks to us. Reading the Bible should bring us closer to Christ, but understanding it is not always easy. Many people tell us they have tried time and again to prayerfully read Scripture, but they get frustrated because they "just don't get it."

The Great Adventure is designed so that anyone can make sense of the Bible and experience the life-changing power of God's Word. At the core of *The Great Adventure* is the concept that there is a story running through the seventy-three books of the Bible that ties all of Scripture together and makes sense not just of the Bible, but of our lives as well.

That story is God's plan as it has unfolded throughout salvation history and continues to unfold today. Once we grasp this "big picture," the readings at Mass begin to make more sense, our Scripture reading and study come to life, and we see how our lives fit into God's loving plan.

Hundreds of thousands of participants have discovered the riches of Scripture by experiencing one or more *Great Adventure* Bible studies. It is our prayer that you will gain a newfound understanding of God's Word that will transform your life and bring you closer to Christ.

Jeff Cavins, Creator & President, *The Great Adventure*
Sarah Christmyer, Co-developer & Author, *The Great Adventure*

About *The Great Adventure* Catholic Bible Study Program

At the core of *The Great Adventure* is *The Bible Timeline* Learning System: a simple way to get the "big picture" of the Bible by focusing on the story that runs throughout Sacred Scripture. *Great Adventure* Bible studies explore the biblical narrative in light of Catholic teaching and the historical, cultural, and literary context of the Scriptures to discover what Scripture reveals about God's plan and our place within it. Studies of individual books of the Bible are supplemented by thematic and "life application" studies.

Every *Great Adventure* study is designed to foster:

- Familiarity with the Bible and ease of reading it
- Bible study habits consistent with the guidelines of the Catholic Church
- Personal engagement in the Word of God
- Faith sharing based on the Word of God
- Growth in knowledge about Scripture and the Catholic Faith

About *Matthew: The King and His Kingdom*

Matthew: The King and His Kingdom shows how Jesus, the promised Messiah, relives the life and struggles of Israel to become the faithful and victorious King. You will come to see Jesus in a new way and discover what his life and teachings mean for us today. Matthew is an ideal follow-up to the basic narrative of Scripture presented in *The Bible Timeline* study.

Materials

Materials for *Matthew: The King and His Kingdom* include:

- **Study Set.** Contains session summaries, home reading assignments, engaging study questions, responses to the questions, talk notes for the video presentations, as well as helpful maps, charts, and diagrams. *(You will need one Study Set for every participant, study leader, and small-group facilitator.)*
- **Video Presentations** (twenty-four, 55-minute sessions). Presented by Jeff Cavins, these twenty-four video presentations provide comprehensive teaching and commentary on the Gospel of Matthew. *(You will need one DVD Set.)*
- ***The Great Adventure* Bible Study Leader's Companion** (free download) provides step-by-step instructions for leaders on planning, promoting, running, and facilitating a Bible study. *(This Leader's Companion is available at ascensionpress.com.)*

In addition, every participant, leader, and small-group facilitator should have a Catholic Bible and the *Catechism of the Catholic Church.* We recommend *The Great Adventure Catholic Bible.*

How the Study Works

Every *Great Adventure* study includes four essential steps, which are designed to fit together and build upon each other. Following these steps in order will help you to get the most out of each session.

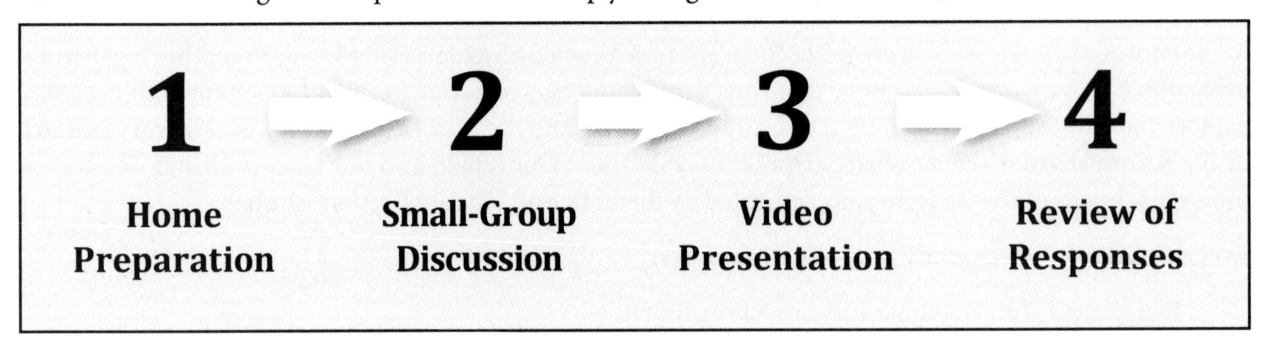

Step 1: Home Preparation

Note: There is no home preparation required for Session 1.

Each session begins with personal study that involves reading Scripture and answering a series of questions that will help you understand and think more deeply about what you have read. Some questions will include additional reading from other parts of the Bible or from the *Catechism of the Catholic Church* to help you consider the passage in light of the bigger picture of salvation history and Catholic teaching.

We recommend that you allow at least 90 minutes to complete the reading and answer the questions for each session. We also suggest that home preparation be done in several sittings over the course of a week. This will help you create a habit of daily Bible reading and prayerful meditation.

Step 2: Small-Group Discussion

The small-group discussion is one of the most effective components of a *Great Adventure* Bible study. During this discussion, members of your small group will have an opportunity to share their insights into the Scripture reading. The goal of the small-group discussion is to help participants obtain a richer understanding of the readings and apply them to their lives. Trained facilitators guide the small-group discussion and keep it on track. To learn how to facilitate a small-group discussion, visit ascensionpress.com. Be sure to follow the "Ten Commandments of Small-Group Discussion" on page xi.

Step 3: Video Presentation

Jeff Cavins wraps up each session with a video presentation that offers unique insights and profound connections to help you gain a deeper understanding of the Bible and its relationship to the Catholic Faith, with a special emphasis on ways to apply what you have learned to your life.

Step 4: Review of Responses

Note: There are no responses for Session 1.

The final step—reviewing the responses at the back of this Study Set—is done at home prior to beginning the reading for the next session. These responses will help you read the Scripture passages for the next session in the proper context.

For the most effective study experience, complete these steps in the following order: (1) Read and answer the questions; (2) discuss them in your small group; (3) view the video presentation; and (4) review the responses. During the discussion, your small-group facilitator will incorporate points found in the responses, but the richness that comes from individual insights can be lost when participants view the responses prior to the discussion.

For more information about how to plan and promote a
Bible study and how to facilitate a small-group discussion,
visit **ascensionpress.com** or call 1-800-376-0520.

Session Outline and Reading Guide

Each session in this Study Set has the following sections. (Note: Session 1 follows a different format.)

1. Session Questions (used during **Step 1: Home Preparation** and **Step 2: Small-Group Discussion**)

A. Establish (or Review) the Context

B. Read the Story

C. Take a Deeper Look

D. Application

2. Session Talk Notes (used during **Step 3: Video Presentation**)

3. Session Responses (used during **Step 4: Review of Responses**)

The following chart offers an overview of the home preparation readings assigned in each session of the study. The main reading is provided in section **B. Read the Story** and should be read before you answer the session questions. Additional Bible readings and *Catechism* readings are provided in section **C. Take a Deeper Look** and should be read as you answer the study questions for each session.

Session (Video Times)	Main Reading	Additional Bible Readings	*Catechism* Readings (CCC)
1. Introduction (49:20)	(none)	(none)	(none)
2. Matthew 1 – Jesus: The Son of David, the Son of Abraham (52:21)	Matthew 1	Genesis 38; Joshua 2:1-16, 6:22-25; Ruth 1:1, 4:13-17; 2 Samuel 6:23; 11; Sirach 46:1-8	430–431, 499–501
3. Matthew 2 – The King in Exile (55:52)	Matthew 2	Numbers 24:15-19; 1 Samuel 16:1, 4-13; Isaiah 11, 60:3-6; Jeremiah 23:5-6; Micah 5:2-4	528, 530
4. Matthew 3 – John: The Forerunner to the King (50:50)	Matthew 3	Joshua 3; 2 Kings 1:8, 5:1, 10-14; Sirach 48:4, 9-10; Malachi 4:5-6; Luke 1:5-36	535–536, 678, 1222–1224, 1265
5. Matthew 4 – The Tempting of the King (56:38)	Matthew 4	Isaiah 9:1-7; Hebrews 4:15-16	85–86, 109–119, 538–540
6. Matthew 5 – The Bar Is Raised by the King (56:53)	Matthew 5	Exodus 20:1-17; Isaiah 42:6-7, 49:5-6; Matthew 6:15	544
7. Matthew 6 – Personal Piety (55:50)	Matthew 6	Philippians 4:6-7	2764, 2803–2854
8. Matthew 7 – Choices in the Kingdom (55:21)	Matthew 7	Deuteronomy 30:15-20; Matthew 6:14-15; 1 Corinthians 4:1-5; James 4:11-12	117, 678
9. Matthew 8 – The King's Power Demonstrated (47:02)	Matthew 8	1 Kings 19:19-21	(none)
10. Matthew 9 – New Wine, New Wineskins (55:57)	Matthew 9	Leviticus 17:11; Isaiah 43:25; Hosea; Mark 2:7; James 5:14-15	(none)
11. Matthew 10 – Jesus Commissions the Twelve (56:23)	Matthew 10	Genesis 3:15; Matthew 4:12-6; 18, 9:9; Luke 22:28-30; Revelation 21:10-14	(none)
12. Matthew 11–12 – Jesus Confronts an Evil Generation (52:41)	Matthew 11–12	Exodus 20:10; 1 Samuel 21:1-6; Sirach 51:23-26; Isaiah 35:4-6; 61:1-2; John 1:11-13, 3:10; 1 John 5:3	679, 994, 1864, 2168–2172
13. Matthew 13 – Parables of the Kingdom (56:16)	Matthew 13	Matthew 7:28; 1 Thessalonians 2:13; Hebrews 4:2	546, 681–682, 827
14. Matthew 14–15 – Instructions to the Twelve (56:31)	Matthew 14–15	Matthew 8:23-27; 14:19; 15:36	1335, 2609–2610
15. Matthew 16 – Jesus Establishes the Church (59:02)	Matthew 16	Genesis 3, 17, 32; Isaiah 22:15-25, 51:1-2; Matthew 4; John 12:24; Romans 8:15-18; Colossians 1:24-26; Revelation 3:7	552–553
16. Matthew 17 –The Transfiguration (54:08)	Matthew 17	Sirach 48; 2 Corinthians 3:18; 2 Peter 1:6-8, 17-18, 4:12-13, 5:10	555
17. Matthew 18 – Characteristics of the Christian Community (59:19)	Matthew 18	John 1:12-13; Galatians 6:1-2	526, 1443–1445, 1461–1463, 2284–2287, 2832–2843

Session (Video Times)	Main Reading	Additional Bible Readings	*Catechism* Readings (CCC)
18. Matthew 19 – Marriage: A Demonstration of God's Love (60:47)	Matthew 19	Genesis 2:20-24; Exodus 20:1-17; Malachi 2:13-16; Matthew 3:1-6; Ephesians 5:31-32	1602–1617
19. Matthew 20–21 – Stepping Down into Greatness (57:23)	Matthew 20–21	1 Kings 1:32-46; 2 Kings 9:13; Psalm 118:22-23; Isaiah 5:1-7, 56:6-12; Jeremiah 8:4-9, 13, 12:10; Hosea 9:10-17; Zechariah 9:9-10; Matthew 16:21, 17:22-23, 26:39, 42	(none)
20. Matthew 22–23 – "Let's Get Real" (57:42)	Matthew 22–23	Deuteronomy 25:5-10; Luke 16:24; John 7:15-19; Acts 7:1-2; Romans 4:12; 1 Corinthians 4:14-16; Philemon 10; Revelation 19:7-9	558
21. Matthew 24–25 – Jesus Predicts the End of an Era (51:09)	Matthew 24–25	Isaiah 13:1, 9-10, 13, 14:4, 12; Ezekiel 32:1-2, 7-8; Matthew 21:13; 23:28	(none)
22. Matthew 26 – The Trial of the Christ (56:16)	Matthew 26	Exodus 12; 24; Psalm 110:1; Daniel 7:1-18; 1 Peter 1:18-19	610, 612–614
23. Matthew 27 – The Passion of the King (56:44)	Matthew 27	Genesis 3:13-24; Psalm 22; Jeremiah 18, 19, 32-33; Zechariah 11:12-13; Matthew 26:75; John 19:1-22; Hebrews 12:18, 21-24, 28	597–598, 1430–1431
24. Matthew 28 and Conclusion – The Triumph of the King (44:53)	Matthew 28	Daniel 7:14; 1 Corinthians 15: 12-24	651–655, 2174–2176

What to Do for Each Session

1. Welcome and Introduction (10 minutes)
2. Small-Group Discussion (40 minutes)
   Note to Study Leaders: There is no small-group discussion for the first week. Instead, use this time to divide participants into small groups of eight to twelve people, ensure that everyone has the study materials, and explain how the study works. Each small group should be led by a trained facilitator.
3. Video Presentation (55 minutes)
4. Closing and Prayer (5 minutes)

Getting the Most Out of This Study

This study will help you understand the Bible in a new way. The "head knowledge" you gain will help you grow in "heart knowledge" as you follow up on what you have learned. The Bible will always remain a mystery, though, and that is part of the beauty of it: We can never exhaust the treasures of Scripture. Fortunately for us, the Bible is not a subject to master; it is a place to encounter the living Word of God.

Whenever you open your Bible to read, *start with prayer,* and place yourself in God's presence. You might take Samuel's prayer as your own: "Speak, LORD, for your servant is listening" (1 Samuel 3:10). When you read, adopt an attitude of listening. Try not to treat Scripture as a text, but as a personal message from God. What is he saying? What does it mean? What does it mean for my life? If you come to the Word focused on having an encounter with the Lord, he will speak to your heart, and you will be transformed.

An Important Note About the Responses to the Study Questions

Responses to the study questions are provided in the back of this Study Set. These responses do not exhaust the meaning that can be found in the Scripture reading. People will have unique insights. The responses have two important functions:

1. The first purpose of the responses is to provide participants with a review of each session, which will help establish a context for the reading and questions in the following session. The best time to read the responses is just before starting on the next session.
2. The second purpose of the responses is to provide guidelines for the small-group facilitators. **Facilitators:** Complete the Scripture reading and answer the questions on your own before reading the responses in preparation for facilitating the small-group discussion.

Participants should not review the responses for each session until after the session is completed. Although it might be tempting to look at these responses in advance, it is important to wait for the following reasons.

1. Bible study is not about simply watching a video presentation or reading a Bible commentary. It is just as important to immerse yourself in the Word of God itself and engage it with your heart and mind. The questions in *The Great Adventure* studies are designed to draw you into the Scriptures so that the Word of God will be planted and grow in your heart. Reading a response written by someone else may satisfy your mind for a moment, but it will not result in the kind of growth that will occur if you attempt to answer the question on your own first.
2. The success of a small group depends on a good discussion. A group of participants who have spent time pondering the Scripture passages on their own will have more varied insights to discuss.

For these reasons, please wait to read the responses until after the session. When you follow the steps of this study as intended, you will explore the Word of God in different ways—in the reading, the small-group discussion, the video presentation, and, finally, in the responses. Follow these steps over time, and you will be more than fed—you will learn to feed yourself.

Ten Commandments of Small-Group Discussion[1]

1. **Enjoy yourself!**
2. **Speak with respect and charity.**
3. **Do not ridicule or dismiss what others say. Keep comments positive.**
4. **Come prepared.**
5. **If you were not able to prepare, let others speak first.**
6. **Stick to the topic and questions at hand.**
7. **Start and end on time.**
8. **Allow silence. Give people a chance to think.**
9. **Listen to others without interrupting.**
10. **Keep personal matters within the group.**

1 Adapted from Thomas Smith's original "10 Commandments of a Small Group."

Matthew: The King and His Kingdom

This study of Matthew's Gospel is the second step in the Foundational Series of *The Great Adventure* Catholic Bible Study Program.

Author

The author of Matthew's Gospel is not mentioned in the Gospel itself; neither are the authors of the other Gospels mentioned in their texts. But the early Church knew who was responsible for each Gospel and titled them accordingly. In modern times, some scholars have questioned whether Matthew is the author of this Gospel, but his authorship has been the uncontested and unanimous opinion of the Church for nearly eighteen hundred years.

Not much is known about Matthew, also called "Levi." He was a tax collector before answering Jesus' call to discipleship. Like many tax collectors of the time, he may also have been a scribe. Matthew once hosted a feast for Jesus and was later chosen by Jesus to be one of his twelve apostles. The only other time he is mentioned in the New Testament is at Pentecost, when he is recorded as being present in the Upper Room.

Date and Language of Composition

The Gospel of Matthew was written between AD 50 and 100. For some time, the consensus has been that Matthew based his Gospel on Mark's Gospel and wrote around AD 80–90. Most New Testament commentaries take this view, but there is also a strong minority view that Matthew's was the earliest Gospel and was written prior to the destruction of Jerusalem in AD 70. This view is supported by the text itself: In Chapter 24, Matthew records Jesus' prophecy of the destruction of Jerusalem. If Matthew had been writing after this prophecy was fulfilled, it is hard to understand why he would not have used this historical event to strengthen the main theme of his Gospel, which is that the Old Covenant would be fulfilled in the New Covenant.

According to Papias (AD 130) and Irenaeus (AD 180), Matthew's Gospel was originally written in Hebrew or Aramaic. This version, which no longer exists, was then translated into the canonical Greek version.

Audience

Matthew most likely wrote his Gospel to Jewish Christians living in and around Palestine. The book assumes that its readers have knowledge of Jewish customs and practices and an intimate familiarity with the Old Testament. Matthew's Gospel quotes or refers to the Old Testament more than one hundred times and reveals the true spiritual meaning of these passages as fulfilled in Jesus Christ.

Structure

The structure of Matthew's Gospel is similar to the Pentateuch. It has five main sections, which we call "books." Each includes a "narrative" section and a "discourse" section, a pattern that weaves together the words and works of Jesus in a way that is easy to remember. These five books come between Jesus' ancestry and infancy narratives (called the "Prologue") and his passion, death, and resurrection narratives (called the "Conclusion"). See the diagram and Outline below for more information on these sections.

Outline

	Prologue	Book 1	Book 2	Book 3	Book 4	Book 5	Conclusion
	Birth of the King	*Announcement of the Kingdom*	*Establishment of the Kingdom*	*The Kingdom Defined*	*Transfer of the Kingdom's Authority*	*Announcement of the End of the Old Kingdom*	*Victory of the King*
NARRATIVE	Mt. 1–2 *Jesus' ancestry and infancy*	Mt. 3–4 *John the Baptist and Jesus' early ministry*	Mt. 8–9 *Miracles; commissioning the Twelve*	Mt. 11–12 *Jesus confronts an evil generation*	Mt. 14–17 *Travels and ministry; instructing the Twelve*	Mt. 19–23 *Events and teaching in Judea*	Mt. 26–28 *Passion week*
DISCOURSE		Mt. 5–7 *Sermon on the Mount*	Mt. 10 *Missionary instructions*	Mt. 13 *Kingdom parables*	Mt. 18 *Life in the Christian community*	Mt. 24–25 *Olivet Discourse (Judgment on Jerusalem)*	

Prologue – Birth of the King (Jesus' ancestry and infancy: Matthew 1–2)

Narrative: Jesus' ancestry and infancy

- Book One – Announcement of the Kingdom (Matthew 3–7)

  Narrative: John the Baptist and Jesus' early ministry (Matthew 3–4)

  Discourse: Sermon on the Mount (Matthew 5–7)

- Book Two – Establishment of the Kingdom (Matthew 8–10)

  Narrative: Miracles; commissioning the Twelve (Matthew 8–9)

  Discourse: Missionary instructions (Matthew 10)

- Book Three – The Kingdom Defined (Matthew 11–13)

  Narrative: Jesus confronts an evil generation (Matthew 11–12)

  Discourse: Kingdom parables (Matthew 13)

- Book Four – Transfer of the Kingdom's Authority (Matthew 14–18)

  Narrative: Travels and ministry; instructing the Twelve (Matthew 14–17)

  Discourse: Life in the Christian community (Matthew 18)

- Book Five – Announcement of the End of the Old Kingdom (Matthew 19–25)

  Narrative: Events and teaching in Judea (Matthew 19–23)

  Discourse: Olivet Discourse: Judgment on Jerusalem (Matthew 24–25)

Conclusion – Victory of the King (Matthew 26–28)

Narrative: Passion week

Historical Perspective and Context

The book of Matthew acts as a bridge between the Old Testament and the New Testament. Using many references to the Old Testament promises of God to his people and the messages he sent them through the prophets, the book of Matthew gives us the key to understanding the rest of the New Testament and Christ as the fulfillment of God's plan. Matthew's genealogy of Christ in Chapter 1 does not make reference to the return of God's people to the Promised Land following their time in Babylonian captivity (see verses 11-12).[1] In his teaching in the Gospel of Matthew, Jesus makes it clear that Judah has not yet returned from spiritual captivity, even though some of the people have physically returned to the land. At the time of Jesus' teaching and ministry, God's people were waiting for the Messiah to liberate them. They thought this liberation would be in the form of freedom from Roman domination. Jesus did come to liberate the people, but he came to liberate them *from their sin.*

Matthew portrays Jesus as the true King who fulfills the Law the people of Israel have failed to keep. All things find new meaning in Christ. He gives the new law, establishes a new leadership, and builds a new Temple. The message of change in Matthew's Gospel is difficult for the Jewish leadership to accept, but it is good news for God's people and for the Gentiles as well.

Jesus shows the people in his teaching that they have relaxed the Law because of their hardness of heart. He "raises the bar" by changing the standars that will be used to judge the people after their return from spiritual exile. He introduces the new law that will acompany the New Covenant. This message is a timeless one. When we examine our own lives, most of us see areas in which we expect less of ourselves than God expects of us. If we read this Gospel carefully, we will see that Jesus is challenging and empowering us to a new level of holiness. To live out the gospel, we must be thoroughly immersed in the kingdom of heaven on earth (the Church).

1 The events of the Return can be found in the yellow section of *The Bible Timeline* Chart.

Geography

The following maps will help you better understand the events in Matthew's Gospel.

Palestine at the Time of Christ

Jesus' Galilean Ministry

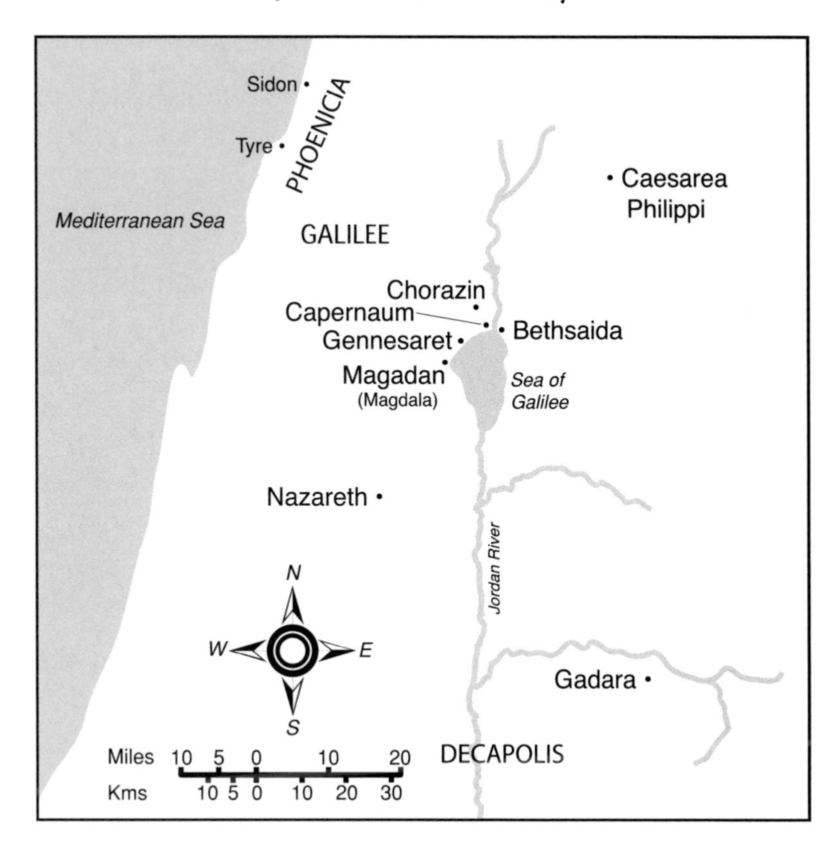

Ministry in Judea

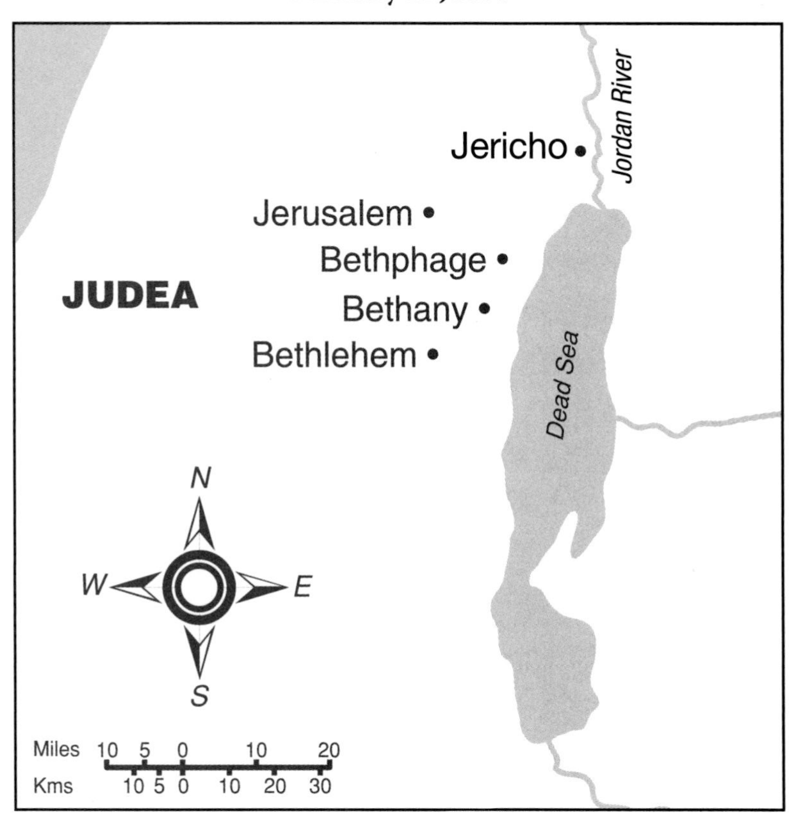

Focus of this Study

Matthew portrays Jesus Christ as the fulfillment of Scripture, the true Messiah sent from God, the One the Jews and all of Israel have been waiting for.

The focus of this study will be the establishment of the Church as the kingdom of heaven on earth. The disciples are given special roles in the kingdom, with Peter in a special place of primacy. Throughout the Gospel of Matthew, Jesus fulfills the Old Testament covenants God made with Abraham, Moses, and David. Jesus fulfills God's promise to Abraham to bless "all the nations of the earth." Jesus is cast in the role of the "new Moses" who ascends a new mountain to give the New Covenant law. He is seen as the "Son of David," sitting on his everlasting throne.

May God richly bless you as you study his Word in Matthew's Gospel.

Reminder: Please complete the Scripture reading and study questions for Session 2 before the next small-group discussion.

Session 1 Talk Notes

Introduction

I. Scripture and Catholic Life

A. Which Bible?

1. New American Bible (NAB)

2. Revised Standard Version–Catholic Edition (RSV-CE)

3. "Ignorance of Scripture is ignorance of Christ" (CCC 133)

B. Two senses of Scripture (CCC 115–117)

1. Literal sense

2. Spiritual sense

a. Allegorical – Christ

b. Moral – me

c. Anagogical – future

C. Interpreting Scripture as a Catholic (CCC 112–114)

1. Context and unity of whole Scripture

2. Living Tradition of the Church

3. Analogy of faith – coherence of truths

D. Application of Scripture study

1. Put into practice

2. Psalm 1 – "blessed" (Heb., *ashrei;* literally, "happy")

3. *Lectio divina* ("divine reading")

4. "Be doers of the word" (James 1:22-24)

II. *Matthew: The King and His Kingdom* – Overview

A. First of four Gospels

B. Author

1. Not identified in the Gospel

2. Traditional understanding – Matthew (Levi)

a. Tax collector, called by Jesus; apostle (Mark 2:14; Luke 5:27; Matthew 9:9)

b. Present at Pentecost (Acts 1:3)

3. Martyred

C. Date

1. Difficult to determine
2. Likely prior to destruction of Temple in AD 70 (Pontifical Biblical Commission, 1911)

D. Style

1. Past events have enduring significance for the Church
2. Matthew 24 foretells destruction of the Temple

E. Audience

1. Jewish
2. Assumed knowledge of Old Testament

F. Focus

1. Christ as fulfillment of Scripture – true Messiah
2. Establishment of Church (kingdom of heaven on earth)

G. Structure (similar to Pentateuch with five divisions)

1. Prologue: Birth of the King (Matthew 1–2)
2. Five sections, "books" – each with a narrative followed by a discourse
   a. Book One: Announcement of the Kingdom (Matthew 3–7)
   b. Book Two: Establishment of the Kingdom (Matthew 8–10)
   c. Book Three: The Kingdom Defined (Matthew 11–13)
   d. Book Four: Transfer of the Kingdom's Authority (Matthew 14–18)
   e. Book Five: Announcement of the End of the Old Kingdom (Matthew 19–25)
3. Conclusion: Victory of the King (Matthew 26–28)

III. Tips for Approaching this Study

A. Stay committed to the small group

B. Take time to do the session questions, and come prepared to discuss them

C. Session sections: "A. Establish (Review) the Context," "B. Read the Story," "C. Take a Deeper Look" (questions), and "D. Application"

D. Pace yourself

E. Familiarize yourself with *The Bible Timeline* Chart

Matthew 1 – Jesus: The Son of David, the Son of Abraham

	Prologue	Book 1	Book 2	Book 3	Book 4	Book 5	Conclusion
	Birth of the King	*Announcement of the Kingdom*	*Establishment of the Kingdom*	*The Kingdom Defined*	*Transfer of the Kingdom's Authority*	*Announcement of the End of the Old Kingdom*	*Victory of the King*
NARRATIVE	**Mt. 1–2** ***Jesus' ancestry and infancy***	Mt. 3–4 *John the Baptist and Jesus' early ministry*	Mt. 8–9 *Miracles; commissioning the Twelve*	Mt. 11–12 *Jesus confronts an evil generation*	Mt. 14–17 *Travels and ministry; instructing the Twelve*	Mt. 19–23 *Events and teaching in Judea*	Mt. 26–28 *Passion week*
DISCOURSE		Mt. 5–7 *Sermon on the Mount*	Mt. 10 *Missionary instructions*	Mt. 13 *Kingdom parables*	Mt. 18 *Life in the Christian community*	Mt. 24–25 *Olivet Discourse (Judgment on Jerusalem)*	

A. Establish the Context

During this first week, read the entire Gospel of Matthew. Do not spend too much time; read through it quickly. Aim for overall impressions rather than trying to absorb everything you read. This will give you the "big picture" you need before you focus on the details. As you read, think about the following questions:

- What were your first impressions?
- What stood out to you about Jesus or his mission?
- What key words or ideas did you notice?
- Are there any concepts you would like clarified or questions you would like answered in the course of this study?

B. Read the Story

Carefully read **Matthew 1.** Ask yourself the questions: *Who? What? When? Where? How? Why?*

As always, pray before you read.

C. Take a Deeper Look

Answering these questions will draw you into the heart of the story. If you do not understand something, make a note of it to bring up in the small-group discussion.

The Genealogy of Jesus Christ (Matthew 1:1-17)

1. Matthew is writing to Jewish Christians living in Palestine. Recall what you learned in Session 1. In writing to this group, why do you think Matthew begins his Gospel with a genealogy of Jesus?

The Difference Between Matthew's and Luke's Genealogies

There are two genealogies of Jesus found in the New Testament. Matthew begins his genealogy with Abraham, most likely because of God's promise to Abraham—"Kings shall come forth from you" (Genesis 17:6). His genealogy also establishes Jesus as heir to the Davidic throne, which God promised would last forever (see 2 Samuel 7:16). Luke's genealogy begins with Jesus and goes all the way back to "Adam, the son of God," probably to emphasize the universal nature of Jesus' kingship. Many theories have been proposed to explain the discrepancies between these two genealogies. It is possible that one list reflects legal descent and the other reflects natural descent. (Note: As the foster son of Joseph, Jesus would have received the same legal rights as a natural child.)

2. What titles does Matthew give Jesus in verse 1, and what do these titles say about him?

3. Matthew includes four women in Jesus' genealogy: Tamar (verse 3), Rahab (verse 5), Ruth (verse 5), and "the wife of Uriah" who was Bathsheba (verse 6). Do you recognize these names?

   a. Read about these women in the following verses and record what you learn.

      Genesis 38:

      Joshua 2:1-16 and 6:22-25:

      Ruth 1:1-22 and 4:13-17:

      2 Samuel 11:

   b. What is unusual about these women? Why do you think Matthew draws attention to them in Jesus' genealogy?

4. **Think About It:** This genealogy is divided into three distinct groups of fourteen names. The first group ends with David, the second with the deportation to Babylon, and the third with the birth of Jesus Christ. Why do you think Matthew draws attention to the deportation but not to Judah's return to the land of Canaan? (For help with this question, review Session 1.)

The Birth of the King (Matthew 1:18-25)

5. In **verses 21 and 23,** what names does Matthew say will be given to the new child, and what is the significance of these names? (For help with the first name, see **CCC 430–431.**)

6. **Think About It:** "Jesus" is the Greek equivalent of the Hebrew name "Joshua" ("Yahweh saves").

   a. Who was Joshua? (There is a good synopsis of his life in **Sirach 46:1-8.**)

   b. How is Jesus a "new Joshua" in a spiritual sense?

7. Consider the names for the Messiah found in Matthew 1, including "Christ," "Son of David," "Son of Abraham," "Jesus," and "Emmanuel." Do any of these names seem particularly appropriate in your own experience of God's Son?

8. Some people interpret verse 25, which says that Joseph "knew [Mary] not until she had borne a son," as meaning that the Holy Couple had sexual relations after Jesus was born. Here, the word "until" has been translated from the Greek word *heos,* which is used elsewhere in the Bible to indicate a discrete period of time and which does not necessarily imply any change in the future. For example, we read in **2 Samuel 6:23** that, "Michal the daughter of Saul had no child to the day of her death." Just as in Matthew 1:25, the word "to" in this passage has been translated from the Greek word *heos.* Read **CCC 499–501.** What does the Magisterium teach about Mary's virginity?

D. Application

These questions will help you apply one of the key themes of the session to your life. After meditating on them, respond to God with a brief written prayer if you choose.

Meditate on the significance of Jesus Christ as "Emmanuel"—"God with us." How is Christ still with us today? If it is sometimes hard for you to believe God is with you, is there anything in this session that might help increase your faith?

Dear Lord …

Session 2 Talk Notes

Matthew 1 – Jesus: The Son of David, the Son of Abraham

I. Matthew's Gospel Begins with a Genealogy (Matthew 1:1-17)

A. Christ as a new beginning
   1. "Genealogy" (Gk., Septuagint uses same word for "Genesis")
   2. Genesis 5:1 – "the generations of Adam"

B. Jesus comes from the lines of David and Abraham (two key Old Testament covenants)
   1. Abraham (Genesis 12 and 15–22)
   2. David (2 Samuel 7)

C. Genealogies are used to make a point

D. Pattern of Jesus' genealogy (verse 17) – three groups of fourteen (equals six groups of seven)
   1. 1:2-6 – Abraham up to David
   2. 1:7-11 – David up to the deportation to Babylon
   3. 1:12-16 – deportation up to Jesus
   4. Jesus begins the seventh "seven" (see Galatians 4:4)

E. Importance of numbers in Judaism
   1. Jewish alphabet of twenty-two consonants used for numbering
   2. David in Hebrew is "DVD" of 4+6+4=14
   3. Importance of David – glory days of Israel; promised eternal throne
      a. Jesus is the Son of David

F. Third set of fourteen years begins with the deportation to Babylon
   1. Kingdom divided in 930 BC
   2. Northern tribes deported to Assyria in 722 BC
   3. Southern tribes deported to Babylon in 587 BC
   4. Genealogy does not mention return, restoration from exile
      a. Daniel 9 – exile will be extended seventy times seven years
      b. In Jesus' view, Israel is still in exile

G. Inclusion of women in Matthew's genealogy
   1. Four "shady ladies"
      a. Tamar – pregnant by father-in-law, Judah
      b. Rahab – Canaanite prostitute
      c. Ruth – Moabite married to a Jew
      d. "Wife of Uriah" – bore Solomon, the illegitimate son of David

2. Inclusion of sinners and Gentiles in the family of God

H. Parallels to the life of Israel

1. Jacob as the father of both the Old and New Testament Josephs
2. Moses' sister, Miriam = Mary

II. The Birth of Jesus (Matthew 1:18-25)

A. Betrothal

1. Period between covenant of marriage and living together
2. Terminable only by death or divorce
3. Who did Joseph think was the unworthy partner?
    a. Suspicion theory – Joseph suspects Mary of adultery and seeks to divorce her (Deuteronomy 24:2)
    b. Reverence theory – Joseph is informed of divine miracle and considers *himself* unworthy

B. Parallels between Old and New Testament Josephs

1. Same name (Matthew 1:18; Genesis 30:24)
2. Fathers named Jacob (Matthew 1:16; Genesis 30:19-24)
3. God spoke to them through dreams (Matthew 1:20-21; Genesis 37:5-11)
4. Righteous and chaste (Matthew 1:19; Genesis 39:7-18)
5. Saved family by bringing them to Egypt

C. Five "formula quotations" in Matthew; first formula quotation is in 1:23

1. A virgin shall conceive and bear a son, Emmanuel, "God with us"
    a. Isaiah 7:14
    b. Matthew 28:19-20
2. Literal sense – birth of King Hezekiah (2 Kings 18:1-6)
3. Allegorical sense: fullness in Christ

D. Jesus = "God saves" (verse 21) – from sin and exile; releases us from bondage

E. "Knew her not until she had borne a son" (verse 25)

1. Catholic teaching – Mary is a perpetual virgin
2. "Until" – Greek, *heos*, "to" or "until" (no implied change in future)
    a. See 2 Samuel 6:23 and 1 Timothy 4:13
3. "Brothers and sisters" = same word for cousins, distant relatives

Session 3 – Questions

Matthew 2 – The King in Exile

	Prologue	Book 1	Book 2	Book 3	Book 4	Book 5	Conclusion
	Birth of the King	*Announcement of the Kingdom*	*Establishment of the Kingdom*	*The Kingdom Defined*	*Transfer of the Kingdom's Authority*	*Announcement of the End of the Old Kingdom*	*Victory of the King*
NARRATIVE	**Mt. 1–2** ***Jesus' ancestry and infancy***	Mt. 3–4 *John the Baptist and Jesus' early ministry*	Mt. 8–9 *Miracles; commissioning the Twelve*	Mt. 11–12 *Jesus confronts an evil generation*	Mt. 14–17 *Travels and ministry; instructing the Twelve*	Mt. 19–23 *Events and teaching in Judea*	Mt. 26–28 *Passion week*
DISCOURSE		Mt. 5–7 *Sermon on the Mount*	Mt. 10 *Missionary instructions*	Mt. 13 *Kingdom parables*	Mt. 18 *Life in the Christian community*	Mt. 24–25 *Olivet Discourse (Judgment on Jerusalem)*	

A. Review the Context

Matthew's Gospel began by giving the messianic credentials of Jesus in the form of a genealogy clearly establishing him as the long-awaited Anointed One, Son of David and Son of Abraham, heir to the royal throne of Israel. The universality of his reign was also hinted at in the inclusion of four Gentile women in his ancestry. Chapter 1 concluded with an account of the Christ child's birth to a virgin and an explanation of his name and mission: He is "Emmanuel," "God with us," and has come to save people from their sins.

B. Read the Story

Carefully read **Matthew 2.** Ask yourself the questions: *Who? What? Where? When? How? Why?*

As always, pray before you read.

C. Take a Deeper Look

Answering these questions will draw you into the heart of the story. If you do not understand something, make a note of it to bring up in the small-group discussion.

The Magi's Visit (Matthew 2:1-12)

1. Jesus is born in Bethlehem of Judea. Find it on the map on page 4. In Hebrew, "Bethlehem" means "house of bread." Read the following Old Testament passages, and note what is important about this little town.

1 Samuel 16:1, 4-13:

This connects Bethlehem to DAVID

Micah 5:2-4:

again: Bethlehem to 'King' DAVID

2. In Matthew 2, four people (or groups of people) are shown reacting to news of the new King. Who are they, and what are their responses?

People	Response
Herod	disturbed - in the end kill all boy 2 yrs - younger
Wise Men	determined to follow star
Chief Priest / Scribes	no interest
People of Jerusalem	troubled

3. **Think About It:** Matthew does not include the visit of the (Jewish) shepherds that is recorded in Luke 2. What conclusion might the reader draw from this omission?

To keep narrative in positive perspective.

4. Read **CCC 528.** What does the Church see in the Magi?

That all Nation can honor "The King".

5. Herod is troubled enough to seek the death of the reported new King of the Jews. His own kingship is not based on blood (Herod is an Edomite descended from Esau), but on political expediency: Rome has appointed him king of the Jews, a position he holds from 37 to 4 BC. Read **Numbers 24:15-19.** This passage records a prophecy of Balaam, with which Herod, as an Edomite, would have been familiar. Why is Herod so disturbed by the words of the chief priests and scribes in Matthew 2:6?

Threatens his position of power. also would devide views of the people

6. Read **Isaiah 60:3-6.** How is this proclamation fulfilled in Matthew 2?

Prophosied Kings on camels bringing gifts

The Holy Family Escapes to Egypt (Matthew 2:13-23)

7. When Matthew says, "Out of Egypt have I called my son" (2:15), he is quoting **Hosea 11:1.** Hosea's reference is to God's delivery of his children from Egyptian slavery. Read **CCC 530.** What point is Matthew trying to make about Jesus?

First to Free Isreal's people - then to Free all God's people

> ### Note on Verses 16-18
>
> Rachel was the beloved wife of Jacob and the mother of his eleventh and twelfth sons, Joseph and Benjamin. Joseph's sons Ephraim and Manasseh became the chief tribes in the North during the time of the Divided Kingdom. Ephraim attained such prominence that Israel (the Northern Kingdom) was often called Ephraim.
>
> Rachel died after giving birth to Benjamin. She was buried either in Bethlehem itself or five miles north in the Benjamite town of Ramah. That geographic area became a focus of sorrow—not just Rachel's sorrow, but the sorrow of Judah and Israel as Ramah became the place where many died and were taken into exile.

8. Read **verses 19-23,** and find Judea, Galilee, and Nazareth on the map on page 4.

   a. Why does the Holy Family decide not to return to Bethlehem?

   Joseph is warned in a dream - Danger because of Herod

   b. "He shall be called a Nazarene" appears to be paraphrased from the words of several prophets. Matthew may be drawing a comparison between the words "Nazareth" and *nester* (Hebrew for "branch"). Read the following verses, and record what the image of the branch represents.

   Isaiah 11: Branch as lineage - Bring all together again after the exile

   Jeremiah 23:5-6: Descendant of DAVID will bring all together N/S

> ### Background: The Divided Kingdom
>
> Nearly one thousand years before, the Davidic kingdom of David and Solomon split in two as a result of sin, and it remained divided until first the North (in 722 BC) and then the South (in 587 BC) were carried into exile by Assyria and Babylon respectively. Although part of the South (Judah) returned to Palestine after seventy years of captivity, the Jewish people continued to mourn the loss of the ten Northern tribes of Israel.

c. How does this image of the "branch" relate to Jesus Christ, the Nazarene?

Jesus is from DAVID Line and Jesus is the "one" promised

D. Application

These questions will help you apply one of the key themes of the session to your life. After meditating on them, respond to God with a brief written prayer if you choose.

Have you ever felt like a "stump," where everything meaningful to you has been cut off? Does the future look bleak? Meditate on this, and praise the God who raised a "branch" of new life from the stump that Israel had become. Do you believe he can do a new work in you?

Dear Lord ...

E. Wrap-Up – Prologue: Birth of the King

How would you summarize the Prologue to Matthew's Gospel (Chapters 1–2)?

Session 3 Talk Notes

Matthew 2 – The King in Exile

I. Old Testament Foundation for Understanding John the Baptist and Jesus

A. Passover as central redemptive event of Old Testament (Exodus 12)

B. Importance of the Exile

1. Royal Kingdom – Saul, David, Solomon
2. Promise of everlasting kingdom to David (2 Samuel)
3. 930 BC – kingdom divides into ten Northern and two Southern tribes
4. 722 BC – Northern Kingdom taken away by Assyria
5. Prophets warn the South – especially Isaiah
    a. Isaiah 1–39 – Book of Woe
    b. Isaiah 40–55 – Book of Consolation
6. Jews in Jesus' time await the consolation of Israel (restoration)

II. Wise Men and Herod (Matthew 2:1-12)

A. Wise men *(Magi)* represent Gentiles

1. Like Balaam in the book of Numbers, they brought blessing

B. Herod is troubled by news of newborn King

1. Appointed king of Jews by Roman senate
2. Replacing collapsing dynasty of priestly rule
3. Renovated Jerusalem Temple
4. Edomite (descendant of Esau)

C. Magi – first Gentiles to recognize kingship of Jesus

1. CCC 528 – Epiphany means pagans can discover Jesus
2. Star – recalls Balaam's prophecy (Numbers 24:17)
    a. Immediately precedes conquest of Canaan
    b. Edom (Herod) will be dispossessed

D. Second formula quotation – Matthew 2:5-6 (quotes Micah 5:2)

E. Magi bearing gifts: reflects prophecy in Isaiah 60:3-6

1. Literal sense
2. Allegorical sense: gifts signify mystery of Christ incarnate (Irenaeus)
    a. Gold = royalty, kingship
    b. Frankincense = worship, divinity
    c. Myrrh (burial ointment) = humanity; Passion and death

3. Moral sense – gifts we present to Christ in daily life (St. Gregory the Great)
    a. Gold = Christ's wisdom shining in us (walking in wisdom)
    b. Frankincense = prayer and adoration
    c. Myrrh = daily sacrifice (cf. Romans 12:1)

F. Magi departed by another way
1. Literal sense – Magi do not go back the way they came
2. Moral sense – conversion when we encounter Christ

III. Escape to Egypt (Matthew 2:13-23)

A. Third formula quotation: Matthew 2:15 (quotes Hosea 11:1)
1. "Out of Egypt have I called my son"
2. Israel and Jesus called out of Egypt

B. Parallels between Jesus and Moses
1. Edict to kill male Hebrew children (Genesis 15; Exodus 1:15-16)
2. Saved by a family member (Exodus 2:1-10)
3. Found protection in Egypt (Exodus 2:5-10)
4. Called back to birthplace (Exodus 4:19)
5. Forty days, nights fasting in wilderness (Exodus 34:28; Matthew 4:2)
6. Commissioned by God to promulgate his covenant law

C. Fourth formula quotation – Matthew 2:18 (quotes Jeremiah 31:15)
1. Rachel weeping for her children
2. Ramah = place of sorrow and exile
3. Bethlehem as new city of sorrows

D. Holy Family moves to Nazareth
1. Fifth Formula Quotation – Matthew 2:23 (quotes Isaiah 11:1)
2. He shall be called a Nazarene

IV. Concluding the Introduction (Matthew 1–2)

A. Theme – the restoration of all Israel (note context of prophets quoted)
1. The "volume of Emmanuel" in Isaiah 7–11 (Isaiah 7:14, 8:14, 9:1-2, 11:1, 11:10-12); Micah 5:2; Hosea 11; Jeremiah 31:15
2. Jesus has come to restore Judah and Israel and bring in the Gentiles

B. Daniel 9 – exile of seventy times seven years leads up to time of Jesus

Session 4 – Questions

Matthew 3 – John: The Forerunner to the King

	Prologue	Book 1	Book 2	Book 3	Book 4	Book 5	Conclusion
	Birth of the King	*Announcement of the Kingdom*	*Establishment of the Kingdom*	*The Kingdom Defined*	*Transfer of the Kingdom's Authority*	*Announcement of the End of the Old Kingdom*	*Victory of the King*
NARRATIVE	Mt. 1–2 *Jesus' ancestry and infancy*	**Mt. 3–4** ***John the Baptist and Jesus' early ministry***	Mt. 8–9 *Miracles; commissioning the Twelve*	Mt. 11–12 *Jesus confronts an evil generation*	Mt. 14–17 *Travels and ministry; instructing the Twelve*	Mt. 19–23 *Events and teaching in Judea*	Mt. 26–28 *Passion week*
DISCOURSE		Mt. 5–7 *Sermon on the Mount*	Mt. 10 *Missionary instructions*	Mt. 13 *Kingdom parables*	Mt. 18 *Life in the Christian community*	Mt. 24–25 *Olivet Discourse (Judgment on Jerusalem)*	

A. Establish the Context

Matthew rounded off the "Prologue" to his Gospel by painting a picture of Christ's early reception by the world. Contrary to what one might expect, it was the Magi who were drawn to worship the newborn King, while the Jews were troubled by the news, and King Herod tried to kill him. Perhaps people were not expecting a king from such humble circumstances. Yet, Matthew's Gospel is full of quotes and allusions to the Old Testament that demonstrate that the birth of this child is the fulfillment of God's promise. Micah prophesied a great king from Bethlehem, and Isaiah foretold Gentile kings bearing gold and frankincense to the Lord. When the Holy Family settled in Nazareth, they fulfilled the prophecies that a righteous "branch" would come to rule from David's line.

Take a look at the diagram on this page. Remember that Matthew's Gospel is divided into five "books," each with a narrative section followed by a discourse (a major "speech" by Jesus). Here, we begin Book One: "Announcement of the Kingdom," which includes an account of John the Baptist and of Jesus' early ministry. This narration will culminate in Jesus' Sermon on the Mount.

B. Read the Story

Carefully read **Matthew 3.** Ask yourself the questions: *Who? What? Where? When? How? Why?*

As always, pray before you read.

What Is the Kingdom of Heaven?

John the Baptist came as a forerunner to Jesus, proclaiming the coming of the "kingdom of heaven." This also will be the central theme of Jesus' mission. What is that kingdom?

The kingdom of heaven (synonymous with "the kingdom of God" or the "kingdom of the Lord") has to do with kingship as much as kingdom. It reflects the Old Testament concept of God's reign over his people Israel. In 1 Chronicles 28:5, King David tells of God's choice of his son Solomon "to sit upon the throne of *the kingdom of the LORD over Israel*" (emphasis added). God promised to establish David's throne (or kingdom) forever—but that throne and kingdom clearly belonged to God.

Thus, the kingdom of God became identified with Israel's everlasting rule over the nations, a rule that all but disappeared when Judah was exiled in 587 BC. Some five hundred years later, at the time of Christ's birth, the Jews continued to hope and pray for the fulfillment of God's promise of a Davidic king to sit upon that throne and reign in justice and righteousness over his everlasting and glorious kingdom.

C. Take a Deeper Look

Answering these questions will draw you into the heart of the story. If you do not understand something, make a note of it to bring up in the discussion.

John the Baptist's Announcement (Matthew 3:1-12)

1. a. Who is John the Baptist, and what has been foretold about him? Read **Luke 1:5-36.**

John is the precurser to Jesus. He was born from a priest – and was "great before the Lord". He turned many Israelites to God. He was filled with the Holy Sipirt

b. Read **verses 2-3.** What is his message and purpose?

Repent, for the kingdom of God is near.
~~Be~~ Prepare

c. What details does Matthew give about where John the Baptist preaches, the clothes he wears, and the food he eats?

John preaches in the wilderness
camel hair clothing & leather belt
eats Locust & wild Honey.

2. Who comes to hear John preach, and how do they respond?

from "all Judea and the region of Jordon.

3. a. The Pharisees and Sadducees were religious leaders in Jesus' day. The Pharisees kept themselves separate from everything "unclean" and insisted the people observe strict adherance to the Law to be considered holy. The Sadducees were descendants of Zadoch, high priest under David, who had become corrupt; they were pawns of the Romans. What do you think John the Baptist means by his warning in verses 8-12?

Position doesn't guarantee being saved. To Act is to be saved

b. What do you think John means when he says, "fruit that befits repentance?" Read **CCC 678.** What will be judged on the Last Day?

Being a good Christian will help future generation and on judgment day

4. Read **2 Kings 1:8; Malachi 4:5-6;** and **Sirach 48:4, 9-10.** What Old Testament prophet does Matthew's description of John the Baptist bring to mind, and what do Malachi and Sirach say about that prophet? (Note: In some Bibles, the Malachi reference will be in verses 23-24.)

John is compared to Elijah - in physical stature also "restorer"

5. **Think About It:** John baptizes people in the Jordan River. What is special about this river that lends meaning to this? Read **Joshua 3; 2 Kings 5:1, 10-14;** and **CCC 1222.**

Jordon River lead ~~Irs~~ Isrealites from exodus
Namaan gets cured here.

6. Compare and contrast the baptisms of Jesus and John the Baptist. (See **verses 11-12** and also **CCC 1265.**)

John baptizes with the idea of repentance
Jesus transforms us with us receiving the Holy Spirit.

Jesus Is Baptized (Matthew 3:13-17)

7. Why do you think Jesus, who is sinless, wants to be baptized by John, who baptizes "with water for repentance"? (For help with this question, see **CCC 535–536 and 1223–1224.**)

Jesus gets baptized to symbolize his aceptance of our SINS. He suffers for our SINS. Took on life as a babe – like us so carried sin like us

8. What do the opened heavens, the descent of the dove, and the voice from heaven signify?

It declares Jesus as the Messiah, the voice identifies him as God's son & the dove symbol of annointed –

D. Application

These questions will help you apply one of the key themes of the session to your life. After meditating on them, respond to God with a brief written prayer if you choose.

John's message is "repent, for the kingdom of heaven is at hand." The kingdom of heaven is here on earth now in a provisional way in the Church. We all need to repent to prepare our hearts for Jesus' coming. Have you borne "fruit that befits repentance"? What can you learn from the preaching of John the Baptist?

Dear Lord ...

Session 4 Talk Notes

Matthew 3 – John: The Forerunner to the King

I. Matthew 3 – The First of Five Narratives in Matthew's Gospel

II. Geography of Israel – "The Fifth Gospel"

A. Wilderness of Judea north of Dead Sea

B. Jordan River

C. Major bodies of water

1. Sea of Galilee – fresh water enters and goes out; small body of water

2. Dead Sea – deep, rich mineral content but no outlet, nothing grows

III. John the Baptist in the Wilderness of the Jordan River

A. Lowest point on earth

B. Israel crossed the Jordan to take Jericho after Exodus and Desert Wanderings

C. Awaiting the Messiah and the consolation of Israel

1. Isaiah prophesies to the South

2. Chapters 1–39 – Book of Woe

3. Chapters 40–55 – Book of Consolation – God will restore Israel

D. Prophets spoke of consolation taking place in the wilderness

1. Hosea 2:14-15 – Valley of Achor (Achan's disobedience – Joshua 7); Matthew 3:3 quotes Isaiah 40:3: new exodus has begun

E. Qumran – Dead Sea Scrolls

1. Essenes – believed end times had come

2. John the Baptist may have been an Essene

IV. Jews and Baptism

A. *Mikveh* (or *mikvah*) = immersion pool for cleansing, purifying

B. John at the Jordan – self-immersion

1. *Baptizo* = to dip or plunge

2. Baptism of preparation for Messiah
3. Exodus symbol
4. Repentance (Gk., *metanoia;* Heb., *shuv* – "to repent")

V. Kingdom References

A. "Kingdom" mentioned more than fifty times in Matthew's Gospel

1. Four times – kingdom "of God"
2. Thirty-two times – kingdom "of heaven" – evasive synonym for the name of God – *malchut shamayim*

B. John as a new Elijah

C. John's clothing reflects Elijah's

D. Jews believed Elijah would come before the Messiah to restore the tribes of Israel[1]

E. Elijah went up to heaven (2 Kings 2:4-6, 9-11) where John appears dressed like Elijah

F. Elijah followed by Elisha who does even greater miracles – 2 Kings 4, 5

VI. Parallels Between Jesus and Elisha

A. 2 Kings 4:1-7 – Elisha transforms vessels of oil; Jesus turns water to wine at Cana

B. 2 Kings 4:32-34 – Elisha raises dead child to life, like Jesus

C. 2 Kings 4:38-44 – Elisha multiplies loaves to feed a multitude

D. 2 Kings 5 – Naaman cured of leprosy when John tells him to wash in the Jordan

1. CCC 1222 – baptism prefigured

VII. Message to Pharisees, Sadducees: "Bear Fruit that Befits Repentance"

VIII. Baptism of Jesus

A. Jesus identifies with Israel – submits to baptism of repentance

B. Language of anointing of a Jewish king

1. 1 Samuel 10:6 – Saul
2. 1 Samuel 16:13 – David

[1] See Malachi 4:5 (NAB: 3:23).

Session 5 – Questions

Matthew 4 – The Tempting of the King

	Prologue	Book 1	Book 2	Book 3	Book 4	Book 5	Conclusion
	Birth of the King	*Announcement of the Kingdom*	*Establishment of the Kingdom*	*The Kingdom Defined*	*Transfer of the Kingdom's Authority*	*Announcement of the End of the Old Kingdom*	*Victory of the King*
NARRATIVE	Mt. 1–2 *Jesus' ancestry and infancy*	**Mt. 3–4** ***John the Baptist and Jesus' early ministry***	Mt. 8–9 *Miracles; commissioning the Twelve*	Mt. 11–12 *Jesus confronts an evil generation*	Mt. 14–17 *Travels and ministry; instructing the Twelve*	Mt. 19–23 *Events and teaching in Judea*	Mt. 26–28 *Passion week*
DISCOURSE		Mt. 5–7 *Sermon on the Mount*	Mt. 10 *Missionary instructions*	Mt. 13 *Kingdom parables*	Mt. 18 *Life in the Christian community*	Mt. 24–25 *Olivet Discourse (Judgment on Jerusalem)*	

A. Review the Context

In Session 4, we learned that God sent John the Baptist to prepare the way for the coming Messiah by calling people to repentance and cleansing them from sin. He also baptized Jesus, thus identifying him with those whose sins he would one day bear on the Cross. Matthew uses language reminiscent of the Creation account in Genesis to describe Jesus' baptism: The dove descended over the waters; God spoke his Word from heaven. This was the beginning of a new creation.

The Messiah has been named by God, has been anointed for service as King, and is ready for ministry. It will be interesting to see what he does first.

B. Read the Story

Carefully read **Matthew 4.** Ask yourself the questions: *Who? What? When? Where? How? Why?*

As always, pray before you read.

C. Take a Deeper Look

Answering these questions will draw you into the heart of the story. If you do not understand something, make a note of it to bring up in the small-group discussion.

The Temptation of Jesus (Matthew 4:1-11)

1. In Matthew 4:1-11, Jesus is tempted by the devil. What is the purpose of the devil's questioning?

The devil is tempting Jesus, to show proof of ~~who~~ his being son of God - Tempting him not to suffer, but be safe on earthy kingdom

2. What weapons does the devil employ against Jesus?

God's own words
If you are the Son of God...

3. How does Jesus fight back? What is the result?

Jesus seems composed - He know this is part of his call. Then he uses God's word on Satan

4. a. Who leads Jesus into the desert in verse 1, and why?

Holy Spirit leads Jesus to desert. Jesus was born in human form. He must understand / feel what humans feel. Makes Jesus strong in his relations with his followers

b. Does this seem odd to you? Why is it important for Jesus to be tempted? Read what the Church has to say about Jesus' temptations in **CCC 538–540.** (See also **Hebrews 4:15-16.**)

5. **Think About It:** If even the devil can quote Scripture, how can we know when it is correctly used and when it is not? How can we avoid being misled? (Try to answer this from what you have learned in this session. (If you need additional help, see **CCC 85–86 and 109–119.**)

Words can be twisted -
praying put yourself in right frame of mine.
Keep yourself in ~~god~~ a god-like frame of mine [illegible]

Jesus Ministers in Galilee (Matthew 4:12-22)

Before answering these questions, re-read verses 12-25, and find all the locations mentioned in those verses on the map on page 5.

6. The tribal areas of Zebulun and Naphtali were the first regions to be carried into exile by the Assyrians. During Jesus' day, there were some Jews (from Judah) living in Galilee, but the population was made up mostly of Gentiles and descendants of the Israelites (Northern tribes) who had returned from exile. Why do you think Jesus chooses to start his ministry there?

Mirrors Old Testament - Those 2 tribes need to be saved & need to believe

7. In verses 15-17, Matthew connects the start of Jesus' ministry with a prophecy from Isaiah. Read the original prophecy in **Isaiah 9:1-7.** What does Matthew want his readers to understand?

The people in darkness. have seen a great light
Jesus is the light Build a City of God.

8. a. Notice that Jesus' message in **Matthew 4:17** is identical to John the Baptist's message in **Matthew 3:2.** Why is this significant?

He continues John the Baptist's work - even stronger
and with more appeal. Repent continues -
John Prepared the way of the Lord

b. Why is this message so important for Israel to hear?

Isreal needs to repent. TURN their hearts to
GOD - this is the way to the Kingdom of
God.

9. How does Jesus call his first disciples (see verse 19), and how do they respond?

Jesus is relatable. He is friendly & calm. He blends
in. He meets fisherman and he urges them to
Continue fishing. They have nothing to lose - and they gain
fish & status. They become followers.

10. a. How does Jesus minister to the people in Galilee (see verses 23-25)?

Jesus teaches about the Kingdom of Heaven.
He heals peoples mind & soul -
He heals their diseases.

b. How is he received?

They are in awe. Believers bring more sick
for Jesus to heal

D. Application

These questions will help you apply one of the key themes of the session to your life. After meditating on them, respond to God with a brief written prayer if you choose.

How well do you know God's Word? The author of Psalm 119 says: "I have laid up thy word in my heart, that I might not sin against thee" (verse 11). How can you do this? How can you resist temptation as Jesus did? If you need courage, remember the words of Hebrews 2:18: "For because he himself has suffered and been tempted, he is able to help those who are tempted."

Dear Lord …

Help me to be strong. Help me to remember how you were tempted, and how strong you needed to be.
Please send me courage.

Session 5 Talk Notes

Matthew 4 – The Tempting of the King

I. The Messiah Confronts Sin and Evil

A. Jesus comes to battle Israel's real enemy – the devil

II. Jesus Is Tempted in the Wilderness (Matthew 4:1-11)

A. Jesus relives the life of Israel, but he trusts the Father

1. Israel came through the Red Sea and was tested for forty years in the desert; Jesus comes through baptism and is tested forty days in the wilderness
2. CCC 538 – Satan's temptations of Jesus recapitulate those of Adam and Israel
3. Jesus faces the same temptations Israel faced, but he triumphs

a. In Deuteronomy, Moses recounts Israel's three major failures

b. Jesus answers Satan by quoting Moses (Deuteronomy 6–8)

B. The Spirit both leads and strengthens him

III. The First Temptation (Matthew 4:3-4)

A. Enemy strikes at identity of Jesus: "If you are the Son of God"

1. Response in Matthew 3:17: "This is my beloved Son"
2. CCC 538 – Satan seeks to compromise Jesus' filial attitude toward God

B. Test deals with hunger, provision, security

1. Exodus 16:2-3 – Israel grumbled about hunger in wilderness and did not trust God
2. "Man shall not live by bread alone" (Matthew 4:3-4, quoting Deuteronomy 8:3)

a. In Hebrew, literally, man can live "by anything God says"

IV. The Second Temptation (Matthew 4:5-7)

A. The Enemy tests Jesus with Scripture

B. Exodus 17:2-3 – Israelites complained to Moses about lack of water and thirst

1. *Massah* = testing

C. Enemy quotes Psalm 91:11-12 to get Jesus to prove he is God

1. "You shall not tempt the Lord your God" (Matthew 4:7, quoting Deuteronomy 6:16)
2. Psalm 91:13 – Serpent trampled underfoot

V. The Third Temptation (Matthew 4:8-11)

A. Enemy tempts Jesus to worship a false god

B. Exodus 32 – worship of the golden calf

C. "You shall worship the Lord your God" (Matthew 4:10, quoting Deuteronomy 6:13-14)

D. Jesus resists the devil, and the devil flees – see James 4:7

VI. Our Temptations and the Tools to Combat Them

A. Lent – experience the wilderness like Israel and Jesus

1. Learning to trust
2. CCC 540 – in Lent, the Church is united to Jesus in the desert

B. Jesus is tempted but not enticed by concupiscence (tendency to sin)

1. 1 John 2:15-17 – lust of flesh, lust of eyes, pride of life
2. Matthew 6 – three forms of piety to combat this – prayer (pride of life), fasting (flesh), and alms (eyes)

C. CCC 2847

1. Trials are necessary for growth
2. Temptation leads to sin and death

D. Sources of strength

1. CCC 1808 – fortitude
2. CCC 2157 – Sign of the Cross
3. CCC 2340 – self-knowledge, ascesis (self-discipline), obedience, exercise of moral virtue, prayer

E. 1 Corinthians 10:13 – God provides a way out of temptation

VII. Jesus Preaches in Galilee (Matthew 4:12-22)

A. Headquarters in Capernaum

1. Zebulun and Naphtali exiled in 722 BC, ten years before other tribes
2. First destroyed will be first restored
3. *Via Maris* = "the Way of the Sea"

B. Isaiah 9:1-2 – the place of bloodshed will be a place of light

C. Jesus begins to bring in twelve apostles (representing twelve tribes)

Session 6 – Questions

Matthew 5 – The Bar Is Raised by the King

	Prologue	Book 1	Book 2	Book 3	Book 4	Book 5	Conclusion
	Birth of the King	*Announcement of the Kingdom*	*Establishment of the Kingdom*	*The Kingdom Defined*	*Transfer of the Kingdom's Authority*	*Announcement of the End of the Old Kingdom*	*Victory of the King*
NARRATIVE	Mt. 1–2 *Jesus' ancestry and infancy*	Mt. 3–4 *John the Baptist and Jesus' early ministry*	Mt. 8–9 *Miracles; commissioning the Twelve*	Mt. 11–12 *Jesus confronts an evil generation*	Mt. 14–17 *Travels and ministry; instructing the Twelve*	Mt. 19–23 *Events and teaching in Judea*	Mt. 26–28 *Passion week*
DISCOURSE		**Mt. 5–7** ***Sermon on the Mount***	Mt. 10 *Missionary instructions*	Mt. 13 *Kingdom parables*	Mt. 18 *Life in the Christian community*	Mt. 24–25 *Olivet Discourse (Judgment on Jerusalem)*	

A. Review the Context

It was not an accident that Jesus began his ministry in Galilee in the lands of Zebulun and Naphtali—the place where Israel's long exile began. The light of Christ would shine out to all nations from that very place, marking the start of a great reversal. "The kingdom of heaven is at hand," he declared. People from all nations would be drawn out of spiritual exile to find their places in the kingdom.

We are halfway through the first of Matthew's five "books." The narrative section described the preparations for Jesus' ministry and led into Jesus' most famous discourse: the Sermon on the Mount (Matthew 5–7). Just like Moses gave the Old Covenant Law to Israel from Mount Sinai, Jesus will climb a mountain to deliver the *spiritual* law of the New Covenant.

B. Read the Story

Carefully read **Matthew 5.** Ask yourself the questions: *Who? What? When? Where? How? Why?*

As always, pray before you read.

C. Take a Deeper Look

Answering these questions will draw you into the heart of the story. If you do not understand something, make a note of it to bring up in the small-group discussion.

The Beatitudes (Matthew 5:1-11)

When God first called Abraham and made a covenant with him and his descendants, he promised them land and an everlasting royal kingdom that would be the source of blessing to the entire world. It is significant, then, that Jesus' first major pronouncement, the Sermon on the Mount, begins with the "Beatitudes"—the blessings of the New Covenant.

1. Look up the definition of "blessed." What does it mean? What do you mean when you call someone "blessed"?

Highly favored and fortunate. 2. They seem at peace with all they have.

2. Who does Jesus proclaim in the Beatitudes will be the "blessed" of the kingdom?

Poor in spirit, those who mourn, the meek, the sorrowing the righteous, the persecuted for his name sake.

3. a. In Jesus' day, "beatitude" (blessedness) would ordinarily be determined by a person's good fortune. On what basis does Jesus determine blessedness?

Dealing with the "beatitude", if we suffer and place our plea before the LORD, we will attain the kingdom of heaven

b. What point is Jesus making about the kingdom of heaven and happiness (blessedness)?

Our Christian goal is the Kingdom of heaven. If "Thy will be done" is in your everyday life, you will attain the blessedness of the Kingdom of Heaven

4. The first beatitude, "Blessed are the poor in spirit, for theirs is the kingdom of heaven," lays the groundwork for the rest. Who are the "poor in spirit"? (For help with this question, see **CCC 544.**)

The Poor in Spirit are those who seek God's love & mercy

Salt and Light (Matthew 5:13-16)

5. Jesus calls his disciples "the salt of the earth" in verse 13. Discuss what it means to be "salt."

Salt is used for seasoning / baking. The disciples are who we need to "season" followers – Help the community believe & expand.

6. a. Read **verses 14-16.** This is not the first time the children of Israel have been called the light of the world. Read Isaiah 42:6-7 and 49:5-6. What is Israel's God-given mission, and how does Jesus expect his disciples to fulfill it?

God used Isreal to bring people out of great darkness. Jesus needs disciples to be the light for people – by actions & deeds.

b. How does the image of light enhance your understanding of what God calls his children to do?

God's children are to enlighten the next generation. Share our faith – Spread the good news – God loves Us.

The Law and the Prophets (Matthew 5:17-48)

7. Part of living out this new law involves being salt and light in the world. How do we put this into practice? Read **Matthew 5:21-48,** in which Jesus applies his New Covenant understanding to Old Covenant laws regarding murder, adultery, divorce, swearing falsely, retaliation, and enemies. How would you summarize his basic message?

Jesus used the Old Covenant laws as proof. Isaiah foretold: —, as an example.

8. Choose one of these laws, and explain how Jesus deepens your understanding of the purpose or intent of the original Law.

9. **Think About It:** The *Catechism* tells us, "In Jesus, the same Word of God, that had resounded on Mount Sinai to give the written Law to Moses, made itself heard anew on the Mount of the Beatitudes" (CCC 581). What similarities and differences do you see between God's Word in the Ten Commandments (Exodus 20:1-17) and God's Word in the Beatitudes? In what sense do the Beatitudes "fulfill" the Ten Commandments or reveal what the earlier Law only pointed to?

The ten Commandments are all negative. Thou shall not
The beatitudes talk about how to ~~attain~~ complete the 10
Commandments with action

10. **Think About It:** What does Jesus' discussion of anger in verses 21-26 say about the connection between our worship of God and our relationships with one another? (See also **Matthew 6:15.**)

Love God & our neighbor:
Forgive us our trepasses –

11. Love of neighbor is one of the two greatest commandments of the Old Testament Law.

    a. How does Jesus expand on the definition of "neighbor" in verses 43-48?

    Everyone - exspecially those in need.

    b. On what basis does Jesus say to love even our enemies?

    God's love is unconditional.
    So must ours be to serve as an example!

D. Application

This question will help you apply one of the key themes of the session to your life. After meditating on it, respond to God with a brief written prayer if you choose.

In his words regarding adultery and lust, Jesus calls us to a radical removal of anything in our lives that leads us to sin and keeps us from living as citizens of the kingdom of heaven. If you are struggling with a particular sin, consider what leads you into that sin and what you can do to "pluck it out" (Matthew 5:29).

Optional: Read CCC 1716–1724, "Our Vocation to Beatitude"; then meditate once more on Matthew 5:3-12. Ask God to speak to your heart. What truths come to mind? What changes do the Beatitudes invite you to make in yourself?

Dear Lord …

Session 6 Talk Notes

Matthew 5 – The Bar Is Raised by the King

I. Introduction to the Sermon on the Mount: The New Law of the New Covenant

II. Beatitudes: The Way to True Happiness

A. St. Augustine – deepest need in life is to find true happiness

B. Four levels of happiness

1. Instant gratification
2. Personal achievement
3. Philanthropy (Acts 20:35)
4. Union with God
    a. Our hearts are restless until they rest in God (St. Augustine)

III. Sermon on the Mount: The New Law of the Kingdom

A. Parallels between Jesus (new law) and Moses (old Law)

1. A new Exodus from bondage
2. A new law on Mount Zion
3. A new Passover, covenant, Israel, temple, priests
4. Jesus' life parallels Moses, Israel

B. Differing views of the Sermon on the Mount

1. Perfectionist perspective (Catholic view) – rule of personal conduct
2. Impossible ideal (Martin Luther) – moves us from Law to grace
3. Interim morality – reserved for a few

IV. Keys to Understanding the Beatitudes

A. The fatherhood of God is disclosed in the Son (Matthew 5:9, 16)

B. They reflect the image of Christ perfectly – what it is like to be him

C. They flow into and build on each other

V. The Beatitudes (Matthew 5:1-12)

A. Blessed are the poor in spirit (verse 3)

1. "Blessed" (Heb., *ashrei*) means "happy"
2. To be happy – become like Christ
3. CCC 2546: Beatitudes reveal an order of happiness and grace
4. "Poor in spirit" means humility
    a. There is no virtue without humility (St. Thomas)
    b. Opposite of pride, the root of all sin
    c. Spiritual poverty (honesty in self-assessment)

d. Emptying self to make room for Christ (Galatians 2:20)
e. Jesus as model (Philippians 2:5-7)
f. Foundation of prayer (CCC 2559)

B. Blessed are those who mourn (verse 4)
1. The humble understand their brokenness, mourn their neediness

C. Blessed are the meek (verse 5)
1. Meek = controlled strength, teachable (like Moses)
2. Submit strength to the Lord, and he entrusts us with the earth

D. Blessed are those who hunger and thirst for righteousness (verse 6)
1. God can satisfy our hunger and thirst for more
2. Psalm 63:1-3
3. God thirsts for you so that you might thirst for him (St. Augustine)
4. Righteousness = right standing with God

E. Blessed are the merciful (verse 7)
1. Mercy is the response of those satisfied with righteousness

F. Blessed are the pure in heart (verse 8)
1. The capacity for truth
2. CCC 2518 – intellects and wills attuned to demands of God's holiness in charity, chastity, love of truth (orthodoxy of faith)

G. Blessed are the peacemakers (verse 9)

H. Blessed are those persecuted for righteousness' sake (verses 10-11)
1. Old Testament – external rewards for obedience (Deuteronomy 28; Leviticus 26)
2. New Testament – reward is the kingdom of God
a. Colossians 1:24 and *Salvifici Doloris* – participation in Christ's suffering
b. CCC 1729 – discernment in the use of earthly goods
c. God gives us what we need: the Giver, not the gift

VI. Salt and Light (Matthew 5:13-16)

VII. Six Antitheses Raise the Bar (Matthew 5:17-48)

A. Jesus is not abolishing the Law, but fulfilling it
1. Focus shifts inward
a. Jeremiah 31 – Law is written on our hearts
b. New Covenant – obey out of love, not fear
c. New law requires internal transformation
d. We need grace, the Eucharist, and the sacraments

B. "You have heard it said ... but I say" – teaching on anger, adultery, divorce, oaths, retaliation, enemies

C. Our reward is relationship with God – the beatific vision

Matthew 6 – Personal Piety

	Prologue	Book 1	Book 2	Book 3	Book 4	Book 5	Conclusion
	Birth of the King	*Announcement of the Kingdom*	*Establishment of the Kingdom*	*The Kingdom Defined*	*Transfer of the Kingdom's Authority*	*Announcement of the End of the Old Kingdom*	*Victory of the King*
NARRATIVE	Mt. 1–2 *Jesus' ancestry and infancy*	Mt. 3–4 *John the Baptist and Jesus' early ministry*	Mt. 8–9 *Miracles; commissioning the Twelve*	Mt. 11–12 *Jesus confronts an evil generation*	Mt. 14–17 *Travels and ministry; instructing the Twelve*	Mt. 19–23 *Events and teaching in Judea*	Mt. 26–28 *Passion week*
DISCOURSE		**Mt. 5–7** ***Sermon on the Mount***	Mt. 10 *Missionary instructions*	Mt. 13 *Kingdom parables*	Mt. 18 *Life in the Christian community*	Mt. 24–25 *Olivet Discourse (Judgment on Jerusalem)*	

A. Review the Context

Jesus began his public ministry like a new Moses, climbing a mountain to give his disciples the new law of the kingdom of God. His opening "Beatitudes" point the way to true happiness and blessing in the kingdom. This can only be obtained by those who are humble, who mourn their sin, who submit their strength to God, and who hunger for righteousness and are merciful. In short, it may be obtained by those who reflect the image of Jesus himself.

The Lord made it clear that, far from doing away with the old Law, he came to fulfill it. What he meant by this became clearer as he began to build upon the Beatitudes with six "antitheses": contrasts between the Old Covenant and the New Covenant that reveal the underlying spirit of the new law.

B. Read the Story

Carefully read **Matthew 6.** Ask yourself the questions: *Who? What? When? Where? How? Why?*

As always, pray before you read.

C. Take a Deeper Look

Answering these questions will draw you into the heart of the story. If you do not understand something, make a note of it to bring up in the small-group discussion.

Personal Piety (Matthew 6:1-4)

1. In this section of Jesus' Sermon on the Mount, he turns to matters of personal piety, or "acts of righteousness."

a. What three practices are discussed in verses 1-18?

acts of giving – to poor
Prayer –
fasting –

b. What is the gist of Jesus' message in these verses?

It's not what is outwardly shown that God is pleased, it is what we do without fanfare.

c. What is revealed about the nature of true piety?

True piety is not an action, but something from the Heart.

2. Matthew uses the title "Father" or "heavenly Father" for God twelve times in Chapter 6.

a. What fatherly traits of God are illustrated in this chapter?

Love, forgiveness and generosity of spirit, like an earthly father

b. What difference does it make to your personal piety, or acts of righteousness, when you relate to God as your Father instead of as a master or judge?

Actions are more out of Love and wonder & awe to follow him and act like him. Instead of fear of judgment – done because I have to!

Prayer (Matthew 6:5-14)

3. In verses 5-14, Jesus introduces prayer as a means of intimate communion with our heavenly Father. The Lord's Prayer gives us a framework so we will understand how to pray.

a. What is the primary focus of the Lord's Prayer (see verses 9-10)?

We praise God, his kingdom, and his will be done.

b. St. Thomas Aquinas once said: "The Lord's Prayer is the most perfect of prayers. … In it we ask, not only for all the things we can rightly desire, but also in the sequence that they should be desired" (CCC 2763).[1] Why do you think these initial requests precede the more personal ones of verses 11-13? (See also **CCC 2764.**)

We ask in love – accepting his willing – and giving him praise – in that order

4. Read **verses 11-13.**

a. What earthly concerns does Jesus direct us to pray about?

on earth as it is in heaven
lead us not into temptation

b. Which one of the petitions speaks most to you? The *Catechism* discusses them in detail in Article 3, (see **CCC 2803–2854**). Read the pertinent section for the petition you choose, and record what you learn from it.

This is hard – This prayer is what | how I want to live each day.

Forgiveness (Matthew 6:15-18)

5. What does Jesus say people must do for their sins to be forgiven?

forgive those who trespass against us.

6. **Think About It:** Why do you think Jesus makes such a point of the need for forgiveness in his instructions on prayer?

~~Only I~~ If we are free from grudges, then we will be free to be completely open to the love of God.

God and Mammon (Matthew 6:19-24)

7. What is Jesus saying in verses 19-24? (Note: The phrase "a sound eye" in verses 22-23 refers to an ancient Hebrew idiom for generosity.)

We should not be worried about material possession, but be free from blongings – give all to God. He will provide

[1] *Summa Theologica II-II*, 83, 9.

Anxiety Versus Trust in the Father's Care (Matthew 6:25-34)

8. a. What reasons does Jesus give us in this passage not to worry about how we will be taken care of?

Jesus says: God cares for his Kingdom - animals and such, so he will take care of us. He knows what we need and will give us only what we need.

b. When Jesus tells us not to worry about what we will eat or wear, is he telling us not to work to provide for ourselves? Read **CCC 2830.**

food, clothes & shelter are necessary, but can cause hardship - anxiety

c. What related point does the apostle Paul make in **Philippians 4:6-7?**

We need to prayer with sincere heart

D. Application

These questions will help you apply one of the key themes of the session to your life. After meditating on them, respond to God with a brief written prayer if you choose.

When Jesus spoke of the traditional works of mercy—almsgiving, prayer, and fasting—he was attempting to combat the tendency of the people of his day to perform these works for the purpose of appearing holy to others. Today, we are more likely to hear a homily on why we should perform these works at all rather than on why we should not flaunt them. Are these acts of piety a regular or only an occasional part of your life? Do you perform these works out of a sense of duty or out of love? How can you make these works a regular part of your life coming from the heart?

Dear Lord ...

Session 7 Talk Notes

Matthew 6 – Personal Piety

I. Personal Piety

A. Almsgiving, prayer, and fasting

1. Common to three monotheistic religions – Judaism, Christianity, Islam

2. A way to combat lust of flesh and eyes, pride of life (1 John 2:15-16)

B. Need for proper motivation

C. Piety = "righteousness" or "covenant behavior" (5:20; also 3:15, 5:6, 6:33)

D. Relationship with God is key – reward comes from God (verses 4, 6, 18)

II. Almsgiving (Matthew 6:1-4)

A. A form of piety and penance

B. Combats the "lust of eyes," covetousness (1 John 2:16)

C. Virtue = habit of doing good

D. CCC 1434 – prayer, fasting, and almsgiving express interior penance

III. Prayer (Matthew 6:5-15)

A. One-quarter of the *Catechism* is devoted to prayer

B. Jesus does not condemn public prayer, but addresses condition of the heart

1. "Hypocrite" = "actor" in Greek

2. Private prayer complements public prayer

3. Integrity – inside matches outside

C. The Lord's Prayer

1. CCC 2765 – Jesus as master and model of prayer

2. CCC 2781 – prayer as communion with the Father and Jesus

3. Provides a framework for prayer

4. The perfect prayer (St. Augustine)

5. First half directed to God, second half to our needs

6. Daily bread = Eucharist (St. Ambrose: receive daily)

7. What it means to call God "Father"

   a. Children of God participate in divine nature (2 Peter 1:4)

8. Hearts not open to forgiveness will be closed to God

   a. CCC 2783 – reveals us to ourselves as it reveals the Father

9. Combats "pride of life" (1 John 2)

IV. Fasting (Matthew 6:16-18)

A. Combats lust of flesh

B. Do not put on a show of fasting; deny yourself to position your heart to hear God

V. Laying Up Treasure in Heaven (Matthew 6:19-21)

A. Hearts yearn for treasure that will bring security and happiness

B. Lay up treasure in heaven for eternity through acts of piety

VI. The Sound Eye and Serving Two Masters (Mathew 6:22-24)

A. Hebrew idiom – "single" (or "sound") eye = generous; "evil" eye = stingy[2]

B. CCC 2113 – idolatry includes divinizing anything that is not God

C. Revelation 13–14 – martyrs died for not worshiping the Beast

VII. Do Not Be Anxious (Matthew 6:25-34)

A. Work hard and be prudent but not anxious

B. Worry is a sin – not trusting God

2 For other instances of this metaphor, see Deuteronomy 15:9 and Sirach 14:8-10.

Matthew 7 – Choices in the Kingdom

	Prologue	Book 1	Book 2	Book 3	Book 4	Book 5	Conclusion
	Birth of the King	*Announcement of the Kingdom*	*Establishment of the Kingdom*	*The Kingdom Defined*	*Transfer of the Kingdom's Authority*	*Announcement of the End of the Old Kingdom*	*Victory of the King*
NARRATIVE	Mt. 1–2 *Jesus' ancestry and infancy*	Mt. 3–4 *John the Baptist and Jesus' early ministry*	Mt. 8–9 *Miracles; commissioning the Twelve*	Mt. 11–12 *Jesus confronts an evil generation*	Mt. 14–17 *Travels and ministry; instructing the Twelve*	Mt. 19–23 *Events and teaching in Judea*	Mt. 26–28 *Passion week*
DISCOURSE		**Mt. 5–7** ***Sermon on the Mount***	Mt. 10 *Missionary instructions*	Mt. 13 *Kingdom parables*	Mt. 18 *Life in the Christian community*	Mt. 24–25 *Olivet Discourse (Judgment on Jerusalem)*	

A. Review the Context

Personal piety is about doing: giving to the poor, nurturing your relationship with God through prayer, and fasting. But these very good and important practices will bring you nothing beyond earthly recognition if they are done for "show." As Jesus explained in Matthew 6, practicing piety belongs between each of us and our heavenly Father. When works of piety are done out of love for him and for his eyes only, we obtain an eternal and indestructible reward in heaven.

The second of these practices, prayer, is important enough that a one-quarter of the *Catechism of the Catholic Church* is devoted to it. Prayer is the secret to intimate communion with God. In the Lord's Prayer, Jesus gives us a framework for Christian prayer so that we can respond in love to the Father's love for us. As the Sermon on the Mount unfolds, it becomes increasingly clear that at the heart of the difference between the Old and New Covenants is the Christian's relationship with God as Father rather than judge. Matthew 6 closed with one of the great consequences of this relationship: We no longer need to be anxious, because we rest in the Father's arms.

In Matthew 7, Jesus concludes the Sermon on the Mount with a series of insights into how we should live in the kingdom of God.

B. Read the Story

Carefully read **Matthew 7.** Ask yourself the questions: *Who? What? When? Where? How? Why?*

As always, pray before you read.

C. Take a Deeper Look

Answering these questions will draw you into the heart of the story. If you do not understand something, make a note of it to bring up in the small-group discussion.

Judging Others (Matthew 7:1-6)

1. a. In verse 1, Jesus says, "Judge not, that you be not judged." What kind of judgment is he talking about, and why does he speak against it? See also **James 4:11-12.**

when we judge people, those people can judge us the same way. We cannot judge others if we behave in the same manner.

b. How do Jesus' instructions regarding judging others relate to his words in **6:14-15?** (See also **CCC 678.**)

if we ~~forg~~ get forgiveness and receive it openly, then we will be free to forgive others.

c. If we refrain from judging others, when will they be judged, and by whom? Read **1 Corinthians 4:1-5.**

All the judgment that counts will be at the end of days.

d. Does Jesus mean we should never make any judgments? Read **verses 6 and 15-19.** What kinds of judgments should Christians make?

I think this means to be mindful when we need or a placed in the situation. Try to be mindful.

Prayer (Matthew 7:7-12)

2. What promises does Jesus make in verses 7-12 about prayer?

~~B~~ Persevere - God knows our needs & desires. We are his children and he will give us what we need, not necessarily what we want

3. The "Golden Rule" in verse 12 is found in a negative form in rabbinic Judaism and other world religions: Do not do things to others you do not want them to do to you. How does Jesus change this? How does this change relate to true righteousness?

Love one another - do good to those who hate.
you will feel great rewards.

Entering the Kingdom – "The Two Ways" (Matthew 7:13-23)

4. Jesus' admonitions in the Sermon on the Mount may seem hard to fulfill. What does Jesus say about the way to the kingdom in verses 13-14?

Pathway to the Kingdom is hard. Many bumps, twists & turns along the way. If we stay focused we shall see the path clearly.

5. **Think About It:** Is this a new message, or has Israel heard something like it before? Compare Jesus' words here about the two gates with God's message to Israel through Moses as the people prepared to enter Canaan (see **Deuteronomy 30:15-20**).

Moses message: follow me to life - if you worship idols you will perish.

still true today in a way. We need to follow the ways to enter the Kingdom - avoid evil.

6. Read **verses 21-23.**

   a. What are some examples of things people might mistakenly rely on to convince themselves they will enter God's kingdom?

   Many "sayers" have there following. There groups are loyal. The Bible sets on the straight path - people need to be open minded to the possibilities

   b. How can you be sure to follow the narrow way and enter the kingdom?

   You can feel it in your heart.

Hearers Versus Doers (Matthew 7:24-29)

7. Jesus compares those who hear and obey his words to a wise man who builds his house upon the rock. What is the "moral sense"—life instruction—of his teaching? (See **CCC 117.**)

The wise man finds it hard to be with the people.
Being with the people helps spread the good news

8. How does the crowd respond to Jesus' teaching?

I think they are amazed by his passion - He
speaks Holy & Truthful. This is new to them

D. Application

These questions will help you apply one of the key themes of the session to your life. After meditating on them, respond to God with a brief written prayer if you choose.

Reflect for a moment on your own life and family. What kind of a spiritual foundation have you laid, and how are you fortifying it? If you think your house is "built on sand," what can you do to build a stronger foundation? Do you have a plan?

Dear Lord …

E. Wrap-Up – Book One: Announcement of the Kingdom

How would you summarize Book One of Matthew's Gospel (Chapters 3–7)?

Session 8 Talk Notes

Matthew 7 – Choices in the Kingdom

I. Judging in Everyday Life (Matthew 7:1-6)

A. Jesus is the judge; we are not

B. Jesus targets moral climate of scribes and Pharisees (see Matthew 5:20)

C. Difference between judging and walking in prudence

1. Luke 6:37 – judge not, condemn not, but forgive

2. Tend to one's own failures first

3. Offer correction with humility

4. Exercise critical discernment (1 Thessalonians 5:21)

5. Try to acquire the virtues you think your brother lacks (St. Augustine)

D. "Do not give dogs what is holy" (7:6) – calls for discernment

1. "Dogs" = Gentiles, unbelievers

2. Lay foundation of elementary teachings first

II. Prayer (Matthew 7:7-11)

A. Problem – not eager enough to ask for the right things (James 4:3)

1. Ask in faith, not double-minded (James 1:5-8)

a. CCC 2609 – pray in filial adherence to God

b. CCC 2610 – pray in filial boldness

B. God is concerned about everyday things – Mary at Cana

1. Relate to God as Father, not master

III. Golden Rule (Matthew 7:12)

A. Summary of the law

B. Underneath this moral lesson is the love of our heavenly Father

IV. Two Ways to Live (Matthew 7:13-23)

A. CCC 1970 – law of gospel requires choice between two ways

1. Wide gate = destruction; narrow gate = life

B. Beware of false prophets

1. Know them by their fruits

C. Road signs on the way

1. Make sure you get through the gate

a. Moses and the two ways (life and good, death and evil)[1]

b. CCC 1696 – importance of moral decisions

2. Watch for people who lead you off track ("false prophets")

a. Old Testament test – do words come to pass? Look for fruit

V. True Obedience (Matthew 7:24-29)

A. Jesus taught as one with authority

B. True obedience to Jesus gives a strong foundation (house built on rock)

1. *Shema* (Deuteronomy 6:4) – hearing is doing

2. Solomon built his house on rock

a. 1 Kings 3:10-12 – wisdom

b. 1 Kings 8:27 – Temple

3. Enduring house – our soul is grounded in Christ (1 Corinthians 3:11-15)

4. Paul to Timothy – lay up a good foundation

5. Herod's Temple not built on rock of Christ, fell AD 70

C. Jesus' house (the Church) built on the rock of Peter (see Matthew 16)

1. Daniel 7 – the kingdom that will last forever

D. James 2:14-26 – show faith by works

---

1 Deuteronomy 30:15-20.

Session 9 – Questions

Matthew 8 – The King's Power Demonstrated

	Prologue	Book 1	Book 2	Book 3	Book 4	Book 5	Conclusion
	Birth of the King	*Announcement of the Kingdom*	*Establishment of the Kingdom*	*The Kingdom Defined*	*Transfer of the Kingdom's Authority*	*Announcement of the End of the Old Kingdom*	*Victory of the King*
NARRATIVE	Mt. 1–2 *Jesus' ancestry and infancy*	Mt. 3–4 *John the Baptist and Jesus' early ministry*	**Mt. 8–9** ***Miracles; commissioning the Twelve***	Mt. 11–12 *Jesus confronts an evil generation*	Mt. 14–17 *Travels and ministry; instructing the Twelve*	Mt. 19–23 *Events and teaching in Judea*	Mt. 26–28 *Passion week*
DISCOURSE		Mt. 5–7 *Sermon on the Mount*	Mt. 10 *Missionary instructions*	Mt. 13 *Kingdom parables*	Mt. 18 *Life in the Christian community*	Mt. 24–25 *Olivet Discourse (Judgment on Jerusalem)*	

A. Establish the Context

First John the Baptist and then Jesus announced the kingdom of God. Then, like a "new Moses," Jesus ascended a mountainside to proclaim the "new law" of this kingdom in his Sermon on the Mount. This new law fulfills the old Law, illuminating its purpose and intent and showing how true righteousness flows from a heart turned toward our heavenly Father. Jesus finishes with an echo of Moses' plea to choose life via the narrow way into the kingdom.

Chapter 8 begins Book Two of Matthew's Gospel, "Establishment of the Kingdom." This book covers Jesus' miracles and his commissioning and instruction of the twelve apostles.

B. Read the Story

Carefully read **Matthew 8.** Follow the narrative of Jesus' movements from town to town on the map on page 4. Ask yourself the questions: *Who? What? When? Where? How? Why?*

As always, pray before you read.

C. Take a Deeper Look

Answering these questions will draw you into the heart of the story. If you do not understand something, make a note of it to bring up in the small-group discussion.

Jesus' Miracles (Matthew 8)

1. In the New Testament, the miracles of Jesus are most often called *dynameis,* or "powers." The focus is not on Jesus as a miracle worker, but on Jesus as the power of God made manifest on earth. How—and over what—does Jesus demonstrate his divine power in Matthew 8?

Matthew focuses on healing (Leprosy) calming people (casting out) and calming nature.

Jesus Cleanses the Leper (Matthew 8:1-4)

2. a. Under the old Law, anyone with leprosy was isolated from the community. Not only were they forbidden from interacting with people who were "clean," they were denied access to the Temple for worship. They lived outside the camp, and if anyone came near, they had to call, "Unclean! Unclean!" so no one would touch them and become defiled themselves. Given this background, what is remarkable about the way Jesus cleanses the leper?

He touches the man - physically with his hand. Not afraid to become unclean. Jesus remains clean & the leper himself is cleaned/healed.

b. **Think About It:** The Church distinguishes between the literal and spiritual "senses" of Scripture, which, taken together, add richness to our understanding of God's Word. The literal sense is the intended meaning of the text; the spiritual senses are based on the literal sense and represent the way in which the text points to or is a sign of a deeper reality. These spiritual senses can be "allegorical"—pointing to Christ; "moral"—pointing to the way we ought to act; or "anagogical"—pointing to our eternal destiny. Can you see a spiritual sense behind leprosy in general or something in the Church that Christ's healing of the leper points to?

Leprosy can be seen as anything that makes us unholy/unclean. We all need to be clean spiritually to be able to receive Jesus in our hearts & on Sunday.

The Centurion's Servant (Matthew 8:5-13)

All Gentiles were by definition "sinners" simply because they did not adhere to Jewish Law. When the centurion says he is not worthy to have Jesus come under his roof, this is not false humility but an acknowledgment that Jesus will become ceremonially defiled if he enters his house.

3. a. Jesus praises the Roman centurion for his faith. What qualities of faith do you see in the words and actions of the centurion?

That he is not worthy— He still asks for help – he believes and is rewarded.

b. What quality, which is lacking in some "sons of the kingdom," does this Gentile have that makes him fit for heaven?

His faith in Jesus is the key.

4. You may recognize the words of the centurion in the following words we say at Mass prior to receiving the Eucharist: "Lord, I am not worthy that you should enter under my roof, but only say the word and my soul shall be healed." What does the story of the centurion add to your understanding of these words?

Beautiful – Reinforces we need to be humble and repented to receive Jesus at Mass in the Eucharist.

The Cost of Discipleship (Matthew 8:18-22)

5. In this passage, Matthew gives us a picture of two potential followers of Jesus. Based on Jesus' replies to their questions, what are they unwilling to let go?

Jesus' followers left everything behind - material & family. The two potential followers had to think.

6. **Think About It:** Read **verses 18-22** along with **1 Kings 19:19-21.** Why do you think Jesus tells the disciple to "leave the dead to bury their own dead" even though Elijah permitted Elisha to take leave of his family?

I think this means - Begin again. Fresh prespective. Leave the past in the past - and return to Jesus.

Jesus Calms the Storm (Matthew 8:23-27)

7. a. Jesus calls the disciples who are with him in the boat "men of little faith." They have enough faith to go to him for help; what do they lack?

Belief that Jesus will keep them safe - Faith - complete faith - human Nature -

b. How might the disciples act differently with stronger faith?

Trust - show unfailing faith after all they have seen. Be humble.

The Gadarene Demoniacs (Matthew 8:28-34)

8. What questions do the demon-possessed men address to Jesus? What do these questions reveal about their knowledge of Jesus?

what do you want - Son of God? - The Demons know Jesus. why are you here? To torture us? - The Demons knew the power of Jesus

Question	What It Reveals

9. **Think About It:** What do the leper, the centurion, and the demoniacs have in common? Is there a reason these are among the first people Jesus reaches out to in Matthew's Gospel?

The are "unworthy", but have interaction with Jesus. The leper is physically unclean – the centurion, is unclean by [illegible], the demoniacs are unclean in mind – But all have faith in Jesus.

D. Application

These questions will help you apply one of the key themes of the session to your life. After meditating on them, respond to God with a brief written prayer if you choose.

Are you experiencing a storm in your life? If so, are you frantic, afraid you will drown? Or are your eyes on the One who can save you? Prayerfully re-read Matthew 8, asking God to give you greater insight into who Jesus is and the power and control he has over everything. Ask also for faith. Are there examples in the reading for this session that can give you strength?

Dear Lord …

Session 9 Talk Notes

Matthew 8 – The King's Power Demonstrated

I. Introduction to the Second Narrative in Matthew

A. Chapters 8 and 9 show the power of the kingdom

B. Ten miracles – power over sickness, demons, nature, death

II. Cleansing the Leper (Matthew 8:1-4)

A. Old Covenant view ("clean, unclean") – separation important to holiness

1. Sin was the superior power
2. Pharisee = *parush,* holiness by separation
3. God had to separate Israel to save them
4. Leprosy identified with sin
5. Home was a small temple *(mikdash me-at),* so act at home as at the Temple
6. Pharisaical pride in being separate
   a. Pride as disordered self-trust, self-reliance (St. Thomas)

B. New Covenant view – for Jesus, holiness is mercy

1. Lenience is not mercy
2. Sickness or accident can be God's mercy
3. Leprosy seen as a sign of mortal sin, which cuts off relationship with God and covenant community (St. Augustine, moral sense)
4. In healing the leper, Jesus reconciles him to the community
5. Leper changes, Jesus does not
   a. God is the same yesterday, today, and forever (Hebrews 13:8)

III. Healing of the Centurion's Servant (Matthew 8:5-13)

A. Centurion demonstrates faith in Christ

1. Right understanding of the nature of God's kingdom and Jesus' authority

B. "Only say the word" (verse 8) – at Mass before receiving the Eucharist

1. Through words of priest, Christ is made present (transubstantiation)
2. Eucharist brings healing, forgiveness of venial sin

C. To "sit at table" alludes to messianic feast (Isaiah 25:6-9)

1. Hints at universal spread of the gospel

a. Promise of worldwide blessing (made to Abraham in Genesis 12)

D. Centurion's servant represents restoration of Gentiles

IV. Healing of Peter's Mother-in-Law (Matthew 8:14-17)

A. Jesus restores and heals so people can serve

B. "He bore our diseases" – fulfills Isaiah 53 (Suffering Servant)

C. The only healing initiated by Jesus

V. Jesus as the "Son of Man" (Matthew 8:18-22)

A. "Son of Man" title (verse 20)

1. Used by Jesus more than any other title for himself

2. Hints *(Heremez)* at Daniel 7:13-14

3. Highest title for Messiah in the first century

4. Daniel 7–8 – Babylon, Persia, Greece, Rome followed by eternal kingdom, the Son of Man

5. Implication – Jesus is the Messiah

6. Jesus responds directly to this title under oath to Caiaphas (Matthew 26)

B. "Leave the dead to bury their own dead" (verse 22)

1. Read Scripture in unity of text – honor your father

2. Burying a loved one took precedence even over daily prayer

3. Hyperbole – his kingdom takes precedence over all

VI. Jesus' Power Over Nature (Matthew 8:23-27)

A. Evokes story of Jonah

VII. Jesus' Power Over Demons (Matthew 8:28-34)

A. Gadarene district – mostly Gentile

B. Old Testament – beasts rise from the sea (example: Daniel 7:1-3)

C. Jesus demonstrates power and authority over the beasts, nations

VIII. Jesus Demonstrates His Power and Gives Us Power

Session 10 – Questions

Matthew 9 – New Wine, New Wineskins

	Prologue	Book 1	Book 2	Book 3	Book 4	Book 5	Conclusion
	Birth of the King	*Announcement of the Kingdom*	*Establishment of the Kingdom*	*The Kingdom Defined*	*Transfer of the Kingdom's Authority*	*Announcement of the End of the Old Kingdom*	*Victory of the King*
NARRATIVE	Mt. 1–2 *Jesus' ancestry and infancy*	Mt. 3–4 *John the Baptist and Jesus' early ministry*	**Mt. 8–9** ***Miracles; commissioning the Twelve***	Mt. 11–12 *Jesus confronts an evil generation*	Mt. 14–17 *Travels and ministry; instructing the Twelve*	Mt. 19–23 *Events and teaching in Judea*	Mt. 26–28 *Passion week*
DISCOURSE		Mt. 5–7 *Sermon on the Mount*	Mt. 10 *Missionary instructions*	Mt. 13 *Kingdom parables*	Mt. 18 *Life in the Christian community*	Mt. 24–25 *Olivet Discourse (Judgment on Jerusalem)*	

A. Review the Context

Matthew 9 continues the narrative portion of Book Two of Matthew's Gospel, "Establishment of the Kingdom," which began with a series of miracles. These miracles were tangible demonstrations of Jesus' power over the things sin brought into the world that separate us from God, such as illness, impurity, isolation, and demon possession. In the Sermon on the Mount, Jesus announced who would be part of the kingdom. In this next chapter, Jesus demonstrates the power that will enable people to enter the kingdom, and he begins to usher them in. By reaching out first to those excluded from the community by the old Law, Jesus opens the door to the kingdom to the Gentiles and offers cleansing and inclusion to all who have faith. By doing so, he radically reinterprets who belongs to the kingdom.

B. Read the Story

Carefully read **Matthew 9.** Ask yourself the questions: *Who? What? When? Where? How? Why?*

As always, pray before you read.

C. Take a Deeper Look

Answering these questions will draw you into the heart of the story. If you do not understand something, make a note of it to bring up in the small-group discussion.

Jesus Heals a Paralytic (Matthew 9:1-8)

Note: "His own city" in verse 1 refers to Capernaum in Galilee. Find it on the map on page 5.

At the end of Matthew 7, we read that the crowds are astonished at the authority with which Jesus teaches. Now, the religious leaders are calling into question the authority with which he acts.

1. a. Why do the scribes, who are experts in Mosaic Law, believe Jesus is blaspheming? (For help with this question, see **Isaiah 43:25; Mark 2:7;** and **Leviticus 17:11.**)

The Scribe believe only God can forgive sins. Jesus is a "Man" bypassing God and forgiving Sins

b. What does Jesus demonstrate to the scribes, and how does he go about it?

Jesus forgives and heals - He does it in the most personal fashion. Healing body & Mind -

c. Whose faith is responsible for the healing of the paralytic and the forgiveness of his sins?

Those who believe and bring the paralytic to Jesus are strong in faith

d. Can we bring the sick before God in faith today and ask him to heal them? Read **James 5:14-15.**

Yes - it's all about faith -

2. **Think About It:** The *Catechism* tells us: "It is the experience of Israel that illness is mysteriously linked to sin and evil, and that faithfulness to God according to his law restores life" (CCC 1502). It is easy to see how the Jewish leaders, focused on attaining holiness, righteousness, and life through strict adherence to the Law and avoidance of everything unclean, might look upon people who are sick as sinners and outcasts. How does Jesus begin to change this thinking?

Jesus heals those who believe - may not follow the religious rules. He also heals out of compassion -

Jesus Calls Matthew (Matthew 9:9-13)

3. The Pharisees object when Jesus and his disciples eat with tax collectors and sinners. Explain what Jesus means when he makes the following three replies in Matthew 9:12-13.

a. "Those who are well have no need of a physician, but those who are sick."

Jesus refers to the Pharasee as those who are sick spiritually

He wants to reach those who need to be spiritually cleansed.

b. "Go and learn what this means, 'I desire mercy, and not sacrifice.'" Jesus quotes from the prophet Hosea, who spoke to the Northern Kingdom about its arrogance, its worship of other gods, and its spiritual sickness. Hosea announced God's judgment, writing: "For I desire mercy and not sacrifice, the knowledge of God, rather than burnt offerings" (Hosea 6:6).

Note: This is a quote from ***Hosea 6:6. Optional:*** *For a deeper understanding of Hosea's general message, read this verse in the context of several chapters, or read your Bible's introduction to Hosea if there is one.*

c. "I came not to call the righteous, but sinners."

what is righteous. Outside - boastful ness. Jesus want to help the humble, those who truly believe, but are afraid.

4. In Matthew 4, we read about how Jesus called his first four disciples. Why do you think Matthew highlighted his own calling in this chapter rather than in the beginning of his Gospel? Think about this in the context of the various accounts of Jesus' healings.

Matthew was a commoner/ one of the Gentiles. Considered an outsider because of being Gentile + tax collector. That Jesus ate with him shows Jesus bradening his range of people for his father's Kingdom.

A Question of Fasting (Matthew 9:14-17)

5. a. A second criticism comes from the disciples of John in verse 14. They ask, "Why do we and the Pharisees fast, but your disciples do not fast?" How does Jesus answer?

Fasting, Jesus said, should be done when appropriate, not as show - Jesus belives his followers were treated as his guests - until the time & purpose changes

b. Jesus' words to his disciples in verses 16-17 about new wine and old wineskins can be applied equally to the Pharisees in verses 10-13. What is he teaching them?

Times change - we are the wine skins - always be open for Religious growth.

More Healings (Matthew 9:18-34)

6. a. What does the woman with the hemorrhage need to do to be healed?

The woman believes and just nees to touch the hem of Jesus' garment.

b. How do you account for the different reactions of the Pharisees and the crowd to Jesus healing the mute demoniac depicted in verses 32-34?

The crowd were in awe - the Pharisees see this as work of a demon.

c. How would you react if you heard about such a miracle occurring today?

I would need to find out more.

7. **Think About It:** Moses performed many miracles in his day; so did Elisha and others. Yet, the people marvel at Jesus' healings: "Never was anything like this seen in Israel," they say in verse 33. What sets Jesus' miracles apart from these other miracles?

God worked through the prophets – they called upon God
Jesus is God and works it himself

The Harvest and Laborers (Matthew 9:35-38)

8. a. After the Southern Kingdom of Judah went into exile, the prophet Ezekiel blasted the "shepherds of Israel" for failing to care for the sheep, God's people. "So they were scattered, because there was no shepherd; and they became food for all the wild beasts" (Ezekiel 34:5). Even though the people have returned physically from exile, how can you tell from this passage in Matthew's Gospel that Jesus sees them in the same situation in his day?

   b. God continues: "I myself will search for my sheep, and will seek them out" (Ezekiel 34:11). "And I will set up over them one shepherd, my servant David, and he shall feed them: he shall feed them and be their shepherd" (Ezekiel 34:23). Who is this "servant David" who will be their shepherd?

9. How does Jesus respond to the needs of these "harassed and helpless," shepherd-less sheep?

He encourages them to join him.

D. Application

These questions will help you apply one of the key themes of the session to your life. After meditating on them, respond to God with a brief written prayer if you choose.

The laws forbidding contact with all that was "unclean" were meant to protect the people from their own weakness and tendency to sin. The Pharisees have turned the Law into a way of measuring their own strength. Are you tempted to make the same mistake? Do you avoid association with, or look down on, some people instead of offering healing or mercy? What can you do to be salt and light in the world?

Dear Lord …

Session 10 Talk Notes

Matthew 9 – New Wine, New Wineskins

I. Continuation of Ten Miracle Stories in Second Discourse (Matthew 8–9)

A. Jesus' power over death

B. Christians share in the power of the kingdom to do Jesus' work

II. Healing of the Paralytic and Forgiveness of Sin (Matthew 9:1-8)

A. "They" bring the man to Christ – cooperation of the family of God

B. Jesus images the Father by forgiving (Jews believed only God could forgive)

C. Old Testament – sickness often associated with sin (see Isaiah 33:24; Psalm 107:17)

D. God's power shown not just in healing, but in our weakness

E. Physical is a sign of the spiritual

F. Common theme of Chapter 9 – rising, resurrection

G. Verse 8 – God has given authority to a man (Jesus) to forgive

H. John 20:23; Matthew 18:18 – basis for the sacrament of reconciliation

1. CCC 1441 – Jesus gives his divine authority to men to exercise in his name
2. CCC 1444 – God gives authority to reconcile sinners to the Church

I. Jesus will take on the sins of the world and "rise"

III. The Calling of Matthew (Matthew 9:9-13)

A. Matthew (Levi) "rose" and followed Jesus

1. Tax collector is unclean (works with Gentiles)

B. Contrast between Jesus and Pharisees as "physicians"

1. Jesus touches; Pharisees cannot
2. Jesus quotes Hosea 6:6
    a. God desires mercy, not sacrifice
    b. Context – restoration of Israel, Judah, and Gentiles
3. Pharisees see themselves as holy *(kadosh)* because they are separate *(parush)*
4. To Jesus, holiness is not separateness, but showing mercy

IV. Fasting and Wineskins (Matthew 9:14-17)

A. Why fast in the presence of the Bridegroom?

1. Old Testament God as Bridegroom (husband)
    a. Isaiah 54:5; Jeremiah 3:20; Hosea 2:16-19
2. Recall the senses of Scripture in CCC 111–117

a. Literal sense – fast when the Bridegroom is not present

b. Moral sense – break fast before Mass when Bridegroom comes in Communion

B. Old and new wineskins

1. Old wineskin = Old Covenant; new wineskin = New Covenant

2. Allegorical sense – Jesus is the new wineskin

3. Moral sense – we are new, born again in Christ

4. New Covenant predicted in Jeremiah 31–33

5. Old Covenant will wear out like a garment (Psalm 102:26)

V. Healing of Woman with a Hemorrhage (Matthew 9:18-22)

A. Unclean woman touches fringe of Jesus' garment

1. Prayer shawl *tallit,* sign of the coming of God's Word

2. *Tallit katan* – four corners (wings) with tassels – *tzittzit*

a. Tassels commanded (Numbers 15:38; Deuteronomy 22:11-12)

b. Reflection of 613 *mitzvot* commandments

3. Jews thought *tzittzit* of Messiah would have healing power

4. Malachi 4:2 (Chapter 3 in NAB) – "healing in its wings"

5. Pharisees extend tassels and enlarge phylacteries[1] to show piety

VI. Other Healings (Matthew 9:23-34)

A. Dead girl "arises," blind men are healed, demon is cast from a mute man

B. "See that no one knows it" (verse 30)

1. Sermon on the Mount – do for the Father, not publicly

2. Knows people will try to make Jesus an earthly king

C. Turning point is healing of demoniac (verses 32-34) – leadership comes against Jesus

VII. The Harvest and the Shepherd (Matthew 9:35-38)

A. Jesus comes as Shepherd, physician, to do what Pharisees failed to do

B. Luke 19:10 – the Son of Man has come to seek and to save the lost

1. *Hekesh* = bang two things together (teaching method)

a. Daniel 7:13-14 – the Son of Man will come, have dominion

b. Ezekiel 34 – shepherds have failed to feed the people, so God will come to seek and save the lost

C. Church does not take the place of the Old Covenant (supersessionism) but fulfills it

---

[1] Phylacteries were small leather boxes Jews wore on their heads and arms during prayer to remind them of God's word (see Deuteronomy 6).

Session 11 – Questions

Matthew 10 – Jesus Commissions the Twelve

	Prologue	Book 1	Book 2	Book 3	Book 4	Book 5	Conclusion
	Birth of the King	*Announcement of the Kingdom*	*Establishment of the Kingdom*	*The Kingdom Defined*	*Transfer of the Kingdom's Authority*	*Announcement of the End of the Old Kingdom*	*Victory of the King*
NARRATIVE	Mt. 1–2 *Jesus' ancestry and infancy*	Mt. 3–4 *John the Baptist and Jesus' early ministry*	Mt. 8–9 *Miracles; commissioning the Twelve*	Mt. 11–12 *Jesus confronts an evil generation*	Mt. 14–17 *Travels and ministry; instructing the Twelve*	Mt. 19–23 *Events and teaching in Judea*	Mt. 26–28 *Passion week*
DISCOURSE		Mt. 5–7 *Sermon on the Mount*	**Mt. 10** ***Missionary instructions***	Mt. 13 *Kingdom parables*	Mt. 18 *Life in the Christian community*	Mt. 24–25 *Olivet Discourse (Judgment on Jerusalem)*	

A. Review the Context

In Matthew 8–9, we read about ten miracles of Jesus that demonstrate the power needed to live the new law Jesus' gave in the Sermon on the Mount. The new life he brought has power over sickness, the elements, demons, and even death. In these chapters, we learned how Jesus established the kingdom of God and used it to welcome "outsiders" and to fling open the doors of the kingdom to all who have faith.

Jesus also called twelve apostles to follow him. Calling attention to the "sheep without a shepherd," he charged them to pray that the Lord would send laborers into the harvest. The stage is set for Jesus' second discourse, in which he will extend the kingdom by sending out the Twelve as missionary laborers.

B. Read the Story

Carefully read **Matthew 10.** Ask yourself the questions: *Who? What? When? Where? How? Why?*

As always, pray before you read.

C. Take a Deeper Look

Answering these questions will draw you into the heart of the story. If you do not understand something, make a note of it to bring up in the small-group discussion.

Jesus Gives His Disciples Authority (Matthew 10:1-4)

Note: The word "apostle" comes from the Greek apostello*—to send forth with a commission. It was used for personal representatives of the king, ambassadors who functioned with the king's authority. This is the spirit in which we see Jesus commissioning his disciples and giving them authority and power to carry out his work on his behalf.*

1. What do you think is the significance of Jesus' selection of twelve apostles? (For help with this question, see **Luke 22:28-30** and **Revelation 21:10-14.**)

i for each of the tribes of Isreal - It is to parallel the prophet Isaiha

2. a. Read the names of the twelve apostles. Whose is the first name on the list?

Peter - always - on whom Jesus would build his Church.

b. Are any of the other apostles' names familiar to you from the preceding chapters of Matthew's Gospel? What kind of men are those described already? (See **Matthew 4:18-22 and 9:9.**)

andrew - James & John - fisherman -

c. **Think About It:** At the end of the list is "Judas Iscariot, who betrayed him." Surely, Jesus knows what kind of man Judas is and that he will betray him; yet, he chooses Judas to be an apostle. Do you sometimes see people in positions of authority in the Church who seem unworthy of those positions? What does Jesus' choice of Judas as an apostle suggest our attitude toward these people and their offices should be?

of Course Judas was last - Jesus knew - but everyone deserves a chance to change. It's not Judas' fault. - this was his destiny.

The Mission of the Apostles (Matthew 10:5-15)

3. a. What charge does Jesus give his apostles, and how does he empower them?

Jesus shares God's message & expects his disciple to do the same. also Jesus shares healing and forgiveness and again expects the disciple to do the same.

b. Who will be the initial recipients of their ministry? Is this significant? (Recall what you learned in **Matthew 4:12-16.**)

He tells them to go to the tribes that were lost & exiled - Tells them to help the lost & forsaken.

4. a. What additional instructions does Jesus give the Twelve?

Go and spread the good news. Do not expect pay - but depend on those who believe. God will provide.

b. When Jews left "unclean" Gentile territory for their own land, it was customary for them to shake the dust from their feet. What is the significance of Jesus' instructions in verses 13-15?

This means:-those who shake the dust from their feet - draw the line - they will not believe

The Cost of Discipleship (Matthew 10:16-39)

5. a. Read **verses 16-24.** Jesus asks his apostles to deliver fantastic news, news that everyone has been longing to hear. Not only that, he gives them the ability to transform people's lives for the better, healing diseases, raising the dead, and casting out demons. In spite of all this, what kind of reception does he tell them to expect?

Not all will accept with open arms.

b. How does Jesus tell them to respond?

Do not be afraid. Bad things will happen. But the Holy Spirit will guide them.

c. What hope and comfort does Jesus give the apostles in these verses?

The Kingdom of Heaven is theirs!

6. a. Following this assurance of persecution, Jesus says in verse 26, "So have no fear of them." How can he say this?

God's love will not change. If we serve the Lord, our reward is with him.

b. **Think About It:** Read **Genesis 3:15** to refresh your memory of the first announcement of the Good News in the Bible. In light of these words of God, why should we not be surprised by Jesus' insistence on the inevitability of persecution—and his admonition not to be afraid?

7. a. Read **Matthew 10:34-39.** Are Jesus' words in verses 34-36, where he says he has come not to bring peace but a sword, a contradiction of his words in John 14:27: "Peace I leave with you; my peace I give to you; not as the world gives do I give to you. Let not your hearts be troubled, neither let them be afraid." Explain your answer.

I think this refers to God's peace – The world cannot give – only God can give

b. What does the cross—a cruel instrument of execution that all Jesus' followers would be familiar with—represent in verse 38?

Jesus died for us as God's will. So must we not be afraid to do God's work. We must be as strong as Jesus – if this is God's will, we accept.

Rewards (Matthew 10:40-42)

8. In verses 14-15, Jesus pronounced judgment greater than that on Sodom and Gomorrah on those who refuse to receive the apostles. In verses 40-42, what does he say is in store for those who do receive them? (Note: Jesus refers to the apostles here as "little ones.")

Everyone who does God's will – will be rewarded.

D. Application

This question will help you apply one of the key themes of the session to your life. After meditating on it, respond to God with a brief written prayer if you choose.

Think about your daily interaction with the Lord. What changes might you make in your life in terms of study, prayer, and action so you can become a better disciple of Christ?

Dear Lord …

E. Wrap-Up – Book Two: Establishment of the Kingdom

How would you summarize Book Two of Matthew's Gospel (Chapters 8–10)?

Session 11 Talk Notes

Matthew 10 – Jesus Commissions the Twelve

I. Apostolic Zeal

A. *Familiaris Consortio* (St. John Paul II on the family)

1. Eucharist is the source of apostolic zeal for the family
2. We go out in the power of the Spirit, fed by Christ

B. Matthew 28 – go out and make disciples

1. Disciple (Heb., *talmid*) – student, disciplined follower

II. Calling and Mission of the Twelve (Matthew 10:1-15)

A. Chapter 10 starts the second discourse in Matthew's Gospel

B. Twelve apostles commissioned to preach the coming of the kingdom

1. Simon Peter is always listed first (Matthew 16 – Peter is made first vicar)
2. Jesus gives the authority he displayed in Chapters 4 and 9

C. Twelve leaders – he is restoring the twelve tribes of Israel

D. Apostle = one who is sent; given his authority

E. Jesus sends them to Israel first

1. Restoration reverses order of exile
2. Exodus 19:5 – Israel is God's own possession; Romans 9: Israel is given special privileges
3. Only after the Resurrection are they sent to the Gentiles

F. Shaking off dust – traditionally when returning to Israel (Matthew 10:14)

1. Jesus says the same about people who reject the gospel
2. See also Luke 10:10-12; Acts 13:51

III. Facing Persecutions (Matthew 10:16-25)

A. Sent as sheep among wolves

1. Christians relive the life of Christ – recapitulation

B. Be wise as serpents, innocent as doves

1. "Without innocence, shrewdness becomes manipulative. Without shrewdness, innocence becomes naive" (New Testament – Wright)
2. Spiritual warfare

C. He is sending us out – be ready ("make your heart a project")

1. Know yourself and your weaknesses
2. Advance in spiritual growth; combat vice with virtue
3. Do not be anxious; he will give you the words

4. Endure to the end

D. He promises to come again within "this generation"

1. Forty-year period leading to destruction of the Temple in AD 70

E. Be like your teacher, master

1. Beelzebul – a Philistine god worshiped in Ekron (2 Kings 1:2-16)
2. "Prince of Baal" = "Lord of Flies" or "Lord of Dung" = Satan
3. What happens to Jesus will happen to us

IV. Do Not Be Afraid (Matthew 10:26-33)

A. The most-often repeated command of Jesus

B. Satan cannot force spiritual death on the soul

1. CCC 363 – soul as innermost, valuable aspect of man

V. A New Way of Being God's People (Matthew 10:34-39)

A. I have not come to bring peace but a sword

1. Jesus did not come to bring division
   a. Analogy of faith, coherence of truth
   b. Jesus is the Prince of Peace
2. His new way of being God's people brings division

B. Setting children against parents – quoting Micah 7:6

1. Context – prophecy of division when God does something new
2. CCC 2232 – family ties are important but not absolute
   a. First vocation of Christians is to follow Christ
   b. Goal of formation – teach our children to love Christ more than us

C. Importance of taking up one's cross

1. The only way to find yourself is to give your life away
   a. When Adam protected his life, he lost it
   b. We are called to self-emptying love
2. To pick up your cross is to die to yourself
3. Acts 1:8 – you shall be my "witnesses" = *martus* (martyr)

VI. He Who Receives You Receives Me (Matthew 10:40-42)

A. CCC 858 – Jesus is the Father's emissary; the apostles are Jesus' emissaries

B. Service to the apostles is service to Jesus – our bishops descend from the apostles

Session 12 – Questions

Matthew 11–12 – Jesus Confronts an Evil Generation

	Prologue	Book 1	Book 2	Book 3	Book 4	Book 5	Conclusion
	Birth of the King	*Announcement of the Kingdom*	*Establishment of the Kingdom*	*The Kingdom Defined*	*Transfer of the Kingdom's Authority*	*Announcement of the End of the Old Kingdom*	*Victory of the King*
NARRATIVE	Mt. 1–2 *Jesus' ancestry and infancy*	Mt. 3–4 *John the Baptist and Jesus' early ministry*	Mt. 8–9 *Miracles; commissioning the Twelve*	**Mt. 11–12** ***Jesus confronts an evil generation***	Mt. 14–17 *Travels and ministry; instructing the Twelve*	Mt. 19–23 *Events and teaching in Judea*	Mt. 26–28 *Passion week*
DISCOURSE		Mt. 5–7 *Sermon on the Mount*	Mt. 10 *Missionary instructions*	Mt. 13 *Kingdom parables*	Mt. 18 *Life in the Christian community*	Mt. 24–25 *Olivet Discourse (Judgment on Jerusalem)*	

A. Establish the Context

Chapter 10 wrapped up Book Two of Matthew's Gospel with Jesus' missionary instructions to the twelve newly appointed apostles. Having demonstrated his power over nature and sin and death, Jesus turned his attention toward getting out the news of the kingdom through the apostles, on whom he bestowed his own power and authority to heal illness and cast out demons. Imagine for a moment the apostles' roller-coaster of emotions as Jesus first announced the apostles would share in his power, then told them to expect the same negative reception he received, and then fortified them against this certain persecution. His answer to their concerns is the most frequently occurring promise of the New Testament: Do not be afraid. Those who persecute you cannot touch your soul, and God has overcome the world.

Find Book Three: "The Kingdom Defined," on the diagram on this page. Jesus has moved from giving the apostles missionary instructions to confronting the people who have given him (and will later give the apostles) the most trouble. The discourse those encounters lead up to centers on parables that help further define what God's kingdom is about and who belongs to it.

B. Read the Story

Carefully read **Matthew 11–12.** Ask yourself the questions: *Who? What? When? Where? How? Why?*

As always, pray before you read.

C. Take a Deeper Look

Answering these questions will draw you into the heart of the story. If you do not understand something, make a note of it to bring up in the small-group discussion.

John the Baptist (Matthew 11:1-19)

John the Baptist had heard reports while in prison of Jesus' miracles. Were they what he had expected from the Messiah? The Bible does not tell us, but John sent this question to Jesus: "Are you he who is to come, or shall we look for another?"

1. a. Although Jesus' answer seems to merely reiterate what John already knows (that Jesus has been healing people and preaching the Good News), it actually says much more. How is Jesus elaborating on what John already knows? (Read **Isaiah 35:4-6 and 61:1-2.**)

he is quoting from the phropet Isaiah to make John see the fillfillment –

b. Jesus tells the crowd that John the Baptist is more than a prophet—he is the Elijah who is to come. He is the greatest of all the prophets, sent to prepare the way for Jesus and the kingdom. Yet, great as John is, Jesus says that even the least in the kingdom is greater than him. What do you think he means by this?

John was blessed by God – We have to struggle with our faith. We need to have faith and than action.

c. What does Jesus say about his generation in verses 16-19?

He belittles them – because they should have faith in him ——

Woe on Unrepentant Cities (Matthew 11:20-24)

2. Read **verses 20-24;** then use the map on page 5 to locate the cities mentioned. Why does Jesus compare the first three cities unfavorably to Tyre and Sidon and pronounce such a harsh judgment on them?

Because Jesus showed them firsthand the power of God and yet the people failed to believe.

Jesus' Yoke (Matthew 11:25-30)

3. a. In contrast to the unrepentant cities that reject Jesus' teaching and miracles, who are those that know the Father and "come" to Jesus?

Share your burden with God and he will help you along the way.

b. What is the "yoke" Jesus refers to in verse 29? (See also **Sirach 51:23-26** and **1 John 5:3.**)

a yoke puls oxen. Figure of speech to share will make your yoke easy & burden light.

Challenges to Jesus' Authority (Matthew 12:1-21)

Following the destruction of the first Temple in 587 BC and during the exile, the Sabbath gained importance as one way the displaced Jews maintained their identity while they lived among strangers. By Jesus' time, keeping the Sabbath was an essential part of Jewish life, and there was a great deal of debate over how it should be observed. Lists of rules were drawn up by the rabbis. Penalties were enforced for breaking the law. As a result, a day set apart for rest in God's image had turned into a day of obligation, stripped of its meaning and intended effect.

4. a. What two charges do the Pharisees bring against Jesus and his disciples in verses 1-14? (See also **Exodus 20:10.**)

   Jesus preaches & heals on the Sabbath

   b. What is Jesus' defense? (Note: If you want to read about the incident Jesus refers to in verses 3-4, it can be found in **1 Samuel 21:1-6.** In verse 5 of this passage, it says that priests who do the work required to offer sacrifice on the Sabbath, do so without guilt.)

   Shepherds are ~~alow~~ allowed to tend to sheep on Sabbath. Are ~~well~~ we less than sheep?

   c. Read **CCC 2168–2172.** What was the original purpose of the Sabbath that the Pharisees have lost in their zeal to enforce the Law?

   Seventh day is Rest - for Man to be like God - and worship.
   Pharisees are more worried about the law than religion.

Challenges to the Source of Jesus' Power (Matthew 12:22-37)

5. a. What serious charge do the Pharisees make against Jesus?

   He casts out demons - by the power of the Devil.

   b. How does Jesus reveal the fallacy in their charge?

   If this is true the kingdom would collapse - They would scatter & work against God If they believe this, they are doomed

   c. In verses 30-34, what grave risk does Jesus say the Pharisees are taking by making this charge? (**Optional:** Read **CCC 1864, 679.**)

Jesus Confronts His Generation (Matthew 12:38-45)

6. a. Read **verses 38-45.** What does Jesus mean by "the sign of the prophet Jonah"? (For help with this question, see **CCC 994.**)

Jesus is comparing himself to Jonah. Three days in the belly of whale = 3 days Jesus in tomb. Jonah release = Jesus resurrection.

~~The Believed~~

b. Jesus gives two examples of Gentiles—one nation (Nineveh) and one person (the queen of the South, or Sheba)—who will arise and condemn his generation. Why would they do this?

Nineveh saw the light & repented –
The Queen of Sheba belived Solomon – and yet they cannot believe Jesus

7. Both Jesus and the Pharisees expel evil spirits. What will happen, though, if that generation ("the man" of Jesus' illustration in verses 43-45) fails to fill the resulting vacuum with acceptance of the kingdom Jesus offers and with the power of the Spirit of God?

Seven spirits more will come and they will be worse.

Jesus' True Family (Matthew 12:46-50)

8. Read **verses 46-50.** How does Jesus broaden the concept of family? (See also **John 1:11-13** and **1 John 3:10.**)

Jesus doesn't only include physical beings, but the spiritual family as well

D. Application

This question will help you apply one of the key themes of the session to your life. After meditating on it, respond to God with a brief written prayer if you choose.

Are you carrying a burden that is too heavy for you? "Come to me, all who labor and are heavy laden, and I will give you rest," says the Lord. Pray and ask God to show you what it means to exchange this burden for his yoke that is easy.

Dear Lord …

Session 12 Talk Notes

Matthew 11–12 – Jesus Confronts an Evil Generation

I. Messianic Signs

A. Are you he who is to come?
   1. Jesus' miracles recall messianic signs (11:5) – Isaiah 26:19, 29:18, 35:4-6, 61:1-2
   2. CCC 549 – Jesus performed messianic signs

II. John the Baptist (Matthew 11:1-19)

A. John as the forerunner of the Messiah (Malachi 3:1)
B. John comes in the spirit of Elijah
   1. Elijah prepared for Elisha as John prepares for Jesus, Moses for Joshua
C. "This generation" (verse 16)
   1. Jesus exposes superficial leadership, Pharisees
   2. Like children playing games, expecting others to follow
   3. True wisdom justified by deeds

III. Woe on Unrepentant Cities (Matthew 11:20-24)

A. "Woe" is judgment formulation in Hebrew
B. Cities that do not respond to Jesus' works will be judged
   1. Compares Capernaum to Sodom

IV. Come to Me (Matthew 11:25-30)

A. Discussion turns to lifting of burdens
B. "Come to me" – turn to him in prayer
C. "Take my yoke upon you" and find rest
   1. Yoke put on ox to steer it in a particular direction
   2. New Covenant has a yoke but also the power to carry it

V. The Sabbath and the Temple (Matthew 12:1-8)

A. Pharisees accuse Jesus' disciples of breaking the Sabbath
   1. Old Covenant – only priests could lift burdens on Sabbath
   2. Jesus is establishing a New Israel with new priests
B. Jesus traps the Pharisees using 1 Samuel 21
   1. David and the men are hungry; Ahimelech gives bread of the presence
   2. Saul sent Doeg the Edomite to spy, wipes out priests of Nob

3. In Jesus' parallel – he is the King; disciples are priests of the new kingdom; Pharisees are spying on the anointed King

C. Mark's account of this story (2:23) makes clear the days of the Pharisees are over

1. Substitutes Abiathar for Ahimilech (Ahimilech's son; last priest under Saul)
2. Zadok first priest under David (2 Samuel 8:7)

D. Jesus uses *remez*[1] to suggest that, like David, he is priest and King

E. Shewbread = bread of the presence; an everlasting covenant

1. Eucharist as the real presence

F. Something greater than the Temple is here

1. God wanted to be Israel's dwelling and King; made provision due to their hardness of heart
    a. 1 Samuel 8 – Israel cried out for a king like other nations
    b. God gave king and Temple provisionally – types of the reality to come
    c. Now something greater than the Temple is here (Jesus)

G. The Son of Man is "lord of the sabbath" (Matthew 12:8)

VI. Lifting Burdens (Matthew 12:9-21)

A. Healing the man with the withered hand – points to deeper healing

VII. Jesus and Beelzebul (Matthew 12:22-32)

A. Pharisees attribute work of God to Satan – Beelzebul

1. CCC 1864 – deliberately refusing God's grace is unpardonable

VIII. The Sign of Jonah (Matthew 12:38-42)

A. Jonah did not want to preach to Assyria

1. Isaiah and Amos prophesied that Assyria would be sent to punish Israel

B. Conversion comes to Nineveh – some repented

C. Jonah 3:4 – in forty days, God will destroy Nineveh

1. Within forty years, it was destroyed

D. Deeper sign – forty years after Jesus, the Romans would destroy the Temple

E. Like Nineveh, Jerusalem had a chance to repent but did not

IX. This Is the End of the Old Regime – End of an Age

X. Next Chapter: Parables

[1] This method of teaching "hints" at the allegoric meaning of a text.

Session 13 – Questions

Matthew 13 – Parables of the Kingdom

	Prologue	Book 1	Book 2	Book 3	Book 4	Book 5	Conclusion
	Birth of the King	*Announcement of the Kingdom*	*Establishment of the Kingdom*	*The Kingdom Defined*	*Transfer of the Kingdom's Authority*	*Announcement of the End of the Old Kingdom*	*Victory of the King*
NARRATIVE	Mt. 1–2 *Jesus' ancestry and infancy*	Mt. 3–4 *John the Baptist and Jesus' early ministry*	Mt. 8–9 *Miracles; commissioning the Twelve*	Mt. 11–12 *Jesus confronts an evil generation*	Mt. 14–17 *Travels and ministry; instructing the Twelve*	Mt. 19–23 *Events and teaching in Judea*	Mt. 26–28 *Passion week*
DISCOURSE		Mt. 5–7 *Sermon on the Mount*	Mt. 10 *Missionary instructions*	**Mt. 13** ***Kingdom parables***	Mt. 18 *Life in the Christian community*	Mt. 24–25 *Olivet Discourse (Judgment on Jerusalem)*	

A. Review the Context

Matthew 13 is Jesus' third discourse and is made up of a series of parables about the kingdom of heaven. In the previous narrative section (Matthew 11–12), Jesus confronted his generation with its failure to repent and receive the Good News of the kingdom; and the Jewish leaders began to challenge Jesus' authority and power.

B. Read the Story

Carefully read **Matthew 13.** Ask yourself the questions: *Who? What? When? Where? How? Why?*

As always, pray before you read.

C. Take a Deeper Look

Answering these questions will draw you into the heart of the story. If you do not understand something, make a note of it to bring up in the small-group discussion.

Parable of the Sower (Matthew 13:1-23)

1. This chapter is filled with Jesus' parables about the kingdom of heaven. The Greek word for "parable" is *parabole*—literally, a "placing beside." In the Gospels, it is a comparison from everyday life that is used to illustrate a spiritual truth. What reason does Jesus give in verses 10-16 for using parables?

CoRupt Leadership - They cannot see themselves
Jesus tries to ~~make things~~ reveal things to the
listner – Makes a point.

2. What is given to the disciples but not to the crowd, and why? (See **verses 11-17** and **CCC 546.**)

The disciples gain insight to the Kingdom of God. The are spiritually enlightened

3. a. Read the parable of the sower in **verses 18-23.** According to Jesus, what do each of the following things refer to?

The seed that falls along the path: hardened heart - hears but doesn't believe

The seed that falls among rocks: -shallow - hears but doesn't allow to seed to grow - short term -

The seed that falls among thorns: -Strangled - hears - belives, but allows outside forces to hold your beliefs back.

The seed that falls on good soil: belwer - Hears - nutures and allows change to build on belief-

b. What is the main message of this parable?

We ~~At~~ must nuture our faith to grow-

c. Why is the Word of God not always effective in our lives? (Read also **1 Thessalonians 2:13** and **Hebrews 4:2.**)

Life gets in the way. We allow human worry's take over.

Parable of the Weeds (Matthew 13:24-30, 36-43)

4. Read the parable of the weeds in **verses 24-30** and what Jesus says about it in **verses 36-43.**

a. What do the following represent?

The sower of the good seed: Jesus

The field: the WORLD

The sower of the bad seed: the Devil

The good seed: Sons of the Kingdom

The bad seed (weeds): Son of the devil.

The reapers: angels

The time of the harvest: end of days

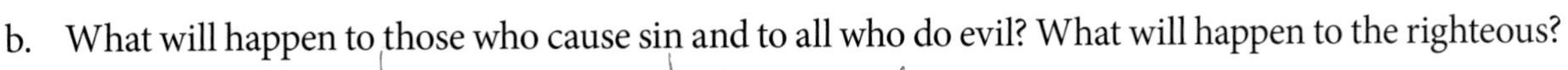

b. What will happen to those who cause sin and to all who do evil? What will happen to the righteous?

we will be seperated in the end -
bad to hell - good to heaven

c. Read **CCC 827 and 681–682.** What ramifications does this parable have for the Church today? (You might ask yourself: Who is responsible for pulling the "weeds"?)

We must be accept all people-

Four More Parables (Matthew 13:31-35, 44-46)

5. Jesus tells four more parables in verses 31-46.

a. What is the connection between the kingdom of heaven and the mustard seed and the way it grows?

Smallest of seeds - but grows strong tree.. Tree = great Nation.
birds in the trees =nations

b. How does Jesus use the concept of yeast to expand our understanding of the kingdom?

shows how a small amount of faith and
multiply.

c. What is the lesson of the two parables in verses 44-46?

The Kingdom of heaven is a treasure. We must
be willing to give up everything for the Kingdom of God.

Parable of the Net: A Prophet Without Honor (Matthew 13:47-58)

6. Read **verses 47-52.** What does the parable of the net tell us about the judgment to come?

we are the fish in the net - as the fisherman go through
their catch & "weed" out the best. There is good & bad
in everyone

7. a. Why are the people of Jesus' hometown "amazed" at him (verse 54)?

Because he was one of them. grew up with them.
No one expects greatness around them.

b. How does their reaction differ from the "amazed" crowd in Matthew 7:28?

This crowd is afraid & cannot believe what is happening. They are threatened

c. What is the consequence of their unbelief?

Jesus doesnot perform any wonderous signs in his home town

D. Application

These questions will help you apply one of the key themes of the session to your life. After meditating on them, respond to God with a brief written prayer if you choose.

Is your heart like the "good soil" in which the seed of the Word can grow readily? You might look at different aspects of your life in light of the four types of soil described in Matthew 13. For example, consider the "soil" of your marriage or your moral life. Is it receptive to the Word, or is it rocky, unreceptive, or choked with care? How can you make sure you hear, understand, and bear fruit?

Dear Lord ...

E. Wrap-Up – Book Three: The Kingdom Defined

How would you summarize Book Three of Matthew's Gospel (Chapters 11–13)?

Session 13 Talk Notes

Matthew 13 – Parables of the Kingdom

I. Jesus Begins to Teach in Parables (Matthew 13:1-13)

A. Matthew 13 – the third discourse

B. Parables

1. Rabbinic use in Old Testament for corrupt leadership (see Judges 9; 2 Samuel 12)

2. Used forty-eight times in the Gospels of Matthew, Mark, and Luke

    a. ("Synoptics" = to see as one)

3. Earthly sketches of heavenly realities – the kingdom is hidden

4. First four parables given to the crowds and the next three given to the disciples

5. One theme of kingdom parables – patience, waiting

II. Purpose of the Parables

A. Jesus answers the "why" with Isaiah 6:9-11

1. People and rulers guilty of covenant infidelity

2. "Hear, O Israel" = *Shema* of Deuteronomy 6

    a. Hearing means doing

    b. God proclaims judgment on faithless generation

B. In the kingdom, the small things matter

C. Isaiah: Great things will happen but not until the old regime falls

D. This generation is not hearing it, but the disciples are

III. The Parable of the Sower

A. Jesus is talking about hearing the Word of God

B. Hearing the words and bearing fruit require "focus" – *kavanah*

IV. The Parable of the Weeds (Matthew 13:24-30)

A. The enemy sows weeds among the wheat

B. Weeds may refer to the darnel plant

C. Our Church consists of wheat and weeds

D. Our job is not to be wheat (weed) "pullers," but "fertilizer" (teach and love)

V. Parable of the Mustard Seed (Matthew 13:31-32)

A. The smallest of all seeds grows into a tree

1. Trees in the Old Testament symbolized great nations (Daniel 4:10-12; Ezekiel 17:22-24)

2. Birds landing in tree symbolize Gentile nations

B. The whole world will find a resting place in the kingdom of God

VI. Parable of the Leaven (Matthew 13:33)

A. Shows the disproportionate power of the kingdom

1. Examples – Blessed Teresa of Calcutta (Mother Teresa) and St. John Paul II

2. Be faithful in the little things

B. Purpose of parables is reiterated (fulfill Psalm 78:2)

VII. Jesus Speaks to the Disciples (Matthew 13:36-51)

A. Meaning of the parable of the weeds

1. This is not a perfect Church; reduces anxiety

B. Treasure, pearls – nothing but the kingdom really matters

1. Allegorical sense – Christ is the great hidden treasure

2. Old and new treasure = Old and New Covenants

Matthew 14–15 – Instructions to the Twelve

	Prologue	Book 1	Book 2	Book 3	Book 4	Book 5	Conclusion
	Birth of the King	*Announcement of the Kingdom*	*Establishment of the Kingdom*	*The Kingdom Defined*	*Transfer of the Kingdom's Authority*	*Announcement of the End of the Old Kingdom*	*Victory of the King*
NARRATIVE	Mt. 1–2 *Jesus' ancestry and infancy*	Mt. 3–4 *John the Baptist and Jesus' early ministry*	Mt. 8–9 *Miracles; commissioning the Twelve*	Mt. 11–12 *Jesus confronts an evil generation*	**Mt. 14–17** ***Travels and ministry; instructing the Twelve***	Mt. 19–23 *Events and teaching in Judea*	Mt. 26–28 *Passion week*
DISCOURSE		Mt. 5–7 *Sermon on the Mount*	Mt. 10 *Missionary instructions*	Mt. 13 *Kingdom parables*	Mt. 18 *Life in the Christian community*	Mt. 24–25 *Olivet Discourse (Judgment on Jerusalem)*	

A. Establish the Context

The parables of the kingdom in Chapter 13 function as a hinge between the two halves of Matthew's Gospel. They draw a "line in the sand" between those who accept Jesus' message and those who reject it. With these parables, there is growing opposition among Jesus' enemies and a fresh comprehension of the truth among his followers. Taken together, the parables paint an interesting and perhaps unexpected picture of the kingdom: It will start out very small, like the tiniest of seeds, hidden so that it must be searched for. Those who seek the kingdom must be willing to give up everything to attain it and should be confident it will be worth the sacrifice. While on earth, the kingdom will contain "weeds" and "wheat"—both "good" and "bad" people—together. People living in the kingdom must exercise the same sort of mercy and patience God offers them. They must be patient and refrain from the temptation to "pull out the weeds" prematurely. Judgment belongs to God.

Look at the diagram on this page before continuing. We are at the start of Book Four of Matthew's Gospel: "Transfer of the Kingdom's Authority." Notice the titles of the narrative and discourse sections of this book.

B. Read the Story

Carefully read **Matthew 14–15.** Ask yourself the questions: *Who? What? When? Where? How? Why?*

As always, pray before you read.

C. Take a Deeper Look

Answering these questions will draw you into the heart of the story. If you do not understand something, make a note of it to bring up in the small-group discussion.

The Death of John the Baptist (Matthew 14:1-12)

1. When Jesus hears that John the Baptist has been beheaded, he does not demand justice or confront Herod but withdraws to a lonely place. Why do you think he does this?

He meditates because he knows it is his time to begin his public ministry -

Jesus Feeds the Five Thousand (Matthew 14:13-21)

2. a. Contrast the disciples' reaction to the needs of the crowd with Jesus' response to their needs.

Jesus is showing by example that all people need help & Love & attention.

b. Jesus asks his disciples to do something that is humanly impossible. What do you think the disciples learn from this experience?

The disciples need to to see a bigger picture. Jesus is the beginning - his Kingdom is small but will be growing - tend to there needs and God will provide.

c. Notice that Jesus does not feed the people himself; he has his disciples pass around the bread and fish in his name; and by his power, they distribute abundance from their meager store. Do you see a parallel to this in the Church today? (For help with this question, see **CCC 1335.**)

Jesus is showing them. Tend to the people. They will grow in number. parallels the priest and the distribution of the bread & wine.

Jesus Walks on Water (Matthew 14:22-33)

3. It is not the storm that first frightens the disciples, but the sight of Jesus walking toward them. How does Jesus respond to their fear?

Tries to calm them - Do not be afraid.

4. a. When Peter realizes it is Jesus, his immediate response is to ask Jesus to permit him to walk on the water. What causes Peter to doubt after his initial success?

The outside elements - the storm - shakes Peter - he panics - doubts - thus begins to fall.

b. What significant confession do the disciples make after this event, and how does it contrast with their reaction the first time they saw Jesus' power over a storm? (For help with this question, see **Matthew 8:23-27.**) The disciples' fear turns to awe & worship. they realize he is truly the son of man

5. What have you learned about faith from the two miracles Jesus performs in Chapter 14?
We should believe that God will provide. It is easy to be afraid.– It is hard to believe!

Clean and Unclean (Matthew 15:1-20)

6. a. In verses 1-9, the scribes and Pharisees once again attempt to catch Jesus and his disciples in an infraction of the Law. What do they accuse the disciples of doing?
The Pharisees accuse Jesus & his disciple of not following the traditions of the elders. Washing before eating– to become pure.

b. How does Jesus reply?
Jesus tells the Pharisees they do not uphold the traditions in other way –

c. How does Jesus explain his parable in verses 17-20?
Jesus explains – outward signs of belief cannot change the inside belief.

The Faith of the Canaanite Woman (Matthew 15:21-28)

Locate the predominantly Gentile district of Tyre and Sidon the map on page 5.

7. a. How does the Canaanite woman obtain healing for her daughter despite Jesus' initial refusal to heal her?
The woman is persistent in her faith she proves to Jesus she is a woman of faith.

b. How can this incident give us confidence as we approach the Father in prayer? (See **CCC 2609–2610.**)
We must be strong & perservere.

Jesus Feeds the Four Thousand (Matthew 15:29-39)

8. a. Before feeding the four thousand, Jesus performs many other miracles in this primarily Gentile region (see **verses 30-31**). List them, and describe how the crowd reacts to them.

   b. Why do you think Matthew includes this list of miracles in his Gospel?

   all things are possible with the belief in God.

9. a. Notice the verbs Matthew uses in **14:19 and 15:36.** Read **Matthew 26:26.** What do the miracles recorded here anticipate? (See also **CCC 1335.**)

   Mimics the Last Supper
   Liturgy of the Eucharist.

   b. **Think About It:** Matthew records not one but two feeding miracles. These miracles have the effect of brackets, focusing the reader's attention on what is between them: the offense the Jewish leaders take at the disciples. Contrast the roles Jesus assigns his disciples in these stories with the role the scribes and Pharisees play. How does this illuminate the difference between the Old and New Covenants?

D. Application

These questions will help you apply one of the key themes of the session to your life. After meditating on them, respond to God with a brief written prayer if you choose.

Are you facing a problem that looks as impossible to solve as feeding five thousand people seemed to the disciples? Look for inspiration to Blessed Teresa of Calcutta (Mother Teresa), who started out with nothing more than a rosary, a few dollars, a Bible, and a change of clothes. What "little" do you have that you can turn over to Jesus so he can work through you?

Dear Lord …

Session 14 Talk Notes

Matthew 14–15 – Instructions to the Twelve

I. The Kingdom in Action

A. How the kingdom plays out in real life

B. Matthew's fourth narrative

II. The Death of John the Baptist (Matthew 14:1-12)

A. Significance of this account here

1. John as the Elijah who is to come

a. 2 Kings 2:6ff – relationship with Elisha

b. 2 Kings 4 – Elisha's miracles

2. Jesus' miracles echo Elisha's miracles

B. Read the Bible in the context and unity of the whole (CCC 112)

III. Feeding the Five Thousand (Matthew 14:13-21)

A. Disciples' solution versus Jesus' solution

B. Church Fathers – tied to Eucharist (allegorical sense)

1. Jesus is the true Bread

2. What God can do with a little (demonstration of the kingdom)

3. The "source and summit" of the Christian life (CCC 1324)

4. The source of apostolic zeal for the family (St. John Paul II, *Familiaris Consortio*)

5. Eucharist as "the great exchange" (Bishop Fabian Bruskewitz)

C. Allegorical sense – Jesus as the Bread multiplied

D. Moral sense – gift of self and talents can become a lot in God's hands

E. Transubstantiation – bread and wine become Body and Blood of Christ

F. The disciples are priests of the New Covenant

G. Significance of numbers

1. Feeding of five thousand (14:13-21)

a. Twelve baskets = twelve tribes; "five thousand" recalls five books of Moses

b. The Eucharist is enough to feed all of Israel

2. Feeding of four thousand (15:32-39)

a. Four corners of the earth, "seven" = covenant fulfillment

b. Gentiles; enough for the world

IV. Jesus on the Mountain and the Sea (Matthew 14:22-33)

A. Jesus draws apart – words and works manifest prayer in secret (CCC 2602)

B. Peter gets out of the boat

V. Jesus Heals the Sick (Matthew 14:34-36)

A. Fringe of garment (see notes on page 62 on *tzittzit*)

VI. Traditions (Matthew 15:1-9)

A. Do Paul and Jesus nullify tradition?

B. 2 Thessalonians 3:6

C. Tradition means to pass on

1. Big "T" Tradition – cannot change

2. Small "t" tradition – can change

D. Jesus is condemning *corban* (emphasis of tradition at the expense of the Law)

VII. Feeding the Four Thousand (Matthew 15:32-39)

Session 15 – Questions

Matthew 16 – Jesus Establishes the Church

	Prologue	Book 1	Book 2	Book 3	Book 4	Book 5	Conclusion
	Birth of the King	*Announcement of the Kingdom*	*Establishment of the Kingdom*	*The Kingdom Defined*	*Transfer of the Kingdom's Authority*	*Announcement of the End of the Old Kingdom*	*Victory of the King*
NARRATIVE	Mt. 1–2 *Jesus' ancestry and infancy*	Mt. 3–4 *John the Baptist and Jesus' early ministry*	Mt. 8–9 *Miracles; commissioning the Twelve*	Mt. 11–12 *Jesus confronts an evil generation*	**Mt. 14–17** ***Travels and ministry; instructing the Twelve***	Mt. 19–23 *Events and teaching in Judea*	Mt. 26–28 *Passion week*
DISCOURSE		Mt. 5–7 *Sermon on the Mount*	Mt. 10 *Missionary instructions*	Mt. 13 *Kingdom parables*	Mt. 18 *Life in the Christian community*	Mt. 24–25 *Olivet Discourse (Judgment on Jerusalem)*	

A. Review the Context

In his two feeding miracles, Jesus demonstrated what he taught in his parables about the kingdom: It might look small at first, but the kingdom possesses great power and potential for growth when Jesus' disciples step out in faith and cooperate. In these miracles, Jesus demonstrated for his disciples the mission he would charge them with before leaving: taking the power and life of the kingdom first to the Jews and then to the Gentiles and all the world. We see this work continued today in the distribution of Jesus' Body and Blood at Mass. The Eucharist provides spiritual nourishment to all people in the Church.

Chapter 16 continues Matthew's account of Jesus' travels, ministry, and instruction of the Twelve. It is a pivotal chapter in which Jesus gives Peter authority to be the first "prime minister" of the kingdom. It is also the first time Jesus announces his coming death and resurrection.

B. Read the Story

Carefully read **Matthew 16.** Ask yourself the questions: *Who? What? When? Where? How? Why?*

As always, pray before you read.

C. Take a Deeper Look

Answering these questions will draw you into the heart of the story. If you do not understand something, make a note of it to bring up in the small-group discussion.

"A Wicked and Adulterous Generation" (Matthew 16:1-12)

1. The Pharisees and Sadducees come to test Jesus in verse 1. In what way does their question reflect Satan's first temptation of Jesus in the desert in **Matthew 4:3?**

Just like Satan - they wanted some sign of proof

2. a. What "signs of the times" do you think Jesus is accusing the Pharisees and Sadducees of being unable to interpret?

Comparing Jonah giving message to the people to Jesus giving a message

b. What kind of sign does Jesus offer them? Explain it. (**Optional:** Read the book of **Jonah,** which contains just four short chapters.)

What is the sign of Jonah - Johan being in belly 3 day & 3 night - 40 days in Nineveh will be overthrone. Hinting at destruction of temple — Jesus is the new beginning.

3. In verses 5-12, Jesus warns the disciples to beware of the "yeast" (teaching) of the Pharisees and Sadducees. What do the uses and properties of yeast add to your understanding of his warning?

The Pharises & Sadduceses want proof that Jesus is the Messiah. Peter proclaims that Jesus is the Son of God - The P & S cannot see the correalitan between OLD Covenant and Jesus.

Peter's Confession (Matthew 16:13-20)

4. a. How does Peter's understanding of who Jesus is compare with the way the religious leaders and other men see Jesus?

Peter was given his proclaimation from God | Holy Spirit.

b. Why is it important to know who Jesus is?

Jesus is the Savior of all. Calling him by any other name may cause people to miss him.

c. Whom does Jesus say is the source of Peter's knowledge?

God the Father

5. a. After Simon acknowledges Jesus to be "the Christ, the Son of the living God," Jesus gives him a new name—Peter—meaning "Rock." Can you remember anyone else who was given a new name by God, and why? (See **Genesis 17 and 32.**)

abraham— he will be father of many

b. The word "rock" was not commonly used as a name in Old Testament times the way "Peter" is used today. It *was* used to describe God, however. (See **Isaiah 26:4** and **2 Samuel 22:32.**) On one occasion, it was used to describe someone else. Who was it? Read **Isaiah 51:1-2.**

↳ Abraham - man a leader for he was one & then was made many -

c. Why is it significant that Jesus gives Simon the new name Peter?

Peter is father of the Church - he is one & his followers many -

*In the original Aramaic, both "Peter" and "rock" are the same word—*kephas. *In Greek, the word for "rock" is* petra. *Because this is a feminine noun, the masculine* petros *("stone") is used for Peter's name in the translation.*

6. a. What does Jesus promise Peter in verse 18, and what does this promise mean for the Church? (See also **CCC 552.**) Peter will be the leader of this New church. The FIRST Pope - It will be unshaken. This means the church will withstand conflicts —

b. In verse 19, Jesus gives Peter "the keys of the kingdom of heaven" and tells him, "Whatever you bind on earth shall be bound in heaven, and whatever you loose on earth shall be loosed in heaven." Read **Isaiah 22:15-25** and **Revelation 3:7.** What insight do these passages give you into the meaning of the keys? Read also **CCC 553.**

The keys are similar to power. whatever the Pope's says is true is true and forbid forbid. JUST Like Keys open the door - truth and CLOSE - forbid.

Jesus Prophesies His Death (Matthew 16:21-28)

7. Verse 21 marks a turning point in Matthew's Gospel. God has revealed Jesus' identity to Peter and made him the foundation stone of the Church. "From that time," Jesus begins to tell his disciples what the establishment of this new kingdom will require.

He must go to Jerusalem - suffer, die and be raised on the 3RD Day.

a. Why are Jesus' words so hard for Peter to take?

Peter cannot believe a leader would suffer and die

b. Why does Jesus reply with such force? (Do you see any parallel between Peter's remark and the words of the Serpent in Genesis 3 or of Satan in Matthew 4 when he tempts Jesus in the desert?)

Because Peter says he belives and the does not really completely understand that Jesus must suffer.

c. **Think About It:** How should we see Peter's error in light of the special revelation he has just received and the fact that he will be the foundation of the Church? For that matter, how do we understand the mistakes of any of the later popes in light of their infallibility?

Human factor. But when we hit a dark place, we hope we come back enlightened.

8. a. It is not only Jesus who will suffer. What does Jesus say will be required of anyone who follows him? (Read also **Romans 8:15-18** and **John 12:24.**)

Not all people will believe. And sometimes that is a threat. We all suffer because of our belief at times

b. How can we do this today?

Be strong & confident, yet humble and full of service

D. Application

These questions will help you apply one of the key themes of the session to your life. After meditating on them, respond to God with a brief written prayer if you choose.

St. Rose of Lima said, "Apart from the cross, there is no other ladder by which we may get to heaven" (CCC 618).[1] Is it difficult for you to suffer and die to yourself—to take up your cross in your daily life and carry it willingly as a share in Christ's burden? Read Colossians 1:24-26 and CCC 618. How can the examples of Jesus' early followers give you encouragement?

Dear Lord …

1 St. Rose of Lima, cf. P. Hansen, Vita mirabilis (Louvain, 1668).

Session 15 Talk Notes

Matthew 16 – Jesus Establishes the Church

I. Overview and Background of Matthew

A. Focus of this session – verses 13-20 and the papacy

B. Up to this point, Jesus has avoided the subject of his death

C. Old Testament provisional kingdom is fulfilled in Jesus

II. The Pharisees and Sadducees Ask for a Sign (Matthew 16:1-4)

A. The sign of Jonah

1. Jonah is in the fish three days, nights
2. Message to Nineveh hints at destruction of Temple

III. "Who Do You Say That I Am?" (Matthew 16:13-20)

A. Simon Bar-Jona (verse 17)

1. Jonah and Peter bring God's message to the Gentiles

B. "Church" (Gk., *ekklesia*)

1. Used in Septuagint to translate the Hebrew *kahal* – "called-out ones"
2. *Kahal* recalls assembly of Jews in the wilderness after the Exodus

C. "Gates of Hades" (verse 18)

1. Jewish tradition about the rock the Temple was built on
   a. Capstone covering gate to Hades *(Sheol)*
   b. Creation, light, Isaac's sacrifice
2. Gate linked to the keys (open the gate; power over death)

D. From this time on, Jesus will suffer

IV. The Papacy and the Primacy of Peter

A. Certitude of Christ's delegated authority

B. Throughout salvation history, God established his authority

C. Role of papacy (CCC 881)

1. Pastoral office of Peter and the apostles belongs to Church's foundation
   a. Continued by bishops under primacy of Peter (pope)
   b. Pope – perpetual, visible source and foundation of unity
2. Pontiff is vicar of Christ and pastor of the entire Church
3. Infallibility = charism for protection of the Faith
   a. *Ex cathedra* = "from the Chair of Peter" (seldom exercised)

V. Jesus Is Building His Church

A. Jesus' plan to establish the New Covenant using the Old Covenant as a type that will go away

1. *Gebira* = queen mother gives way to Mary
2. "Prime minister" gives way to pope

B. "Kingdom" and "Church" are synonymous

C. Simon renamed Peter ("rock")
1. Name change signifies change in vocation (Abram, Jacob)
2. Old Testament meaning of "rock"
    a. Metaphor for protection and refuge
    b. Refers to God (Psalm 95:1)
    c. Refers to Abraham as "father" (Isaiah 51:1-2)
3. Peter will be known as rock, like Abraham and Yahweh
4. Temple built on rock at Mount Moriah – *Even Hash'tiya* (2 Chronicles 3:1)

D. Jesus is building his new temple—the Church—on a new "rock"
1. Matthew 7:24 – wise man built house on the rock
2. Gates (powers) of hell will not prevail – *Even Hash'tiya* covered Hades
3. Jesus as the new Solomon (Matthew 12:42), building his house on the rock that is Peter
4. Believed Messiah would build Temple without hands
    a. Mark 14 – Jesus is accused of saying he would destroy the Temple and build one not made with hands

VI. Old Testament Texts and the Papacy

A. *Al biet*[2] in kingdom of David – "steward"; office like "prime minister"
1. *Biet* = home, house
2. Held authority in king's absence
3. Another Old Testament example: Joseph "over the household" in Egypt

B. Jesus draws from Isaiah 22:15-24
1. Isaiah upbraids the *al biet* (Shebna), brings in Eliakim
2. Characteristics of steward – office; clothed with robe; authority; "father"; keys of house of David; power to bind and loose; fastened like a peg in sure place; throne of honor; weight of father's house hangs on him

VII. Power to Bind and Loose

A. Keys to kingdom = authority given to Peter

B. "Bind and loose" = juridical term of first-century rabbinic canon law
1. Authority to prohibit or permit
    a. Protestant M. Vincent – powers of rabbinic office transferred to Peter
    b. George Lamsa – authority to declare lawful, unlawful
2. Christ rules through papacy, leadership
    a. Guidance of Holy Spirit – John

---

[2] Can also be *al ha-bayit,* which means "over the house" in Hebrew.

Session 16 – Questions

Matthew 17 – The Transfiguration

	Prologue	Book 1	Book 2	Book 3	Book 4	Book 5	Conclusion
	Birth of the King	*Announcement of the Kingdom*	*Establishment of the Kingdom*	*The Kingdom Defined*	*Transfer of the Kingdom's Authority*	*Announcement of the End of the Old Kingdom*	*Victory of the King*
NARRATIVE	Mt. 1–2 *Jesus' ancestry and infancy*	Mt. 3–4 *John the Baptist and Jesus' early ministry*	Mt. 8–9 *Miracles; commissioning the Twelve*	Mt. 11–12 *Jesus confronts an evil generation*	**Mt. 14–17** ***Travels and ministry; instructing the Twelve***	Mt. 19–23 *Events and teaching in Judea*	Mt. 26–28 *Passion week*
DISCOURSE		Mt. 5–7 *Sermon on the Mount*	Mt. 10 *Missionary instructions*	Mt. 13 *Kingdom parables*	Mt. 18 *Life in the Christian community*	Mt. 24–25 *Olivet Discourse (Judgment on Jerusalem)*	

A. Review the Context

In Matthew 7, Jesus said that the wise man will build his house upon a rock and it will withstand the onslaught of the elements. Centuries earlier, King David's son, Solomon, blessed with wisdom above all other men, built a house for the LORD—the Jerusalem Temple—on a massive rock. But one greater than Solomon is now here: Jesus Christ. And in Matthew 16, he expressed his intention to build his house, the Church, upon the "rock" of Peter. The kingdom that Jesus established on earth is a spiritual fulfillment of the kingdom God established in Israel. This is the fulfillment of God's original promise to David—that he would make David's name great and would establish his house.

At the close of Chapter 16, Jesus told his disciples for the first time that he must suffer, die, and rise again. They did not yet understand. The people of Israel have been suffering for five hundred years. They are looking for someone to deliver them from suffering. They are pre-conditioned to think of a kingdom and glory in earthly terms, and Jesus has to teach them what these things mean in heavenly terms. How does Jesus do this, even as he transfers the authority of the kingdom to them? The events of Chapter 17, which bring the narrative section of Book Four to a close, are an important first step.

B. Read the Story

Carefully read **Matthew 17.** Ask yourself the questions: *Who? What? When? Where? How? Why?*

As always, pray before you read.

C. Take a Deeper Look

Answering these questions will draw you into the heart of the story. If you do not understand something, make a note of it to bring up in the small-group discussion.

The Transfiguration (Matthew 17:1-13)

1. The Transfiguration takes place in the context of the events of Matthew 16, in which Peter declares Jesus to be the Christ, Son of the living God, and in which Jesus foretells his passion and speaks of the cost of discipleship.

   a. Six days later, who does Jesus take up a mountain, and what is revealed to them there?

   Peter, James & John & he is revealed in all his divine majesty.

   b. In what way will this experience prove significant for the apostles later on? (See **2 Peter 1:17-18** and **CCC 555.**)

   The experience gives them strength - in their preaching. Gives them insight as to the events that were to come.

2. a. Moses and Elijah represent the Law and the Prophets. Why do you think these two "greats" appear on the mountain for this occasion? (A brief ode to Elijah can be found in the first part of **Sirach 48.**)

   To reinforce the parallel of Jesus' life and the life of Isreal. Elijah did not die, he is raised where John the Baptist begins there. - Then Jesus picks up after John

   b. From Luke's Gospel, we know that on this occasion, Moses and Elijah speak with Jesus about his "departure, which he was to accomplish at Jerusalem" (Luke 9:30-31). The literal meaning of "departure" here is "exodus." What would calling it an "exodus" add to the disciples' understanding of Jesus' mission?

   To ~~a~~ align with Moses - but this is the new exodus - freeing people from sin. Jesus is the new Moses

3. Peter wants to extend Moses' and Elijah's stay by building tents for them. What do we learn from the fact that they do not stay?

   Peter doesn't want to let go. He sees this is a spiritual moment. We learn - The pass must go - so the New Covenant can be achieved.

4. How does the Transfiguration relate to our own hopes for the future? (See **2 Corinthians 3:18.**)

   We hope to see Jesus on Judgment Day.

The Healing of a Boy with a Demon (Matthew 17:14-23)

5. a. Why are the disciples unable to drive the demon from the man's son?

The disciples need more faith. Not just prayers and fasting. They need to beome stronger in beliveing who Jesus is.

b. What does Jesus say they need?

They need more faith in Jesus. Their faith will grow like a mustard seed - which grows.

c. What do you make of the disciples' failure?

It is hard to believe even for those who were close to him.

6. a. In verses 22-23, Jesus again says he will be betrayed, killed, and raised to life on the third day. The first time he said this in Matthew 16:21-22, Peter was shocked, and the disciples misunderstood him. Do they understand him this time? How do you know?

The transfiguration and now again, the disciples understand, but they are understanding. They are distressed.

b. **Think About It:** By the time Peter wrote his epistles, his view of Christ's suffering—and of suffering in general—had changed markedly. Read **1 Peter 1:6-8, 4:12-13, and 5:10.** Do you think witnessing the Transfiguration had an impact on his change of view? Explain your answer.

Yes - He saw Jesus - heard Moses & Elijah and all the pieces come together. And we understand how our suffering will bring us to eternal life

The Temple Tax (Matthew 17:24-27)

7. The half-shekel tax (literally, *didrachma*—"two-drachma tax") represented about two days' wages; it was an annual tax on adult males for the Temple upkeep and was a symbol of the people's redemption, or purchase, from Egypt.

a. Who does Jesus say is exempt from the tax, and why?

The son's - compares to King's not taking their son's money.

b. By implication, of whom is he speaking specifically?

Jesus is the "Son" of God and Peter is his successor - so both should be free from taxes

8. If they are exempt, why does Jesus ask Peter to pay the tax for the two of them?

He does not want to offend the collectors

9. Do you think Jesus accomplishes more by submitting to the authorities in this way than he would by insisting on his rights?

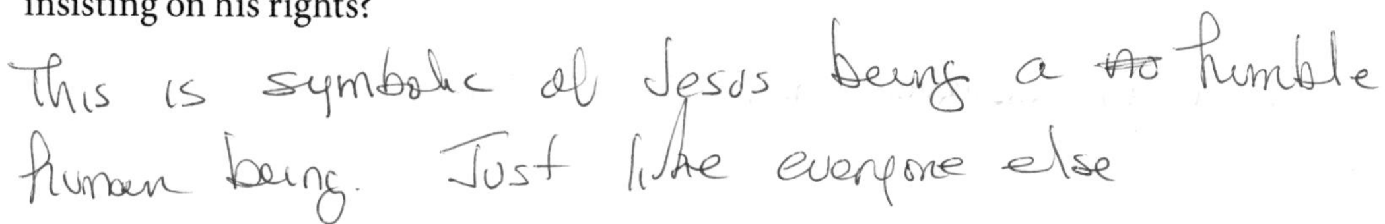

D. Application

This question will help you apply one of the key themes of the session to your life. After meditating on it, respond to God with a brief written prayer if you choose.

We often speak about "mountaintop" and "valley" experiences. What can you take from the mountaintop experience of the Transfiguration that will help you walk through the "valleys" in your own life?

Dear Lord …

Session 16 Talk Notes

Matthew 17 – The Transfiguration

I. Review

A. Structure of Matthew

B. Jesus' life recapitulates the life of Israel and reconstitutes Israel around himself

C. Chapter 1 – genealogy

D. Chapter 2 – infancy narrative

E. Chapter 3 – John the Baptist and Jesus parallel Elijah and Elisha

F. Chapter 4 – baptism and testing

G. Chapter 5–7 – Sermon on the Mount as the law of the New Covenant

H. Chapter 6 – piety

I. Chapter 7 – judging, Golden Rule, building house on rock

J. Chapters 8–9 – miracle stories demonstrate power of the kingdom

K. Chapter 10 – disciples are sent out

L. Chapters 11–12 – Jesus is the new king

M. Chapter 13 – Jesus teaches in parables

N. Chapters 14–15 – miracles; feeding the five thousand

O. Chapter 16 – Peter as first vicar of the new kingdom

II. The Transfiguration (Matthew 17, 1-13)

A. Luke's account (Chapter 9) – Moses, Elijah speak of Jesus' departure (Gk., *exodus*) from Jerusalem

1. The true exodus from bondage to sin

2. Revelation 11:1 – Jerusalem as the new Egypt

a. The two witnesses are Elijah (1 Kings 17:1-2) and Moses (Exodus 7:17)

3. Revelation 11:7-8 – Jerusalem allegorically called Sodom (Lot's exodus) and Egypt (Moses' exodus)

4. Destruction of harlot city Babylon refers to the fall of Jerusalem (Revelation 17:4-6, 18:2, 18:10, 18:21, and 12:1-9)

B. Moses and Elijah represent the Law and the Prophets

C. Matthew 17 shows Jesus as a new Moses, leading an exodus from sin

1. Parallels between them – seventh day; on a mountain; three companions; faces shine with God's glory; glory cloud of God's presence (*Shekinah* – glory; *Parousia* – coming of the Lord) at epiclesis at Mass; God speaking through a heavenly voice (Exodus 24 and 34)

D. Peter's idea to build three booths

1. Old Testament Feast of Booths (Feast of Tabernacles) celebrated the people coming out of Egypt

2. Jesus is predicting a Passover event

E. "Listen to him" (verse 5)

1. Moses spoke of a future prophet – "listen to him" (Deuteronomy 18:15; see also Acts 3:22-23)

F. Moses and Elijah both make pilgrimages to Sinai (Exodus 24; 1 Kings 19)

G. Elijah to come to restore all things (Matthew 17:12)

1. Hints at Sirach 48:10 and the prophetic role of Elijah

III. The Temple Tax (Matthew 17:24-27)

A. Are Jesus and his followers loyal to the Temple?

B. Peter is spokesman – primacy of Peter (see Matthew 14:28-33 and Matthew 16 and 17)

C. Jesus is the King; apostles are sons of the King

D. Should not owe tax, yet do not give offense

Session 17 – Questions

Matthew 18 – Characteristics of the Christian Community

	Prologue	Book 1	Book 2	Book 3	Book 4	Book 5	Conclusion
	Birth of the King	*Announcement of the Kingdom*	*Establishment of the Kingdom*	*The Kingdom Defined*	*Transfer of the Kingdom's Authority*	*Announcement of the End of the Old Kingdom*	*Victory of the King*
NARRATIVE	Mt. 1–2 *Jesus' ancestry and infancy*	Mt. 3–4 *John the Baptist and Jesus' early ministry*	Mt. 8–9 *Miracles; commissioning the Twelve*	Mt. 11–12 *Jesus confronts an evil generation*	Mt. 14–17 *Travels and ministry; instructing the Twelve*	Mt. 19–23 *Events and teaching in Judea*	Mt. 26–28 *Passion week*
DISCOURSE		Mt. 5–7 *Sermon on the Mount*	Mt. 10 *Missionary instructions*	Mt. 13 *Kingdom parables*	**Mt. 18** ***Life in the Christian community***	Mt. 24–25 *Olivet Discourse (Judgment on Jerusalem)*	

A. Review the Context

We have reached the end of the narrative portion of the fourth book of Matthew: "Transfer of the Kingdom's Authority." Fittingly, the narrative begins with the death of John the Baptist: The old is passing away, and the new has arrived. Jesus is passing on his authority to the disciples and establishing them as leaders of the new kingdom. Their positions will not give them the kind of personal power that leaders in earthly kingdoms have, but they will rely on Jesus' power and cooperate with him to provide heavenly food, cast out demons, and heal.

In this next narrative, Jesus is seen investing his kingly authority in Peter as the foundation stone of the Church. In this position, Peter will exercise authority "over the house" in Jesus' absence. Any doubts Peter might have had as to whether Jesus is the Son of God would have vanished on the Mount of Transfiguration, where Jesus was revealed as the new Moses preparing to lead a new exodus of his people from slavery to sin. It would be natural in the context of Jesus' day that the rest of the disciples would wonder where they fit within the new kingdom. A hierarchy would be expected. In Jesus' time, a person's position at formal gatherings would have been determined by rank, and a seating hierarchy was commonly maintained, even at regular mealtimes. Peter's installation as the head of the Church would lead to the questions: Who will be the greatest in the kingdom of heaven? By what standards will the leaders of the new kingdom rule? What values will characterize this kingdom community? Jesus' fourth discourse will get to the heart of these questions.

B. Read the Story

Carefully read **Matthew 18.** Ask yourself the questions: *Who? What? When? Where? How? Why?*

As always, pray before you read.

C. Take a Deeper Look

Answering these questions will draw you into the heart of the story. If you do not understand something, make a note of it to bring up in the small-group discussion.

Humility (Matthew 18:1-4)

1. a. In verse 1, the disciples ask Jesus, "Who is the greatest in the kingdom of heaven?" How does Jesus answer their question?

He really doesn't answer just
you have to be like little children to enter the Kingdom

b. What do you think Jesus has in mind when he says to "turn and become like children"?

to be like a child is to need God and depend on God to give us what we need

2. What must we do to enter the kingdom of heaven? (See also **John 1:12-13** and **CCC 526.**)

We must be humble not pride-ful.

Purity (Matthew 18:5-9)

3. What warning does Jesus issue to those who would cause "one such child" to sin?

This is a serious issue. One who makes another sin is doomed.

4. a. In Matthew 5, Jesus said to take drastic measures if necessary (figuratively, to cut off or pluck out the offending member) to combat personal temptation and avoid sin. In this illustration in Matthew 18, how does he extend this concern to the community as a whole?

He relates the body to heavenly life -
if we abuse the body we are ill, if we take of body we are healthy. Same with religion.

b. What is the goal of these drastic measures?

to obtain our place in the kingdom of heaven

5. **Think About It:** When the *Catechism* discusses "Life in Christ," it includes a section called "Respect for the souls of others: scandal." Read it in **CCC 2284–2287.** What does this add to your understanding of Jesus' words in Matthew 18:5-9?

Family (Matthew 18:10-14)

6. What does the parable of the lost sheep tell you about God?

We all get lost in life – we may stray but God will find us when we are open to him to find us.

Justice . . . (Matthew 18:15-20)

7. a. As the earthly shepherds of God's flock on earth, the disciples will need to know how to deal with lost sheep and problems in the sheepfold. What are Jesus' instructions for dealing with sin in the Christian community?

family to court room.

1. Try a reconciliation
2. if this fails, ~~come~~ go back & confess.
3. If doesn't listen should be bought to the church

b. In verse 17, Jesus says that if the offender refuses correction by the Church, "Let him be to you as a Gentile and a tax collector." What does this mean?

Gentile's & tax collector are outsiders.

c. What is the ultimate goal of this process? (See also **Galatians 6:1-2.**)

To help with the correction of issues people have issues with.

8. a. How does Jesus' assurance that what the disciples bind or loose on earth will be bound or loosed in heaven relate to this? (See also **CCC 1443–1445.**)

Our goal is to be reconciled to reach the Kingdom of Heaven - forgive all.
everyone needs correction

b. Who has this authority today, and how is it practiced? (See **CCC 1461–1463.**)

Pope, Cardinals, Bishops & Priests.

. . . and Mercy (Matthew 18:21-35)

9. What does Jesus mean by saying that even seven times is not enough, but "seventy times seven"?

Relationship - from exile to return –
and many times we need to forgive.

10. a. How does Jesus illustrate the foolishness of putting limits on forgiveness? (Note: One "talent" would represent about twenty years' wages for a laborer; one "denarius" could be earned in a day.)

There is no limits on forgiveness.
almost an impossible amount.

b. What does this parable teach about justice in the kingdom of heaven? (Read also **CCC 2832–2843.**)

God's mercy has no end.

c. **Think About It:** Forgiving others sounds good on paper, but it can be the hardest thing we have to do. How is it possible to carry this out in our lives?

I need to take a breath & remember
to forgive.

D. Application

This question will help you apply one of the key themes of the session to your life. After meditating on it, respond to God with a brief written prayer if you choose.

Forgiveness is not so much a matter of feelings as it is an act of the will. Jesus has released us from our sin and asks us to release others who have sinned against us. Is there someone in your life you have not forgiven? If so, release them today, and say a prayer for them.

Dear Lord . . .

E. Wrap-Up – Book Four: Transfer of the Kingdom's Authority

How would you summarize Book Four of Matthew's Gospel (Chapters 14–18)?

Session 17 Talk Notes

Matthew 18 – Characteristics of the Christian Community

I. Become Like a Child (Matthew 18:1-6)

A. Recognize dependence on the Father

II. Caring for "Little Ones" (Matthew 18:10-14)

A. God's protection, guardian angels

B. St. Paul's care of churches

C. The powerful witness of loving and forgiving

III. Conflict Management (Matthew 18:15-20)

A. Go privately to the one who offended you

B. If unsuccessful, take witnesses – covenant is familial and juridical

C. If that does not work, take the conflict to the Church

D. Last resort – excommunication

1. Drawing a line in love – saying, "You have moved outside by your actions"

2. Authority of the Church to bind and loose

a. Peter's authority extends to the apostles

b. Example – 1 Corinthians 5:1-5; 2 Corinthians 2:5-11

E. The Church has a way of dealing with problems

1. Jesus is in the midst of two or three who are gathered together – spoken in the context of ecclesiastical discipline (Matthew 18:19-20)

IV. Response to Those Who Hurt Us – Forgiveness (Matthew 18:20-22)

A. Salvation history as a tale of exile and return

1. Israel's failure led to exile – being taken physically to where they already were spiritually

2. Jacob's sons in Egyptian bondage (Genesis 15, 37–39), released by Joseph

3. God delivered Israel out of bondage, expected them to do the same

a. The Great Jubilee – every fiftieth year, forgive debts, release slaves (Exodus 25:10; Deuteronomy 15:1-3; Deuteronomy 31:10)

b. Within Israel every seven years, a small jubilee

c. Israel exiled after failure to release others (Jeremiah 34; 2 Kings 25:7)

d. Daniel 9 – seventy years of exile not enough; will be extended seventy times seven years

B. How often should I forgive? Seventy times seven – echoes the return from exile

C. Jesus starts ministry, announcing the Jubilee, end of exile – Luke 4:16-19, quoting Isaiah 61

V. Parable of the Unmerciful Servant (Matthew 18:23-35)

A. Context is Jesus' teaching on forgiveness

1. Servant forgiven debt of ten thousand talents[1]

2. Refusal to forgive a small debt lands him in prison

3. "So will my Father do to you, if you do not forgive"

a. Marcionism (heresy) – New Testament God (forgiving); different from Old Testament God (vengeful)

B. The ability to forgive is a gift from God that maintains harmony

1. John 16:33 – warning of tribulation, "to be pulled apart on the inside"

2. Jesus shows us how to suffer – to unite our pain with his

3. Forgiveness (release) is a better way

C. Being offended can lead to unforgiveness

1. The enemy wants us to take the bait – to be scandalized, offended

a. *Skandalon* – where the bait is put in a trap

b. Nature of a trap – we do not expect it; it is stronger than we are

2. Forgiveness springs the trap

a. An act of the will

b. Die to yourself

D. Jesus paid the debt we cannot pay

[1] One talent = fifteen years' wages.

Session 18 – Questions

Matthew 19 – Marriage: A Demonstration of God's Love

	Prologue	Book 1	Book 2	Book 3	Book 4	Book 5	Conclusion
	Birth of the King	*Announcement of the Kingdom*	*Establishment of the Kingdom*	*The Kingdom Defined*	*Transfer of the Kingdom's Authority*	*Announcement of the End of the Old Kingdom*	*Victory of the King*
NARRATIVE	Mt. 1–2 *Jesus' ancestry and infancy*	Mt. 3–4 *John the Baptist and Jesus' early ministry*	Mt. 8–9 *Miracles; commissioning the Twelve*	Mt. 11–12 *Jesus confronts an evil generation*	Mt. 14–17 *Travels and ministry; instructing the Twelve*	**Mt. 19–23** ***Events and teaching in Judea***	Mt. 26–28 *Passion week*
DISCOURSE		Mt. 5–7 *Sermon on the Mount*	Mt. 10 *Missionary instructions*	Mt. 13 *Kingdom parables*	Mt. 18 *Life in the Christian community*	Mt. 24–25 *Olivet Discourse (Judgment on Jerusalem)*	

A. Establish the Context

Book Four of Matthew's Gospel closed with Jesus' discourse on the characteristics of the kingdom. Only the truly humble and childlike can enter, and mercy is the hallmark of relationships within it. The kingdom more closely resembles a family than a courtroom. Reconciliation and restoration is the goal of correction when it is needed. The key to all is to have the attitude of the heart that is like Christ's—to offer to him the little we have and allow his power to work within us and through us.

Matthew 19 begins before the Passion. Find it on the diagram on this page. This chapter begins the fifth book of Matthew's Gospel, "Announcement of the End of the Old Kingdom." It covers this and the next six chapters of Matthew's Gospel and culminates in the "Olivet Discourse," in which Christ pronounces judgment on Jerusalem.

B. Read the Story

Carefully read **Matthew 19.** Ask yourself the questions: *Who? What? When? Where? How? Why?*

As always, pray before you read.

C. Take a Deeper Look

Answering these questions will draw you into the heart of the story. If you do not understand something, make a note of it to bring up in the small-group discussion.

Marriage and Divorce (Matthew 19:1-12)

1. The action shifts from Galilee in the north to "Judah beyond the Jordan." Locate this area on the map on page 5. Do you remember what this region is associated with? (See **Matthew 3:1-6.**)

2. We have seen the Pharisees plotting to kill Jesus since Matthew 12. Forbidden under their own law from carrying out a death sentence, they will need to find him guilty of breaking Roman law or get him to provoke the secular authorities. In 19:3, they test Jesus by asking, "Is it lawful to divorce one's wife for any cause?" What do you think is behind this question? Can you think of any way in which it represents a potentially lethal trap for Jesus? (Hint: Remember the fate of John the Baptist.)

He cannot win with any answer - He reminds them of of the law a man shall leave his mother & two become one -

3. a. How does Jesus avoid the trap?

   b. What is the next objection of the Pharisees, and how does Jesus handle it?

   Pharises bring up Moses - saying Moses commanded, but Moses did not command - he allowed.

The Meaning of "Except for Unchastity ..."

The meaning of the phrase, "except for unchastity," in Matthew 19:9 has been strenuously debated. Three interpretations exist in Catholic tradition: (1) Separation or divorce is permitted under serious conditions (such as adultery), but remarriage is not; (2) "unchastity" refers to invalid marriages that should never have taken place and which should be ended—for example, a marriage between close relatives; and (3) "except for unchastity" means something like, "regardless of the Old Testament grounds for divorce."

In any of these cases, while there might be some grounds for separation or divorce, there are no grounds for a divorced person to remarry. (See also CCC 2380–2391.)[1]

4. a. According to the following Bible and *Catechism* references, what does marriage represent? (**Optional:** Read **CCC 1602–1617.**)

   Ephesians 5:31-32: Marriage is compared to Christ & church & their bond

   CCC 1604: both are a union & unfailing love

   CCC 1611: Martial love mirror love of God & his love for Isreal

   CCC 1613: sign of God's Prescence

   CCC 1617: Sancrament = scantity of God's new covenant

[1] For a concise view of the conflict, see the essay, "Jesus on Marriage and Divorce," on page 51 in the *Ignatius Catholic Study Bible.*

b. In Matthew 19:5, Jesus quotes from **Genesis 2:20-24.** Read this passage. What was God's original plan for marriage?

that man & woman would be ~~unsep~~ unseperable – Like one flesh

c. Read **Malachi 2:13-16.** What do these verses say about God in regard to divorce?

~~He~~ God hates divorce, because it breaks his covenant – Not the fabric of life.

d. How does the reaction of the disciples in verse 10 support the Catholic teaching that the marriage bond is created by God and cannot be broken except by death?

the disciples would chose celibacy before breaking the covenat of marrige

5. Is the Church's teaching on the indissolubility of marriage impossible to bear? (See **CCC 1615.**)

The Rich Young Man (Matthew 19:16-30)

6. Why do you think Jesus responds the way he does when the rich young man asks what good thing he can do to attain eternal life?

Jesus wants to change the way the young man thinks. "Stuff" means nothing to God. Your attitude ~~is~~ towards holiness does.

7. a. Jesus says the young man has to obey the commandments to "enter life." For a list of the Ten Commandments, read **Exodus 20:1-17.** Which of the commandments does Jesus omit in the list he gives the young man in verses 18-19 that pertain to the young man's situation?

worship other God's & Covet –

because of his love for external pleasures.

b. Why do you think he omits those at first?

8. a. Why do you think the disciples are astonished at what Jesus says in verses 23-24?

The disciples think wealth means you have favor from God - ~~what~~ olds thoughts confused them

b. Can you explain Jesus' reply in verse 26?

Only God's favorable judgement can get you into the kingdom - It cannot be bought

9. **Think About It:** In reviewing Matthew 19, what is the cost of commitment to the kingdom?

For some, like priests, it means giving up on a family life for celibacy. Others sacrifice other things for God's grace and do God's work.

10. Peter is quick to note that he and the other disciples have left everything to follow Christ. What will be their reward?

If they are true their reward is in heaven - while on earth God will provide, when things seems bleak - remember - ~~with~~ all things are possible with God

D. Application

This question will help you apply one of the key themes of the session to your life. After meditating on it, respond to God with a brief written prayer if you choose.

All Christians find themselves in a marriage relationship. If you are single, you are married to the Lord. If married, you are also married to the Lord. In your state of life what three things might you do to improve your marriage so that the covenant you have may be stronger?

Dear Lord …

Session 18 Talk Notes

Matthew 19 – Marriage: A Demonstration of God's Love

I. Overview of Matthew 19:1-12 (on Divorce)

A. Matthew 19 is the fifth narrative of the Gospel

B. Importance of geography – Judea beyond the Jordan

1. John the Baptist was here before his arrest (14:4)

2. Pharisees try to trap Jesus

a. First-century debate regarding marriage

i. Hillel – divorce, remarriage only after adultery (Deuteronomy 24:1)

ii. *Shammai* – divorce for any unclean thing

b. "Any cause" (verse 3) brings to mind Herod's actions

3. Same location where Moses promulgated laws on divorce (Deuteronomy 24)

II. Jesus' Teaching on Divorce

A. Pharisees appeal to Moses; Jesus refers back to Genesis

1. God is the Author of marriage

B. Jesus condemns the Pharisees, not Herod

C. Moses did not command divorce but permitted and regulated it (Deuteronomy 24:1-4)

1. Certificate of divorce was permitted due to hardness of heart

2. Divorce was permitted to save lives

D. Jesus does not confirm this but teaches that marriage is indissoluble

1. Marriage points to the relationship between God and the Church

2. Marriage bond is created by God, dissolved only on death

a. Romans 7:1-3

E. "Except for unchastity" – *porneia* (19:9)

1. Does Jesus provide an exception clause?

a. The disciples' response (verses 10-12) indicates he does not

2. Meaning of "except for unchastity"[2]

a. Patristic view – divorce allowed for serious sexual sin, but remarriage was not allowed (see Paul's teaching in 1 Corinthians 7:10-11)

---

[2] See "Jesus on Marriage and Divorce" in the commentary on Matthew 19 in the *Ignatius Catholic Study Bible*.

b. Levitical Law view – "unchastity" refers to an invalid marriage where spouses are too closely related; not divorce, but annulment (Leviticus 18:6-18)

c. "No comment" view – Jesus revokes the debate over the grounds for divorce by showing they are irrelevant

3. The Church upholds Jesus' prohibition of divorce and remarriage

III. Annulments

A. Are not divorce

B. Conclude there never was a sacramental bond

C. Not infallible, but binding

IV. The Disciples' Response (Matthew 18:10-12)

A. Shows seriousness of Jesus' teaching

B. Those who "make themselves eunuchs" for the kingdom: priests

V. The Sacrament of Matrimony

A. Sacrament of martrimony allows channel of grace into our lives

1. Sacrament – a direct encounter with Christ (Ephesians 5)
2. Marriage as a participation in the life of the Trinity
3. Key – die to self, live for the other

B. Leave, cleave, become one (Genesis 2:24)

1. Leave = departure from the old way of life
2. Cleave = in Hebrew, to stick or be glued together, to hotly pursue
3. Become one = more than just personal intimacy

C. Kinds of love in marriage

1. *Storge* = "I like you"
2. *Eros* = "I want you"
3. *Philia* = "You are my friend"
4. *Agape* = "I love you unconditionally"

D. Jewish idea of marriage (example: Genesis 24:67, Isaac and Rebekah)

E. Love is a verb – "I give myself to you"

Session 19 – Questions

Matthew 20–21 – Stepping Down into Greatness

	Prologue	Book 1	Book 2	Book 3	Book 4	Book 5	Conclusion
	Birth of the King	*Announcement of the Kingdom*	*Establishment of the Kingdom*	*The Kingdom Defined*	*Transfer of the Kingdom's Authority*	*Announcement of the End of the Old Kingdom*	*Victory of the King*
NARRATIVE	Mt. 1–2 *Jesus' ancestry and infancy*	Mt. 3–4 *John the Baptist and Jesus' early ministry*	Mt. 8–9 *Miracles; commissioning the Twelve*	Mt. 11–12 *Jesus confronts an evil generation*	Mt. 14–17 *Travels and ministry; instructing the Twelve*	**Mt. 19–23** ***Events and teaching in Judea***	Mt. 26–28 *Passion week*
DISCOURSE		Mt. 5–7 *Sermon on the Mount*	Mt. 10 *Missionary instructions*	Mt. 13 *Kingdom parables*	Mt. 18 *Life in the Christian community*	Mt. 24–25 *Olivet Discourse (Judgment on Jerusalem)*	

A. Review the Context

The narrative section of Matthew's fifth book began with Jesus moving south from Galilee to the region of Judea beyond the Jordan. There, he was tested by the Pharisees with a question about divorce that was designed to trap him into offending Herod Antipas. Jesus deftly avoided the trap and turned it on the Pharisees, exposing the hardness of their hearts while asserting that his authority to proclaim law is greater than that of Moses. This is the beginning of the events that lead to Jesus' announcement of the end of the old kingdom and the judgment he will pronounce on Jerusalem.

B. Read the Story

Carefully read **Matthew 20–21.** Ask yourself the questions: *Who? What? When? Where? How? Why?*

As always, pray before you read.

C. Take a Deeper Look

Answering these questions will draw you into the heart of the story. If you do not understand something, make a note of it to bring up in the small-group discussion.

"The Last Shall Be First" (Matthew 20:1-16)

1. This parable continues and further clarifies Jesus' reply to the disciples' question in Matthew 18—"Who then can be saved?" Jesus' replies: "Many that are first will be last, and the last first." Keep in mind when reading verses 1-16 that this is a parable. It is not something that actually happened, nor is it proposed as a model for labor relations today. Jesus is telling this story to help his disciples understand who will be part of the kingdom of God.

a. What or who do the following represent?

The vineyard (see Jeremiah 12:10 and Isaiah 5:1-7):

Harvest time:

The employer:

The first group:

The later groups:

b. How does this parable illustrate God's justice and mercy?

c. What is the parable's message to Israel?

The "Cup" of Christ (Matthew 20:17-28)

2. a. Twice already in Matthew's Gospel, we have heard Jesus prophesy his passion. Review **Matthew 16:21 and 17:22-23.** What new information does Jesus give the disciples in 20:17-19?

b. What "cup" is Jesus talking about in verse 22? (See also **Matthew 26:39, 42.**)

c. How is greatness achieved in God's kingdom?

The Triumphal Entry into Jerusalem (Matthew 20:29–21:17)

3. To better understand the significance of the way Jesus enters Jerusalem, read **Zechariah 9:9-10; 1 Kings 1:32-46;** and **2 Kings 9:13.** With these verses as the background, what does **Matthew 21:4-5** say is being fulfilled, and how do you know?

4. In verse 13, Jesus says to those who are changing money and selling pigeons in the Temple: "It is written, 'My house shall be called a house of prayer'; but you make it a den of robbers." Jesus does not want the Temple profaned by being turned into a marketplace. Read that verse from its original context in **Isaiah 56:6-12.** What else does Jesus indict the Jewish leaders for when he quotes this verse? *(It may help you to know that during the Passover in Jesus' day, the Temple became a veritable marketplace as people came from all over Israel to worship. Many sacrificial animals were required, and pilgrims often needed to change currency. Merchants made a profit by taking advantage of this demand. There was not much room outside the Temple, so the outer court—the "court of the Gentiles"—was used to sell animals and exchange money. Normally, the outer court was the only place in the Temple Gentiles could enter to worship.)*

Jesus Curses the Fig Tree (Matthew 21:18-22)

5. a. How is what Jesus does to the fig tree in this passage prophetic? (For help with this question, read **Jeremiah 8:5-9, 13** and **Hosea 9:10-17.**)

   b. What is the message of this incident for us?

Jesus Is Challenged by the Religious Authorities (Matthew 21:23-45)

6. a. What challenge does Jesus face from the chief priests and elders?

   b. How does Jesus handle their question?

7. Jesus tells the leaders two parables. Summarize the message behind the parable of the two sons in verses 28-32.

8. In the parable of the tenants in verses 33-41, the servants represent the Old Testament prophets, many of whom were killed. The son represents Christ, condemned by the religious leaders. The other tenants are the "outcast" Jews and the Gentiles.

   a. In verse 40, Jesus asks what the owner will do to the unfaithful tenants. How do the religious leaders respond?

   b. Do the Pharisees understand the meaning behind the parable? Who is the message of the parable directed to?

   c. How do the Pharisees react to this, and what keeps them from overt action against Jesus?

9. What message is Jesus trying to send when he refers to **Psalm 118:22-23** (in **Matthew 21:42**)?

D. Application

This question will help you apply one of the key themes of the session to your life. After meditating on it, respond to God with a brief written prayer if you choose.

The secret of true greatness lies in a life of self-donating love. Think about someone in your life you consider great. What attributes does this person exhibit that you might incorporate into your own life?

Dear Lord …

Session 19 Talk Notes

Matthew 20–21 – Stepping Down into Greatness

I. The Parable of the Kingdom (Matthew 20:1-16)

A. Parable moves from contractual relationship to family covenant relationship with God
  1. Verse 15 – Can I do what I choose with what belongs to me?
  2. Verse 13 – "friend"
    a. John 15:15 – Jesus calls us friends, not servants
    b. Israel's role as firstborn of many

B. God grants eternal life even to those who come to him late in life

C. Rewards for obedience
  1. Old Testament – gold, silver
  2. New Testament – God himself

II. Jesus Foretells His Death (Matthew 20:17-19)

III. A Mother's Request for James and John (Matthew 20:20-28)

A. "The cup" links baptism and the Eucharist (see Mark 10:38-39)
  1. To take the cup – to die to oneself
  2. Metaphor "to drink the cup" – God's wrath on the wicked (Psalm 75:8; Isaiah 51:17; Jeremiah 25:15)
  3. Denotes Jesus' passion endured for sinners
  4. Jesus shares his ministry; we participate as the body of Christ
    a. Colossians 1:24: "In my flesh I complete what is lacking in Christ's afflictions"
    b. We have a small particle of the infinite treasury of God's redemption (St. John Paul II)
    c. James partook of the cup (see Acts 12:2)

B. The Mass: entering God's rest
  1. Old Testament – most holy day was the Sabbath (Saturday) – enter God's rest
  2. Hebrews 4 – Israel's failure to enter the rest
  3. Sunday Liturgy fulfills the Sabbath rest
  4. Christians gather on Sunday, the first day (Acts 20:7)

IV. Jesus Heals Two Blind Men (Matthew 20:29-34)

A. Literal sense – blind men who want to see

B. Moral sense – do we have vision? What do we pray for?

C. Hosea – without a vision, the people perish

V. Jesus' Entry into Jerusalem (Matthew 21:1-11)

A. Signs of the Messiah (see Zechariah 9–14)
  1. Enters Jerusalem like Solomon (1 Kings 1:32-40)
  2. Verse 5 combines Isaiah 62:11 and Zechariah 9:9-10

3. Isaiah speaks of salvation coming; Jesus' name means "the salvation of God"
4. Messiah will come humbly, riding a donkey (Zechariah 9:9-10)
    a. Allegorically – donkey = Israel; colt = Gentiles (St. Augustine)
5. Spreading garments – sign of homage to a king (2 Kings 9:13)
6. Palm branches – royal significance (Example: 2 Maccabees 10:7)
7. "Hosanna" = "Save us O Lord"
8. Jesus the Paschal (Passover) Lamb (Exodus 12)
    a. Inspect lambs – days ten to fourteen of Nisan
    b. Sacrifice the lamb at twilight (3 PM)
    c. Sacrificial flock outside Jerusalem
    d. Jesus' triumphal entry – tenth of Nisan; inspected until fourteenth day

VI. Jesus Cleanses the Temple (Matthew 21:12-17)

A. Jesus hints at Isaiah 56:7 and Jeremiah 7:11 *(remez)*
1. Isaiah 56 – God gathers all nations, including Gentiles, to the Temple
    a. All nations will gather in him (new Temple)
2. Jeremiah 7 – message of judgment – Temple will be destroyed
    a. Temple is destroyed in AD 70

VII. Three Prophetic Gestures Point to Jesus as the Messiah

A. Triumphal entry – Jesus is the sacrificial Lamb
1. Since Abraham and Isaac (Genesis 22), Israel has been waiting for God's Lamb
2. *Jehovah-jireh* – the LORD will provide
3. CCC 559
    a. "Hosanna" is repeated at Mass before we allow the Lord in to cleanse our temple *(Preface of Acclamation of Eucharistic Prayer)*

B. Jesus makes a triumphal entry at every Mass

C. Jesus cleanses the Temple (verses 12-13)

D. Jesus curses the fig tree (verses 18-19) – symbol of Israel and the prophets (see Jeremiah 8; Hosea 9)

VIII. Parable of the Householder (Matthew 21:33-41)

A. Householder = God

B. Vineyard = Jerusalem

C. Tenants = Israel's leaders

D. Servants = Old Testament prophets

E. Son = Jesus

Session 20 – Questions

Matthew 22–23 – "Let's Get Real"

	Prologue	Book 1	Book 2	Book 3	Book 4	Book 5	Conclusion
	Birth of the King	*Announcement of the Kingdom*	*Establishment of the Kingdom*	*The Kingdom Defined*	*Transfer of the Kingdom's Authority*	*Announcement of the End of the Old Kingdom*	*Victory of the King*
NARRATIVE	Mt. 1–2 *Jesus' ancestry and infancy*	Mt. 3–4 *John the Baptist and Jesus' early ministry*	Mt. 8–9 *Miracles; commissioning the Twelve*	Mt. 11–12 *Jesus confronts an evil generation*	Mt. 14–17 *Travels and ministry; instructing the Twelve*	**Mt. 19–23** ***Events and teaching in Judea***	Mt. 26–28 *Passion week*
DISCOURSE		Mt. 5–7 *Sermon on the Mount*	Mt. 10 *Missionary instructions*	Mt. 13 *Kingdom parables*	Mt. 18 *Life in the Christian community*	Mt. 24–25 *Olivet Discourse (Judgment on Jerusalem)*	

A. Review the Context

Jesus has told the disciples how to achieve greatness in his kingdom. The last will be first. Whoever wants to be great must be a servant and must bear fruit. In these final chapters before Christ's passion, his glory is juxtaposed with images of suffering and judgment. The old is going out, and the new is coming in. Jesus gives many examples that he is the Messiah, the true Son of David come to establish his reign and kingdom. The inevitable clash with the religious leaders now intensifies. Chapters 22–23 complete the fifth book of Matthew's Gospel and end in a scathing judgment on the scribes and Pharisees.

B. Read the Story

Carefully read **Matthew 22–23.** Ask yourself the questions: *Who? What? When? Where? How? Why?*

As always, pray before you read.

C. Take a Deeper Look

Answering these questions will draw you into the heart of the story. If you do not understand something, make a note of it to bring up in the small-group discussion.

Parable of the Wedding Banquet (Matthew 22:1-14)

1. a. To what does Jesus compare the kingdom of God in this parable?

b. In what way does this parable tell the story of salvation history?

c. What is the significance of the man without wedding clothes who is thrown outside? (See **Revelation 19:7-9.**)

Three Challenges (Matthew 22:15-40)

2. a. What trap is laid for Jesus in verses 16-17, and how does he escape it?

b. How do the Sadducees try to trick Jesus in verses 23-28? (For help with this, see **Deuteronomy 25: 5-10.**)

c. How does Jesus answer them, and what does his answer reveal about their knowledge?

3. Jesus' reply to the ethical question posed in verse 36 pairs the familiar *shema* of Deuteronomy 6:4-8—"Hear, O Israel: The LORD our God is one LORD; and you shall love the LORD your God with all your heart, and with all your soul, and with all your might"—with a second law: Love your neighbor as yourself (Leviticus 19:18). What point is Jesus making by joining these laws and saying they are the greatest commandments?

Jesus Silences the Opposition (Matthew 22:41-46)

4. a. What question does Jesus ask that finally silences the Pharisees, and why does it have this effect on them? (**Think About It:** If the Messiah is not David's son, whose son is he?)

   b. Why do they not answer him or dare to ask him any more questions?

5. **Think About It (optional):** Why do the Pharisees not "get it"? Why do they fail to recognize Jesus for who he is? (For help with this question, read **John 7:15-19.**)

Jesus Denounces the Scribes and Pharisees (Matthew 23:1-12)

6. a. "That the scribes and the Pharisees sit in Moses' seat" is a metaphor for their teaching and ruling authority as successors of Moses. According to Jesus, what practical implications does this have for the people regarding their teaching?

   b. What do you think Jesus means when he instructs them not to call anyone "rabbi," "father," or "master"? How literally should we take this? (To see how literally the disciples took this instruction in the early Church, read one or more of the following: **Luke 16:24; Romans 4:12; Acts 7:1-2; 1 Corinthians 4:14-16;** and **Philemon 10.**)

The "Seven Woes" (Matthew 23:13-32)

In Deuteronomy 27 and 28, Moses pronounced the blessings and curses of the covenant: blessings on those who kept the Law, curses on those who did not. Leviticus 26:18ff enumerates the consequences to Israel of breaking its covenant with God: a "sevenfold" chastisement for its sins. In the Beatitudes, Jesus explains who will attain the blessings. The "seven woes"—curses tantamount to the sevenfold chastisement—are also spelled out in Leviticus. Throughout Matthew's Gospel there are hints of these "woes"; here, Jesus gives a full critique and pronounces judgment on the religious leaders who have been leading the people astray and who refuse to recognize him.

7. a. Jesus calls the scribes and Pharisees "hypocrites" six times in these verses. Look up the definition of "hypocrisy." What does it mean?

   b. What other words and images does Jesus use when talking about the scribes and Pharisees? What do these say about the leaders?

   c. How does Jesus illustrate the hypocrisy of the scribes and Pharisees in the following verses?

   Matthew 23:13-14:

   Matthew 23:15:

   Matthew 23:16-22:

   Matthew 23:23-24:

   Matthew 23:25-28:

   Matthew 23:29-36:

Jesus' Final Curse and Lamentation Over Jerusalem (Matthew 23:33-39)

8. What judgment does Jesus say will fall on the leaders, and when will it come?

9. What is Jesus' attitude in this rebuke of Jerusalem's false shepherds? Is there any hope? (See also **CCC 558.**)

D. Application

This question will help you apply one of the key themes of the session to your life. After meditating on it, respond to God with a brief written prayer if you choose.

Spend some time in prayer, and ask God to show you if there are areas in which you are hypocritical. Think about your relationships. Are you genuine? Ask the Lord to help you be true to who he created you to be.

Dear Lord …

Session 20 Talk Notes

Matthew 22–23 – "Let's Get Real"

I. Matthew 22–23: Series of Teachings ("Stringing Pearls")

II. Pharisees, Herodians Try to Trap Jesus (Matthew 22:15-22)

A. Nature of the trap

1. Approve the tax and Pharisees will accuse him of unfaithfulness
2. Refuse the tax and Herodians will accuse him of revolt

B. Jesus' response

1. He turns the trap on them, answering a question with a question
2. Jesus makes three points
    a. A coin with Caesar's image should be given to Caesar
    b. Those made in God's image should be given to God
    c. They must pay taxes because they gave themselves to man and not to God (see Leviticus 26:18)

C. Israel pays the price for the disobedience of breaking the covenant

1. Leviticus 26:18-29 consequences – sevenfold chastisement
2. In AD 70, Jerusalem experienced these punishments (see Josephus)
3. Seven woes of Matthew 23 evoke Leviticus 26

D. CCC 2242 – Jesus affirms civic duty; but God's law takes precedence

III. Sadducees Try to Trap Jesus (Matthew 22:23-33)

A. The Sadducees do not believe in bodily resurrection and ask about Moses' teaching in Deuteronomy 25:5

B. Jesus' response is to tell them they do not know the Scriptures or the power of God

1. The resurrection ends marriage as we know it
    a. Marriage is to raise up children and to help spouses become saints
    b. Life in heaven (Isaiah 6:2-3; Revelation 5:11-12)
2. "I am the God of Abraham" (quotes Exodus 3:6)

IV. Another Test: What Is the Greatest Commandment? (Matthew 22:34-40)

A. Jesus gives the standard answer (Deuteronomy 6:5) – love God

B. Jesus adds a second command – love your neighbor (Leviticus 19:18)

1. "Like it" – our relationship with God is related to our relationship with our neighbor

V. Jesus Asks the Pharisees a Question (Matthew 22:41-46)

A. Whose son is the Christ?

1. Pharisees answer – Son of David

B. Jesus' reply – but David calls the Christ "Lord"

1. Implies the Messiah is greater than David – Psalm 110

VI. Jesus Pronounces Seven Woes on the Leaders (Matthew 23)

A. "Woe"

1. Covenant judgment, curse (see Leviticus 26)
2. Seven woes stand against the blessings of the Beatitudes (Matthew 5)
3. Curses, blessings of Old Covenant (Deuteronomy 27, 28)

B. Reasons for denouncing leaders

1. They speak with authority – "sit on seat of Moses" (verse 4) but do not practice
2. They bind heavy burdens on others
3. Their holiness is an outward show (large phylacteries,[1] long *tallit* – fringes)

C. "Call no man your father" (verse 9)

1. Hyperbole – do not seek lofty titles
2. Rules of interpretation of Scripture (see CCC 112–114)
   a. Be attentive to content and unity of the whole Scripture
      i. Example – Hebrews 12:7-11; 1 Corinthians 4:15
   b. Read within the living Tradition of the whole Church
   c. Be attentive to the analogy of faith

D. Examples of the seven woes (verses 13-36)

1. Strain a gnat (smallest unclean animal), yet swallow a camel
2. Whitewashed tombs

E. Lament over Jerusalem (verses 37-39)

1. "Your house is forsaken"
   a. The exit from the Temple (24:1) recalls Ezekiel 10:18, 11:23
   b. The glory has departed

[1] See Deuteronomy 6:8, 11:18.

Session 21 – Questions

Matthew 24–25 – Jesus Predicts the End of an Era

	Prologue	Book 1	Book 2	Book 3	Book 4	Book 5	Conclusion
	Birth of the King	*Announcement of the Kingdom*	*Establishment of the Kingdom*	*The Kingdom Defined*	*Transfer of the Kingdom's Authority*	*Announcement of the End of the Old Kingdom*	*Victory of the King*
NARRATIVE	Mt. 1–2 *Jesus' ancestry and infancy*	Mt. 3–4 *John the Baptist and Jesus' early ministry*	Mt. 8–9 *Miracles; commissioning the Twelve*	Mt. 11–12 *Jesus confronts an evil generation*	Mt. 14–17 *Travels and ministry; instructing the Twelve*	Mt. 19–23 *Events and teaching in Judea*	Mt. 26–28 *Passion week*
DISCOURSE		Mt. 5–7 *Sermon on the Mount*	Mt. 10 *Missionary instructions*	Mt. 13 *Kingdom parables*	Mt. 18 *Life in the Christian community*	**Mt. 24–25** ***Olivet Discourse (Judgment on Jerusalem)***	

A. Review the Context

Matthew 24 and 25 form what is known as the "Olivet Discourse," which is the final discourse before the "Conclusion" and the Passion narratives in Matthew's Gospel. These chapters concern the end of the Old Covenant and the establishment of the New Covenant. These chapters are not easy to read. Matthew 24 has given rise to much speculation about "end times." As Catholics, we interpret Scripture according to the living Tradition of the Church and the unity of God's plan. The Church considers the literary genre and historic context of Scripture as well as the "literal" and "spiritual" senses of Scripture. The "literal" sense of Scripture is the immediate meaning of the words: what they intend to convey. The "spiritual" senses of Scripture concern the ways in which the literal sense of the Scriptures points to spiritual realities. There are three spiritual senses of Scripture: (1) allegorical—the event's significance in Christ; (2) moral—how the events show us we should live; and (3) anagogical—the eternal significance of the events in Scripture.

B. Read the Story

Carefully read **Matthew 24–25.** Ask yourself the questions: *Who? What? When? Where? How? Why?*

As always, pray before you read.

C. Take a Deeper Look

Answering these questions will draw you into the heart of the story. If you do not understand something, make a note of it to bring up in the small-group discussion.

Signs of the End of the Age (Matthew 24:1-35)

1. The Jews saw the Temple as a microcosm of the world and an image of the universe in miniature. God met his people there; his presence filled the Holy of Holies and from there, spread out to the world. Read **Matthew 24:1-2,** and review **21:13 and 23:38.** If the Temple is God's house and the center of worship, why does Jesus condemn it?

2. The disciples respond to Jesus' prophecy of the destruction of the Temple with the question: "When will this happen, and what will be the sign of your coming and the end of the age?" (See **verse 3.**) Thus, the destruction of the Temple is the context for Jesus' reply, which equates it with his coming and the end of the age. Summarize the signs Jesus gives in verses 4-31.

3. a. Notice how Isaiah and Ezekiel use apocalyptic imagery in the following passages, and record the historic events they describe.

   Isaiah 13:1, 9-10, 13:

   Isaiah 14:4, 12:

   Ezekiel 32:1-2, 7-8:

   b. In light of this literary tradition, how should we interpret the apocalyptic imagery found in Matthew 24?

Be Watchful and Faithful (Matthew 24:36-51)

The "coming" of the Son of Man is literally his Parousia. *In ancient times,* Parousia *was a term used for a returning conqueror: He would leave the conquered city under an agreement that they would follow certain stipulations of the conquest. Some time later, he would pay them a surprise visit to determine whether or not they were behaving as loyal subjects to their new master.*

Remember that God had made a covenant with Israel. Before establishing them in the Promised Land, he put before them blessings if they would obey, curses if they would not. He has sent his emissaries time and time again to warn them of the consequences of continued disobedience. Now, the time of his Parousia *is "coming."*

4. Whether we are looking at the immediate or future fulfillment of these events, people commonly respond to apocalyptic messages by trying to determine the exact date on which the events will occur.

   a. Does Jesus mean for his followers to do this? How do you know?

   b. How does Jesus advise people to occupy themselves while they wait for his return?

Two Parables (Matthew 25:1-30)

5. The parable of the ten virgins reflects a Jewish custom in which the bridegroom brings his bride home at the head of a procession that ends with a weeklong celebratory banquet.

   a. Why are some of the bridesmaids in Jesus' story admitted while others are not?

   b. A wedding banquet often represents the wedding of Christ and the Church, when he will come to establish his kingdom in glory. What is the message of this parable?

6. a. This parable is about the kingdom of heaven. Who do the people in this story represent?

   b. Why are the servants treated differently when the man returns?

c. What does this teach us about the kingdom of God?

The Last Judgment (Matthew 25:31-46)

7. a. When the Son of Man comes and sits on his throne in glory and gathers the nations before him, on what basis will he separate the "sheep" from the "goats," and what will be the destination of each group?

   b. What do the people fail to understand in verses 37-39 and 44?

8. What does this parable say about how we should live while we wait for Christ's return?

D. Application

This question will help you apply one of the key themes of the session to your life. After meditating on it, respond to God with a brief written prayer if you choose.

What are some practical things you can do to prepare for Christ's return? Think about both the physical and spiritual aspects of preparedness.

Dear Lord …

E. Wrap-Up – Book Five: Announcement of the End of the Kingdom

How would you summarize Book Five of Matthew's Gospel (Chapters 19–25)?

Session 21 Talk Notes

Matthew 24–25 – Jesus Predicts the End of an Era

I. Review: Warnings of the End

A. All this will come upon "this generation" (23:36; recall 12:39-41, 45)

B. The Temple is forsaken and desolate (23:38)

C. Jesus leaves the Temple and goes to the Mount of Olives (foretold by prophets)

II. Jesus' Coming and the Close of the Age (Matthew 24:1-8)

A. Jesus prophesies destruction of the Temple (24:1-2)

  1. End-times prediction or in their lifetime? (key date: AD 70)

B. "The close of the age" (verse 3) – the end of time?

  1. Preterist view – close of the age in AD 70
  2. Spiritual sense applies also to today and future
  3. "Coming" (verse 3) = *Parousia;* presence, appearance, visitation
  4. Other Scripture references that refer to Jesus' coming and the last days
     a. Acts 2:17; Joel 2:28 – the last days of what?
     b. Hebrews 1:1-2 – last days of the Old Covenant
     c. Ephesians 2:4-7 – the coming ages = messianic age

C. False Christs, persecutions, and sacrilege (Matthew 24:4-28)

  1. Prophet Agabus foretells famine (Acts 11)
  2. Verse 14 – gospel preached throughout the world (Colossians 1:6, 23; 1 Thessalonians 1:8)
  3. Verse 15 – desolating sacrilege (Daniel 9:27)
  4. Christians flee in AD 66 based on "inside information" (24:16)
  5. Prediction of atrocities is borne out

D. Jesus speaking from perspective of the Old Testament

III. Coming of the Son of Man (Matthew 24:29-31)

A. Cataclysmic signs in the heavens (verse 29) – end of an age, not of time

  1. Old Testament examples
     a. Isaiah 13:1, 6-8, 10 (destruction of Babylon by Persians)
     b. Isaiah 19:1 (destruction of Egypt)
     c. Isaiah 34:4-5 (demise of Edom)
     d. Ezekiel 32:7-8 (against Egypt)

2. Theological significance behind political, military action
3. Ancients told time by sun (days), moon (months), and stars (ages)
4. Literal meaning of this language – "it is over!"

B. Son of Man coming on the clouds (verse 30)

1. Allusion to Daniel 7:13

C. A hint of the end of the world

1. Balance between preterist and futurist views
2. The Second Coming – Jesus coming to judge
3. Destruction of Temple (AD 70) prefigures Last Judgment
    a. Temple as a microcosm of the world
    b. Temple as a sign of creation

D. The key to understanding Chapter 24 and the meaning of the Temple: senses of Scripture (CCC 112–114)

1. Literal – AD 70 destruction of the Jerusalem Temple
2. Allegorical – Christ, the Temple destroyed and raised in three days
3. Moral – our bodies are temples of the Holy Spirit
4. Anagogical – we will die, and if we have been faithful, we will rise (1 Corinthians 10)

IV. Watchfulness and Warning: The Coming of the Lord (Matthew 24:36-51, 25:1-13)

A. Past – judgment on Jerusalem

B. Present – be ready to receive Christ in the Eucharist (1 Corinthians 11)

C. Future – the Second Coming at the end of history (Matthew 25:34-36)

V. Parable of the Talents (Matthew 25:14-30)

A. Stewardship

B. The delay between the Ascension and God's judgment

VI. Judgment of the Nations (Matthew 25:31-46)

A. Judgment of the Old Covenant of Israel

B. Particular judgment at the end of a person's life (see CCC 1021)

C. General (Last) Judgment at the end of time after the resurrection of the dead (See CCC 1038)

Session 22 – Questions

Matthew 26 – The Trial of the Christ

	Prologue	Book 1	Book 2	Book 3	Book 4	Book 5	Conclusion
	Birth of the King	*Announcement of the Kingdom*	*Establishment of the Kingdom*	*The Kingdom Defined*	*Transfer of the Kingdom's Authority*	*Announcement of the End of the Old Kingdom*	*Victory of the King*
NARRATIVE	Mt. 1–2 *Jesus' ancestry and infancy*	Mt. 3–4 *John the Baptist and Jesus' early ministry*	Mt. 8–9 *Miracles; commissioning the Twelve*	Mt. 11–12 *Jesus confronts an evil generation*	Mt. 14–17 *Travels and ministry; instructing the Twelve*	Mt. 19–23 *Events and teaching in Judea*	**Mt. 26–28** ***Passion week***
DISCOURSE		Mt. 5–7 *Sermon on the Mount*	Mt. 10 *Missionary instructions*	Mt. 13 *Kingdom parables*	Mt. 18 *Life in the Christian community*	Mt. 24–25 *Olivet Discourse (Judgment on Jerusalem)*	

A. Establish the Context

Find Chapter 26 on the diagram on this page. Matthew's Gospel is drawing to a close. The five books have all been leading to the conclusion—the "Victory of the King." This section is the heart of Matthew's Gospel. Everything we have read in Matthew 1–25 and the entire Old Testament has been leading up to this. We may wonder what the disciples expect and whether they think Jesus has been talking about the literal destruction of the Temple. Following the Olivet Discourse, they are almost certainly anticipating tremendous upheaval. The world as they know it is about to end, and Jesus will be at the center of both the end and the new beginning.

B. Read the Story

Carefully read **Matthew 26.** Ask yourself the questions: *Who? What? When? Where? How? Why?*

As always, pray before you read.

C. Take a Deeper Look

Answering these questions will draw you into the heart of the story. If you do not understand something, make a note of it to bring up in the small-group discussion.

Plan or Plot? (Matthew 26:1-5)

1. When Jesus tells his disciples that the time is near for his crucifixion, he links it to an important event in Israel's history and ongoing tradition: the Passover. What is the Passover? (See **Exodus 12** for help with this question.)

2. Jesus says he will be crucified at Passover. In spite of the Jewish leaders' determination not to crucify Jesus during the feast, that is exactly what they do. What does this suggest about Jesus' death?

Anointing and Betrayal (Matthew 26:6-16)

3. Why do you think Matthew includes the story of the woman anointing Jesus with expensive ointment at the start of his Passion narrative?

4. Compare the price of the ointment "wasted" on Jesus with the price the priests place on his head. (For purposes of comparison, note that the owner of a slain slave was reimbursed thirty shekels of silver in Exodus 21:32.) What does this say about Judas and about the woman?

The True Passover Lamb (Matthew 26:17-29)

5. a. When the time comes during the Passover meal for the disciples to eat the lamb, what does Jesus ask them to eat instead? What is he doing?

   b. Explain how you know Jesus is the Passover Lamb the other lambs only pointed to. (For help with this question, read **Exodus 12** and **1 Peter 1:18-19.**)

c. In Exodus 24, the blood of the covenant was splashed on the altar and on the people to seal Israel in a family relationship with God. What does Jesus mean when he says, "For this is my blood of the covenant, which is poured out for many for the forgiveness of sins"? (See **verse 28** and **CCC 610, 613–614.**)

Prayer in the Garden (Matthew 26:30-46)

6. What does Jesus' prayer in Gethsemane teach us about how and why to pray when we are in difficult circumstances?

Betrayal and Arrest (Matthew 26:47-56)

7. In the garden, Jesus is faced by an angry crowd of armed men. Who is in control of the situation, and how do you know?

8. a. The picture Matthew paints is one of Jesus walking deliberately toward the crucifixion. Because he is God's Son, it would be a small matter to get rid of his enemies and avoid capture. What does he do instead? Read also **CCC 612.**

   b. What does this suggest about the role of the betrayal of Jesus in God's plan?

Trial and Denial (Matthew 26:57-75)

The Sanhedrin was the Jewish high court. It was made up of chief priests, elders, and teachers of the Law. Counting the high priest, there were seventy-one members. Under Roman law, they were given a great deal of authority but could not impose the death penalty without Roman approval.

9. What charges are brought against Jesus, and how does he answer them?

10. a. Jesus takes his answer from **Psalm 110:1** and **Daniel 7:1-18.** Read these passages. What do the beasts represent in Daniel's vision?

    b. What happens to the Son of Man in those verses, and who is defeated when he appears?

11. In light of this background, what is Jesus saying about himself—and about his accusers—when he claims to be the Son of Man, and why does this evoke their immediate condemnation?

12. How does Peter fulfill the prophecy Jesus makes in verse 34?

D. Application

These questions will help you apply one of the key themes of the session to your life. After meditating on them, respond to God with a brief written prayer if you choose.

Have you ever denied knowing Jesus? Have you fallen asleep rather than waiting with him hidden in someone else? Do you feel your own suffering is too great for you to help bear the suffering of another person? Using Jesus' suffering as the model, how should you proceed in your own ordeal?

Dear Lord ...

Session 22 Talk Notes

Matthew 26 – The Trial of the Christ

I. The Anointing of Jesus (Matthew 26:6-13)

II. Judas Agrees to Betray Jesus (Matthew 26:14-16)

III. The Last Supper and Institution of the Eucharist (Matthew 26:26-29)

A. Location, timing of the Last Supper

1. "Upper Room" – Essene quarter of Jerusalem

a. Essenes followed solar calendar – (Passover early?)

B. The bread

1. Blessing – first century blessed God, not things

2. Unleavened bread = Passover bread (Exodus 12)

3. "Host" comes from *hostia* = victim

4. Frees from bondage (Eucharist: forgiveness of venial sin)

5. "This *is* my body" – transubstantiation

a. Not Jesus *with* the bread (consubstantiation – Lutheran view)

b. Not just a symbol (Baptist, Assembly of God view)

C. In the Eucharist, the whole Christ is truly, really present (see CCC 1374–1375)

1. Body and Blood, Soul and Divinity

2. Jesus promised he would not leave us alone (John 14, 16)

3. Real presence is apprehended by faith, not senses (CCC 1381)

4. Eucharist is "an anticipation of the heavenly glory" (CCC 1402)

D. "He took a cup" and gave thanks (verse 27)

1. Four cups at the Passover *seder* meal

a. The third cup is the cup of blessing (see 1 Corinthians 10:16)

b. After the third cup, they sing *The Great Hillel* (Psalms 113–114)

c. After the meal, Psalms 115–118

2. "He gave thanks" (Gk., *eucharistia;* Heb., *todah*)

a. *Todah* (thank) offering involves meal, unleavened bread, thanks for deliverance from mortal threat

b. Example – Psalm 22 – thanksgiving of David for deliverance

c. In the coming age, all sacrifices will cease except the *todah*

3. *Todah* continues in the Eucharist

    a. "The blood of the covenant" – language parallels Moses (see Exodus 24:3-8)

E. Passover meal interrupted (verse 29)

1. "I shall not drink again" until "I drink it new … in my Father's kingdom"

2. Jesus did not drink the fourth cup of consummation

IV. Jesus Prays in Gethsemane – Parallels to Garden of Eden (Matthew 26:36-46)

A. Verse 39: next mention of cup ("Let this cup pass from me")

B. Jesus in Gethsemane goes through what Adam and Eve went through in Eden

1. See Hebrews 5:7-8 – learned obedience

2. St. Paul – "the last Adam"

3. One person, two natures, two wills (hypostatic union) CCC 475 – his human will submits to divine will

4. Judas enters the Garden as Satan did

5. Unlike Adam, Jesus trusts the Father completely

V. Jesus Completes the Passover

A. "Seamless garment" also worn by the high priest offering sacrifice (John 19:23)

B. No broken bones (John 19:33)

C. Sour wine on hyssop (John 19:29; echoes Exodus 12:22): the fourth cup

1. "It is finished" – the Passover is complete

D. The Lamb slain on the fourteenth of Nisan

E. Hanging of Judas parallels 2 Samuel 17:1-3, 23 (Ahithophel's plot foiled)

VI. Jesus Before the High Priest

A. "You will see the Son of man …" – alludes to Psalm 110:1 and Daniel 7:9-13

1. Will ascend to the heavenly throne room

2. Royal Messiah will reign with God

3. Son of Man triumphs over enemies

B. Caiaphas tears his garments – prohibited: Leviticus 10, 21

C. Jesus is charged with blasphemy

VII. Peter's Denial (Matthew 26:69-75)

Session 23 – Questions

The King and His Kingdom

Matthew 27 – The Passion of the King

	Prologue	Book 1	Book 2	Book 3	Book 4	Book 5	Conclusion
	Birth of the King	*Announcement of the Kingdom*	*Establishment of the Kingdom*	*The Kingdom Defined*	*Transfer of the Kingdom's Authority*	*Announcement of the End of the Old Kingdom*	*Victory of the King*
NARRATIVE	Mt. 1–2 *Jesus' ancestry and infancy*	Mt. 3–4 *John the Baptist and Jesus' early ministry*	Mt. 8–9 *Miracles; commissioning the Twelve*	Mt. 11–12 *Jesus confronts an evil generation*	Mt. 14–17 *Travels and ministry; instructing the Twelve*	Mt. 19–23 *Events and teaching in Judea*	**Mt. 26–28** ***Passion week***
DISCOURSE		Mt. 5–7 *Sermon on the Mount*	Mt. 10 *Missionary instructions*	Mt. 13 *Kingdom parables*	Mt. 18 *Life in the Christian community*	Mt. 24–25 *Olivet Discourse (Judgment on Jerusalem)*	

A. Review the Context

Matthew 26 contrasted Jesus' precious worth—demonstrated by the woman willing to spend a fortune anointing him—with the paltry sum he was betrayed for by men who hated him and wanted to kill him. Now, it is Passover, and Jesus prepares to lead his own "Exodus." He has struggled with temptation in the Garden of Gethsemane and set aside his own will to do his Father's will. He has stood before Ciaphas following his arrest and said he is the Messiah. The leaders are preparing to condemn him for blasphemy. "The hour" has come.

B. Read the Story

Carefully read **Matthew 27.** Ask yourself the questions: *Who? What? When? Where? How? Why?*

As always, pray before you read.

C. Take a Deeper Look

Answering these questions will draw you into the heart of the story. If you do not understand something, make a note of it to bring up in the small-group discussion.

Judas Hangs Himself (Matthew 27:1-10)

1. a. Compare Judas' remorse in verse 4 over his sin of "betraying innocent blood" with Peter's bitter sadness in **Matthew 26:75.** How do they differ?

b. Read **CCC 1430–1431.** Would you say Judas experiences true repentance? Why, or why not?

2. **Think About It:** Matthew says Jeremiah's prophecy is fulfilled in the purchase of the potter's field with the thirty pieces of silver. Similar images are found in both the books of Jeremiah and Zechariah. **Optional:** Read **Jeremiah 18 and 19; Zechariah 11:12-13;** and **Jeremiah 32–33.** What insights do these passages provide into the wider meaning of Judas' betrayal of Jesus, his death, and the purchase of the potter's field?

Jesus Before Pilate (Matthew 27:11-26)

3. a. Why does Pilate decide to offer the crowd Barabbas in Jesus' place?

   b. Read John's account of this trial in **John 19:1-22.** What is behind Pilate's final decision? Does he believe in it?

4. Barabbas is a "notorious prisoner," guilty of insurrection and murder. He is possibly one of the Zealots, a group of Jews who seek to change Israel's fortunes by political rebellion and force. What does the crowd's choice to spare Barabbas over Jesus say about their understanding of God's way of accomplishing things? What are they really choosing?

5. In verse 25, the crowd cries, "His blood be on us and on our children!" Some people have interpreted that to mean that all Jews are cursed as a result. What does the Church have to say about this? Are the Jews as a people responsible for the crucifixion of Christ? Why, or why not? (See **CCC 597–598.**)

The Death of the King (Matthew 27:27-56)

6. **Think About It:** Jesus' passion should be seen in light of the curse that resulted from mankind's original sin, which Jesus has come to set right (see **Genesis 3:14-24**). Now read **1 Corinthians 15:45,** where Paul calls Jesus "the last Adam." What elements of the curse do you see reflected in Jesus' ordeal or redeemed by him?

7. **Think About It:** Jesus' final words on the Cross are, *Eli, Eli, lama sabachthani?*—or, "My God, my God, why hast thou forsaken me?" (verse 46). To anyone familiar with the psalms, this should immediately bring to mind Psalm 22, which begins with the same line. Jesus could quote another psalm; there are many with similar sentiments. Why do you think he chooses this particular verse? Is he simply crying out in loss, or is there more in this cry?

8. a. Review **Matthew 27:51-54**. What do you think is the significance of these events? Read also **Hebrews 10:19-22 and 12:18, 21-24, 28.**

   b. Of what do these signs convince the centurion and those who are with him?

The Burial of the King (Matthew 27:57-66)

9. What precautions are taken in sealing Jesus' tomb, and why?

D. Application

These questions will help you apply one of the key themes of the session to your life. After meditating on them, respond to God with a brief written prayer if you choose.

Matthew 27 ends with what appears to be the end of all the hopes and dreams of Jesus' followers. Have you ever felt the crushing impossibility of circumstance? Have you felt that God has abandoned you or that hope is dead and lying in a sealed and guarded tomb? What have you learned in this session that can help you avoid despair?

Dear Lord …

Session 23 Talk Notes

Matthew 27 – The Passion of the King

I. The Betrayal of Jesus (Matthew 27:1-10): Judas and Repentance

A. Thirty pieces of silver – "blood money" – used to buy potter's field

1. Verses 8-10 – fulfills Jeremiah (could also be Zechariah 11:7-14)

a. Zechariah – thirty shekels of silver

b. Jeremiah 19 – breaks potter's flask in Valley of Hinnom (field of blood, Gehenna)

2. Jeremiah talks of New Covenant (Jeremiah 31), buys a field as sign of hope, restoration (Chapter 32)

B. True penance

1. CCC 1430–1431 – involves interior conversion

2. Judas repents but has no deep conversion

II. Jesus Before Pilate (Matthew 27:11-26)

A. Twofold purpose to Christ's death

1. Make right the broken covenant by taking the curses on himself (Deuteronomy 28; Leviticus 26, 28)

2. Restore mankind from original sin

B. Jesus takes on himself the charge of rebellion – Luke 23

1. Jesus becomes the Suffering Servant

a. The Servant, Messiah will suffer (Psalm 89)

b. The Suffering Servant will be restored (Isaiah 49, 53)

C. Release of prisoner at Passover (Barabbas; verses 13-23)

1. Passover speaks of release from bondage (Exodus 12)

a. Israel went into exile after failing to release others

2. Jesus is delivered up out of envy

a. Difference between jealousy and envy

3. Jesus is turned over to the Gentiles (see curses of Deuteronomy 28)

4. The Son of the Father takes the place of Barabbas (means "son of the father")

D. Pilate delivers Jesus to be crucified

1. The blessing of Abraham comes upon the Gentiles

a. Galatians 3:13-14

b. Genesis 12:1-3 – third promise, worldwide blessing

2. Jesus takes on the curses of the Fall (Genesis 3:17-18)

a. The "last Adam" makes right what Adam made wrong

b. Mary, the second Eve, unties the knot of Eve's disobedience – "co-redemptrix," works with Jesus

III. The Crucifixion and Death of Jesus (Matthew 27:27-54)

A. The Cross

1. The new Tree of Life
2. The fruit of the tree is Jesus' Body and Blood (John 6:50-51)

B. Crucifixion

1. "King of the Jews"
    a. Israel asked for a king in 1 Samuel 8
    b. Jesus comes, but they refuse him (John 1)

C. Death

1. "Why have you forsaken me?" (verse 46)
    a. Jesus quotes Psalm 22 – ends in triumph

D. Use of crucifixion by Romans

E. Church is born when blood and water flow from his side (John 19:34)

F. Passion of Christ is efficacious in two ways

1. Jesus offers himself for the broken covenant
    a. Israel is freed from the Old Covenant for the New Covenant (Deuteronomy 28; Romans 7:1-6)
    b. Freed by death to the Law through Christ's body
    c. Freed by new life to join Christ, New Covenant
2. Takes on the curses of the Fall
    a. Jesus does what Adam did not, Mary does what Eve did not: trust the Father
    b. Redeemed through weakness of flesh

G. Simon the Cyrene; pick up your cross

1. Colossians 1:24 – fill up what is lacking in Christ's suffering
2. *Salvifici Doloris* – redemptive participation in Christ's suffering

H. Temple veil is torn

1. Grief in heaven over the death of the Son
2. Access to God the Father is now wide open

I. You can trust the Father

Session 24 – Questions

Matthew 28 and Conclusion – The Triumph of the King

	Prologue	Book 1	Book 2	Book 3	Book 4	Book 5	Conclusion
	Birth of the King	*Announcement of the Kingdom*	*Establishment of the Kingdom*	*The Kingdom Defined*	*Transfer of the Kingdom's Authority*	*Announcement of the End of the Old Kingdom*	*Victory of the King*
NARRATIVE	Mt. 1–2 *Jesus' ancestry and infancy*	Mt. 3–4 *John the Baptist and Jesus' early ministry*	Mt. 8–9 *Miracles; commissioning the Twelve*	Mt. 11–12 *Jesus confronts an evil generation*	Mt. 14–17 *Travels and ministry; instructing the Twelve*	Mt. 19–23 *Events and teaching in Judea*	**Mt. 26–28** ***Passion week***
DISCOURSE		Mt. 5–7 *Sermon on the Mount*	Mt. 10 *Missionary instructions*	Mt. 13 *Kingdom parables*	Mt. 18 *Life in the Christian community*	Mt. 24–25 *Olivet Discourse (Judgment on Jerusalem)*	

A. Review the Context

The hopes of the disciples for a new messianic kingdom appear to be swallowed in defeat. Jesus is dead. The band of twelve apostles has lost one to suicide, and the others have run rather than stand by the Lord. The Jewish people have chosen a "son of the father"—Barabbas—in place of the Son of the Father. The sun has gone down on another Sabbath, and things look very bleak.

Is this the end, or is it a beginning? Jesus became a man so he could suffer and die to free men from the curse of sin. But he also came to defeat death and give mankind new life, his own life. For that, something else is needed. Jesus will have to rise from the dead.

B. Read the Story

Carefully read **Matthew 28.** Ask yourself the questions: *Who? What? When? Where? How? Why?*

As always, pray before you read.

C. Take a Deeper Look

Answering these questions will draw you into the heart of the story. If you do not understand something, make a note of it to bring up in the small-group discussion.

The Resurrection (Matthew 28:1-15)

1. a. Compare the reaction of the women to the news of Jesus' resurrection with the reaction of the guards.

b. Why do you think these two groups react in different ways to their fear?

2. Read **CCC 2174–2176.**

   a. What is the significance of Jesus rising on the dawn of the first day of the week after the Sabbath?

   b. What is the difference between the Jewish Sabbath and the Christian Sunday?

3. a. The elders bribe the guards to lie and say the disciples have stolen Jesus' body. Is this lie convincing? Why, or why not?

   b. What are the religious leaders afraid of that prompts them to spread this story?

4. a. Read St. Paul's reflections on Jesus' resurrection in **1 Corinthians 15:12-24.** Why is it so important for Jesus' to be raised from the dead?

   b. Read **CCC 651–655.** What does this add to your understanding of the significance of the Resurrection?

The "Great Commission" (Matthew 28:16-20)

5. Jesus instructs the women to send the disciples to Galilee where they will see him for themselves. It is there that he appears to the disciples to give them the instructions that are often called "the Great Commission" (verses 16-20). On the map on page 4, note the relationship of Galilee to Jerusalem. Why would Jesus call his disciples to this location to see him and hear these important instructions?

6. a. List the things Jesus tells the disciples to "go therefore" and do.

   b. Why does Jesus tell them to do this? Read also **Daniel 7:14.** Do you see a connection?

7. **Think About It:** The *Catechism* says: "Missionary endeavor requires *patience.* It begins with the proclamation of the Gospel to peoples and groups who do not yet believe in Christ, continues with the establishment of Christian communities that are 'a sign of God's presence in the world,' and leads to the foundation of local churches" (CCC 854).[1] How can you help your Christian community be "a sign of God's presence in the world"?

8. a. What comforting promise does Jesus leave with his disciples, and why do they need it?

   b. What name of Jesus (a name that Matthew emphasizes in Chapter 1) are these words a reminder of?

[1] Cf. *Redemptoris Missio* 42-47; *Ad Gentes* 15§1; Cf. *Redemptoris Missio* 48-49.

c. What does this name mean to you today?

D. Application

This question will help you apply one of the key themes of the session to your life. After meditating on it, respond to God with a brief written prayer if you choose.

Jesus' resurrection is evidence that we can trust our heavenly Father even if it means we will suffer and die. How does Christ's resurrection change the way you will face hardship in the future?

Dear Lord …

E. Wrap-Up – Conclusion: Triumph of the King

How would you summarize the Conclusion to Matthew's Gospel (Chapters 26–28)?

F. Review

Take the time to review what you learned in this study of Matthew's Gospel. Consider the following questions, and record anything you want to remember.

- What did you learn about Jesus?
- What did you learn about the kingdom of heaven?
- Which parables and teachings of Jesus' made a particularly strong impression on you?
- Did any of the sessions hit home, minister to you, or stand out?
- Have any of your thoughts, attitudes, or behavior changed?
- Review the prayers you wrote in response to the application questions at the end of each session. Were there any instances where you decided to make a change in your life? How can you continue to apply what you learned in this study during the coming weeks and months?

Session 24 Talk Notes

Matthew 28 and Conclusion – The Triumph of the King

I. Review Matthew's Gospel

A. The kingdom of heaven on earth

B. Jesus' life as a recapitulation of the life of Israel

1. Unlike Israel, Jesus is a faithful Son
2. The Old Covenant is fulfilled in Christ; Israel is invited to join the New Covenant
3. Jesus reconstitutes Israel around himself

C. Chapter 1 – genealogy

D. Chapter 2 – parallels between two Josephs

E. Chapter 3 – parallels of Elijah and Elisha, John and Jesus (2 Kings 2–5; Malachi)

F. Chapter 4 – water and wilderness, Moses and Jesus, temptations

1. Hunger, provision, security (Exodus 16:3; Deuteronomy 8:3)
2. Putting God to the test (Exodus 17:3; Deuteronomy 6:16)
3. Worshiping a false god (Exodus 32; Deuteronomy 6:13-14)

G. Chapters 5–7 – the new law of the New Covenant

1. Jesus as the new Moses (Numbers; Luke 10)
2. Beatitudes
   a. Humility as chief virtue
   b. Antitheses raise the bar

H. Chapter 6 – piety (prayer, fasting, almsgiving)

I. Chapter 7 – judging, Golden Rule, two ways to live, building on rock

J. Chapters 8–9 – miracles (power of the kingdom)

K. Chapter 10 – disciples invested with Jesus' authority and power

L. Chapters 11–12 – Jesus as the new King; disciples are the new priests (1 Samuel 21)

1. Something greater than Solomon, Jonah, and the Temple
2. Leadership wants Jesus dead

M. Chapter 13 – parables for corrupt leadership

N. Chapters 14-15 – multiplication of the loaves – enough for the whole world

O. Chapter 16 – the Son of Man (Daniel 7:13-14); the first pope (Isaiah 22)

P. Chapter 17 – Transfiguration, exodus from sin

Q. Chapter 18 – forgiveness and exile (Jeremiah 34)

R. Chapter 19 – marriage and divorce

S. Chapter 20–21 – triumphal entry into Jerusalem

1. Paschal Lamb (Exodus 12)
2. Cleansing the Temple

T. Chapter 22–23 – leadership tries to trap Jesus; the greatest commandment

U. Chapter 24–25 – end of the age and the *todah*

V. Chapter 26 – Last Supper, Garden of Gethsemane

W. Chapter 27 – Passion and death; Jesus and Barabbas, sons of the Father

II. The Resurrection of Jesus (Matthew 28:1-15)

A. We can trust the Father

B. Jesus defeats death, hell, and the grave (1 Corinthians 15:35-44)

C. True resurrection of the flesh – incorruptible, spiritual body (infallible teaching)

1. Supported by Creeds (Apostles', Nicene, Athenasian)
2. Fourth Lateran Council, AD 1215
3. CCC 999

III. Jesus Commissions the Disciples (Matthew 28:16-20)

A. Gospel ends: "All authority … has been given to me. Go therefore and make disciples"

B. A disciple believes and does what he is taught

1. *Talmid* = disciplined follower, student
2. "Covered in the dust of the rabbi" (*Pirke avot,* "The Sayings of the Fathers")
3. Faithfulness *(emunah)* – show belief by doing (see James)

Responses to the Study Questions

How to Use These Responses

After completing the home preparation, discussing the questions, and viewing the video presentation, the final step is to review the responses to the questions. These responses summarize the main points from the session and help you continue your Bible study in the next session.

Although it can be tempting to read these responses ahead of time, please wait until after you have completed the questions for each session and engaged in the small-group discussion. It is not necessary to have the "right" answers before going to the small-group discussion. In fact, one purpose of the discussion is for participants to learn by sharing their insights and questions with each other and, through that discussion, coming to a better understanding of the Scripture passages. This makes for a better Bible study experience for everyone.

For best results, follow these steps in order:

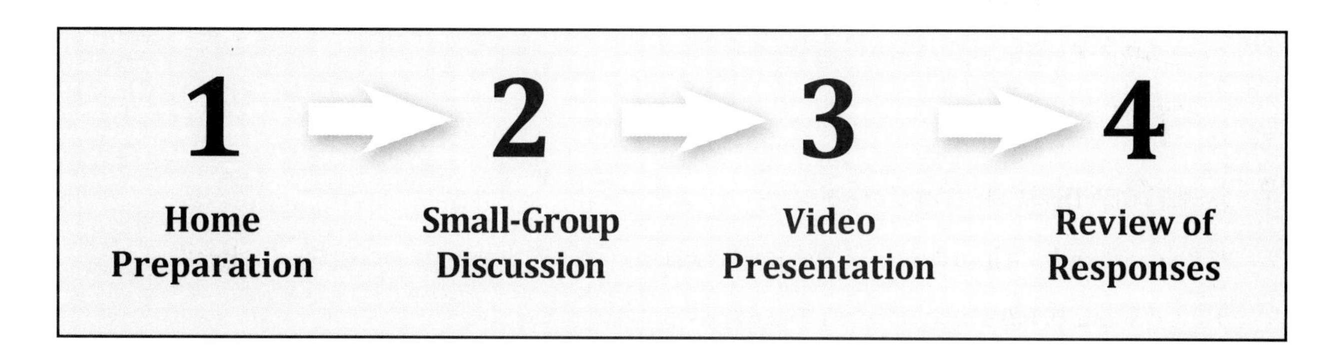

Session 2 – Responses

Matthew 1 – Jesus: The Son of David, the Son of Abraham

***Facilitators:** Read these responses to the questions ahead of time to help you prepare to lead the small-group discussion.*

***Participants:** Reinforce what you have learned by reviewing these responses after the small-group discussion and before you go on to the next session.*

A. Establish the Context

Facilitators: Ask participants to share their first impressions of Matthew's Gospel. If you like, use the following questions to encourage discussion:

- *What were your first impressions?*
- *What stood out to you about Jesus or his mission?*
- *What key words or ideas did you notice?*
- *Are there any concepts you would like clarified or questions you would like answered in the course of this study?*

B. Read the Story

Facilitators: To help set the context for the session, point out the diagram on page 2. We begin with Matthew's "Prologue"—"Birth of the King." This session covers Jesus' ancestry and infancy. If there is time, have someone read each passage aloud before it is discussed.

C. Take a Deeper Look

The Genealogy of Jesus Christ (Matthew 1:1-17)

1. *Matthew is writing to Jewish Christians living in Palestine. Recall what you learned in Session 1. In writing to this group, why do you think Matthew begins his Gospel with a genealogy of Jesus?*

   The Jews in first-century Palestine were waiting and longing for the Messiah—someone in the line of David, anointed by God, to rule over Israel and save it from its enemies; someone to fulfill the promises God gave Abraham. Matthew is presenting Jesus as that Messiah, so it is natural that he begins his Gospel by answering the question that would have been at the forefront of people's minds: "Who is this man?" Matthew answers this question by providing Jesus' credentials, starting with a genealogy that traces his Davidic heritage and his roots in Abraham.

2. *What titles does Matthew give Jesus in verse 1, and what do these titles say about him?*

   Matthew gives Jesus the following three titles in the introduction to his genealogy:

   - **"Christ":** This comes from the Greek *Christos,* which means "Anointed One," a translation of the Hebrew word *Messiah.* "The Anointed One" was one way of referring to the Davidic king in Old Testament times. Jesus is the Messiah the Jews have been waiting for, the one anointed by God to be King over Israel.

   - **"Son of David":** In 2 Samuel 7:8-16, God promised to establish David's kingdom forever through his son Solomon and his heirs—a royal dynasty that one day would give rise to a universal King. Jesus, "the Son of David," comes from this line and is heir to the Davidic throne.

   - **"Son of Abraham":** refers to the role Jesus will play in fulfilling the promises made to Abraham, father of Israel, which include the promise that kings and worldwide blessing will come from him and his descendants (see Genesis 22:18).

3. *Matthew includes four women in Jesus' genealogy: Tamar (verse 3), Rahab (verse 5), Ruth (verse 5), and "the wife of Uriah" who was Bathsheba (verse 6). Do you recognize these names?*

   a. *Read about these women in the following verses and record what you learn.*

      Genesis 38: Tamar, a Canaanite, was Judah's daughter-in-law. After her husband died, she posed as a harlot to bear Judah's child when he failed to give his youngest son to her in marriage.

      Joshua 2:1-16 and 6:22-25: Rahab, also a Canaanite, was a harlot who sheltered the Israelite spies before their entrance into the Promised Land. Joshua saved Rahab and her family in the destruction of Jericho, and they subsequently lived in Israel.

      Ruth 1:1-22 and 4:13-17: Ruth was a Moabite woman who married an Israelite. When he died, she left her family and moved with her mother-in-law, Naomi, to Israel, pledging to be faithful to Naomi's people and God. She later married Boaz, her father-in-law's next of kin.

      2 Samuel 11: Bathsheba, "the wife of Uriah," was a Hittite—a married woman whom King David seduced. When she became pregnant, David had her husband killed and then married her. That child died; her second child was Solomon, who became king after David.

   b. *What is unusual about these women? Why do you think Matthew draws attention to them in Jesus' genealogy?*

      The fact that these women were Gentile in origin, yet still became ancestresses of the Messiah, foreshadows the international scope of the gospel. The fact that three of these women (particularly King Solomon's mother) were associated in some way with sexual immorality may have been intended for those who would think the unusual circumstances of Jesus' birth should disqualify him from the throne.

4. ***Think About It:*** *This genealogy is divided into three distinct groups of fourteen names. The first group ends with David, the second with the deportation to Babylon, and the third with the birth of Jesus Christ. Why do you think Matthew draws attention to the deportation but not to Judah's return to the land of Canaan? (For help with this question, review Session 1.)*

   Although some of the Jews had returned from Babylonian exile by the time of Christ, they had not fully returned to God. They were physically free, but they remained in spiritual captivity. Jesus comes as the promised Davidic King to release them from a far worse captivity than what they experienced in Babylon: He comes to release them from the captivity of sin.

The Birth of the King (Matthew 1:18-25)

5. *In* ***verses 21 and 23,*** *what names does Matthew say will be given to the new child, and what is the significance of these names? (For help with the first name, see* ***CCC 430–431.****)*

   In verse 21, we read: "You shall call his name Jesus, for he will save his people from their sins." The name "Jesus" literally means "God saves." God accomplishes the salvation of mankind through his Son, Jesus. By saving people from their sins, Jesus saves them from a domination worse than that imposed by Rome. He saves them from the exile of permanent separation from God.

   In verse 23, we read: "Behold, a virgin shall conceive and bear a son, and his name shall be called Emmanuel." "Emmanuel" means "God with us." Until Jesus' coming, God had only been "with" his people in isolated instances: when he appeared to individuals; in his Word; in the Tabernacle; and in the Jerusalem Temple. Now, he is coming to walk among his people as a man. The words of the prophecy come from Isaiah 7:14 (in a prophecy of the birth of King Hezekiah who rescued Israel from harm). Matthew sees a deeper level of meaning here, a prophecy of the One who will truly be "God with us"—God incarnate—and save his people from the ultimate harm of sin.

Facilitators: As optional background for further discussion of the name "Jesus," continue reading in the *Catechism* through CCC 435.

6. ***Think About It:*** *"Jesus" is the Greek equivalent of the Hebrew name "Joshua" ("Yahweh saves").*

   a. *Who was Joshua? (There is a good synopsis of his life in* ***Sirach 46:1-8.****)*

      Joshua succeeded Moses as leader of the children of Israel and led them victoriously into the Promised Land.

   b. *How is Jesus a "new Joshua" in a spiritual sense?*

      Under Joshua's leadership, Israel was saved from sin. Jesus leads the children of God into the "Promised Land" of heaven, making him a "new Joshua" in a spiritual sense.

7. *Consider the names for the Messiah found in Matthew 1, including "Christ," "Son of David," "Son of Abraham," "Jesus," and "Emmanuel." Do any of these names seem particularly appropriate in your own experience of God's Son?*

   Answers will be personal and will vary. Encourage discussion.

8. *Some people interpret verse 25, which says that Joseph "knew [Mary] not until she had borne a son," as meaning that the Holy Couple had sexual relations after Jesus was born. Here, the word "until" has been translated from the Greek word* heos, *which is used elsewhere in the Bible to indicate a discrete period of time and which does not necessarily imply any change in the future. For example, we read in* ***2 Samuel 6:23*** *that, "Michal the daughter of Saul had no child to the day of her death." Just as in Matthew 1:25, the word "to" in this passage has been translated from the Greek word* heos. *Read* ***CCC 499–501.*** *What does the Magisterium teach about Mary's virginity?*

   The Church confirms that Mary is "ever virgin"—she had no natural children other than Jesus. Her virginity is "real and perpetual"; and in giving birth to God's Son, that virginity was sanctified. Some people misinterpret scriptural references to Jesus' "brothers and sisters" as meaning Mary had other children with Joseph. The Church answers these concerns by explaining that the words translated "brother" and "sister" referred to close relatives at the time of Jesus. Even though Mary had no other natural children, she is a spiritual mother to all who become God's children through her son, Jesus.

In the words of St. Pius X, "Mary, by bearing the Savior in her womb, can be said to have borne all those whose life was contained in the life of the Savior. All of us, therefore, who are united with Christ and are, as the apostle says, 'members of his body, made from his flesh and bones,' have come forth from the womb of Mary, after the manner of a body that is joined to its head. Hence, in a spiritual and mystical sense we are called the children of Mary and she is Mother of us all."[1]

D. Application

Facilitators: If time allows, have group members share their responses to the following application questions.

Meditate on the significance of Jesus Christ as "Emmanuel"—"God with us." How is Christ still with us today? If it is sometimes hard for you to believe God is with you, is there anything in this session that might help increase your faith?

After the small-group discussion, watch Jeff Cavins' video presentation on *Session 2* – Matthew 1: Jesus – The Son of David, the Son of Abraham.

1 John E. Rotelle, ed., *Day by Day with Mary,* Augustinian Press, 2001).

Facilitators: *Read these responses to the questions ahead of time to help you prepare to lead the small-group discussion.*

Participants: *Reinforce what you have learned by reviewing these responses after the small-group discussion and before you go on to the next session.*

A. Review the Context

Facilitators: Take a moment to review the context and what was learned in the previous session. If you like, use the following questions to encourage discussion:

- *Try to imagine yourself living in first-century Palestine. What effect would you expect Matthew's proclamation in Chapter 1 to have on the Jewish leaders? On ordinary people? On the Romans?*

B. Read the Story

Facilitators: If there is time, have someone read each passage aloud before it is discussed.

C. Take a Deeper Look

The Magi's Visit (Matthew 2:1-12)

1. *Jesus is born in Bethlehem of Judea. Find it on the map on page 4. In Hebrew, "Bethlehem" means "house of bread." Read the following Old Testament passages, and note what is important about this little town.*

   1 Samuel 16:1, 4-13: According to Samuel, Bethlehem was the hometown of David and his family and the place where David was anointed king.

   Micah 5:2-4: The prophecy in this passage says that although Bethlehem is small, a great king will come from it. This prophecy was given to the Southern Kingdom (Judah) long after King David reigned over Israel and shortly before the Northern Kingdom was taken into exile.

2. *In Matthew 2, four people (or groups of people) are shown reacting to news of the new King. Who are they, and what are their responses?*

People	Response
Wise men (Gentile astronomers)	They leave their homes and travel far to worship the new King. They persist even when Jewish leaders do not point the way and even though the star stands over an unlikely place, a humble stable.
Herod	Troubled; he plots and kills all boys two years old and younger in Bethlehem.
All Jerusalem	Troubled
Chief priests and scribes	Even though they know the location (Bethlehem), they do not seem interested or excited, nor do they try to find the young King.

3. ***Think About It:*** *Matthew does not include the visit of the (Jewish) shepherds that is recorded in Luke 2. What conclusion might the reader draw from this omission?*

   The fact that Matthew does not record the visit of the Jewish shepherds emphasizes the contrast between the positive reception Jesus receives from the the Gentile Magi and the negative reception he receives from his own people.

4. *Read* ***CCC 528.*** *What does the Church see in the Magi?*

   In the Magi, the Church sees the "first-fruits of the nations," an initial indication of the many non-Jews who will welcome Christ and the salvation he will bring them. Not only are those of Jewish birth welcomed by the King of kings, but people of all nations are welcomed as well.

5. *Herod is troubled enough to seek the death of the reported new King of the Jews. His own kingship is not based on blood (Herod is an Edomite, descended from Esau), but on political expediency: Rome has appointed him king of the Jews, a position he holds from 37 to 4 BC. Read* ***Numbers 24:15-19.*** *This passage records a prophecy of Balaam, with which Herod, as an Edomite, would have been familiar. Why is Herod so disturbed by the words of the chief priests and scribes in Matthew 2:6?*

   Before Israel ever entered the land of Canaan, the prophet Balaam foretold the dispossession of Edom and other enemies of Israel at a future time when a new king would arise from Israel. The wise men follow a star that proclaims the birth of just such a king.

6. *Read* ***Isaiah 60:3-6.*** *How is this proclamation fulfilled in Matthew 2?*

   Isaiah foresaw "other nations and kings" coming "on camels bringing gold and frankincense" to praise the Lord. Seven hundred years later, Matthew describes kings from far-off countries arriving on camels and bearing gifts of gold and frankincense for the Christ child.

The Holy Family Escapes to Egypt (Matthew 2:13-23)

7. *When Matthew says, "Out of Egypt have I called my son" (2:15), he is quoting* **Hosea 11:1.** *Hosea's reference is to God's delivery of his children from Egyptian slavery. Read* **CCC 530.** *What point is Matthew trying to make about Jesus?*

   Israel's deliverance from slavery by God was the great touchstone in their history. Here, Matthew brings that liberation to mind and puts Jesus forward as the ultimate redeemer of God's children.

8. *Read* **verses 19-23,** *and find Judea, Galilee, and Nazareth on the map on page 4.*

   a. *Why does the Holy Family decide not to return to Bethlehem?*

      The Holy Family does not return to Bethlehem because of the danger they face there even after the death of Herod. Joseph is warned in a dream not to return, so they settle north in the town of Nazareth near the Sea of Galilee.

   b. *"He shall be called a Nazarene" appears to be paraphrased from the words of several prophets. Matthew may be drawing a comparison between the words "Nazareth" and* nester *(Hebrew for "branch"). Read the following verses, and record what the image of the branch represents.*

      Isaiah 11: The branch can be likened to part of a family genealogy chart. In Isaiah 11, the "branch" is a righteous judge who will come from the line of Jesse (David's youngest son). God will recover the remnant of his people who have been scattered in exile, and he will reunite his torn kingdom.

      Jeremiah 23:5-6: Jeremiah 23 tells us that God will raise a "righteous branch," or descendant, of David to rule wisely and justly. In his days, the kingdom of Israel (North and South together) will be secure.

   c. *How does this image of the "branch" relate to Jesus Christ, the Nazarene?*

      Jesus the "Nazarene" is the promised "Branch," the shoot from the line of Jesse who will sit on David's throne and rule over God's reunited kingdom in justice, wisdom, and righteousness.

D. Application

Facilitators: If time allows, have group members share their responses to the following application questions.

Have you ever felt like a "stump," where everything meaningful to you has been cut off? Does the future look bleak? Meditate on this, and praise the God who raised a "branch" of new life from the stump that Israel had become. Do you believe he can do a new work in you?

E. Wrap-Up – Prologue: Birth of the King

Facilitators: If there is time, ask if anyone can summarize the "Prologue" of Matthew's Gospel (Chapters 1–2). Answers will vary. The point is not to find a "correct" answer, but to explore the major points of the chapters. You might ask questions like:

- *What facts does Matthew establish about the new King?*
- *How does he say the King will fulfill the prophecies of the Old Testament?*
- *What is the new King's mission?*

After the small-group discussion, watch Jeff Cavins' video presentation on *Session 3* – Matthew 2: The King in Exile.

Session 4 – Responses

Matthew 3 – John: The Forerunner to the King

Facilitators: *Read these responses to the questions ahead of time to help you prepare to lead the small-group discussion.*

Participants: *Reinforce what you have learned by reviewing these responses after the small-group discussion and before you go on to the next session.*

A. Establish the Context

Facilitators: Take a moment to review the context and what was learned in the previous session and to establish the context of "Book One" of Matthew's Gospel. If you like, use the following question to encourage discussion:

- *What have you learned about the way God fulfills his promises?*

B. Read the Story

Facilitators: If there is time, have someone read each passage aloud before it is discussed.

C. Take a Deeper Look

John the Baptist's Announcement (Matthew 3:1-12)

1. a. *Who is John the Baptist, and what has been foretold about him? Read* ***Luke 1:5-36.***

   John the Baptist has been sent by God as the forerunner of Jesus Christ, to prepare the way for the Lord. He is born to the priest Zechariah and his wife, Elizabeth, in their old age. An angel of the Lord says that John will "be great before the Lord" (Luke 1:15). He will be filled with the Holy Spirit from his conception and will turn many Israelites to God. The angel also says that John will go before the Lord "in the spirit and power of Elijah, to turn the hearts of the fathers to the children, and the disobedient to the wisdom of the just, to make ready for the Lord a people prepared" (Luke 1:17).

   b. *Read* ***verses 2-3.*** *What is his message and purpose?*

   John calls on Israel to "repent, for the kingdom of heaven is at hand." His purpose is to prepare the way for Christ's coming.

   c. *What details does Matthew give about where John the Baptist preaches, the clothes he wears, and the food he eats?*

   John preaches in the wilderness of Judea. He wears camel's hair clothing and a leather belt and eats locusts and wild honey.

2. *Who comes to hear John preach, and how do they respond?*

   People from "all Judea and all the region about the Jordan"—not just from Jerusalem—and even many Jewish religious leaders come to hear John preach, to confess their sins, and to be baptized.

3. a. *The Pharisees and Sadducees were religious leaders in Jesus' day. The Pharisees kept themselves separate from everything "unclean" and insisted the people observe strict adherance to the Law to be considered holy. The Sadducees were descendants of Zadoch, high priest under David, who had become corrupt; they were pawns of the Romans. What do you think John the Baptist means by his warning in verses 8-12?*

   John the Baptist delivers a stern rebuke to the Pharisees and Sadducees, who think it is enough to obey the letter of the Law but ignore its spirit. He says they need to repent and change their actions, rather than presuming they are saved based on their positions. God's purifying judgment is at hand in the coming of Jesus.

   b. *What do you think John means when he says, "fruit that befits repentance?" Read* **CCC 678.** *What will be judged on the Last Day?*

   People who are truly repentant bear fruit and do not presume to be God's children simply because of the circumstances of their birth. On the Last Day—the Day of Judgment—attitudes and actions will be revealed and judged, and those who have refused the grace and love of God will be condemned.

4. *Read* ***2 Kings 1:8; Malachi 4:5-6;*** *and* ***Sirach 48:4, 9-10.*** *What Old Testament prophet does Matthew's description of John the Baptist bring to mind, and what do Malachi and Sirach say about that prophet? (Note: In some Bibles, the Malachi reference will be in verses 23-24.)*

   John's clothes match the description of the great prophet Elijah, who did not die but was taken up into heaven by a whirlwind of fire. The prophets foretold that God would send Elijah back before the Day of the LORD to bring reconciliation between father and son and restore the tribes of Jacob. The angel's message to Zachariah regarding John the Baptist echoes this prophecy.

   Elijah is the appointed restorer of all things; John the Baptist is "Elijah" returned to restore and to pave the way for the Lord.

5. ***Think About It:*** *John baptizes people in the Jordan River. What is special about this river that lends meaning to this? Read* ***Joshua 3; 2 Kings 5:1, 10-14;*** *and* ***CCC 1222.***

   The Jordan River is rich in association. The people of Israel crossed through it on dry land, much as they did the Red Sea when God brought them triumphantly into the Promised Land from their wanderings in the desert. Later, Namaan, a Syrian commander, was cleansed from his leprosy there.

   Because of the initial crossing of the Jordan in particular, it is associated with God's deliverance and is a place of new beginnings. That John baptizes people there before Christ's coming, hints of an even greater beginning than either that first deliverance or Namaan's cleansing: Soon, people will be cleansed of and delivered from their sins.

6. *Compare and contrast the baptisms of Jesus and John the Baptist. (See* ***verses 11-12*** *and also* ***CCC 1265.)***

   John baptizes with "water for repentance," while Jesus baptizes with the Holy Spirit and with fire. John's baptism washes away, while Jesus' baptism transforms. What John's baptism represents, Jesus' baptism achieves: The baptized person is purified, filled with the new life of the Holy Spirit, and made an adopted member of the family of God.

Jesus Is Baptized (Matthew 3:13-17)

7. *Why do you think Jesus, who is sinless, wants to be baptized by John, who baptizes "with water for repentance"? (For help with this question, see* ***CCC 535–536 and 1223–1224.****)*

   In being baptized by John, Jesus identifies himself with those whose sins he will later bear on the Cross and demonstrates submission to the Father. Jesus has no sin of his own to wash away. His baptism is a powerful symbol of what he has come to do—to die and rise to new life. It points to his death and rebirth, which we are also baptized into.

8. *What do the opened heavens, the descent of the dove, and the voice from heaven signify?*

   These images clearly identify Jesus as the Messiah, the "Anointed One": The voice identifies Jesus as God's Son; the dove identifies him as the Anointed One; and the opened heavens indicate the presence of God in the announcement. The entire Trinity—God the Father, God the Son, and God the Holy Spirit— is present at this announcement of the Messiah.

   In addition, the Spirit descending as a dove over the water brings to mind the creation of the world. Here begins a new, albeit spiritual, creation.

Facilitators: Jesus is both King and High Priest in the New Covenant, so it should not surprise us that his reign begins in a similar way to those who preceded him in the Old Covenant. In the Old Covenant, a new high priest was washed with water and anointed before taking office (see Exodus 29:4), and the Davidic kings were anointed to mark the beginning of their reigns. An echo of this practice can be seen in the priestly ordination rites of the Church today.

D. Application

Facilitators: If time allows, have group members share their responses to the following application questions.

John's message is "repent, for the kingdom of heaven is at hand." The kingdom of heaven is here on earth now in a provisional way in the Church. We all need to repent to prepare our hearts for Jesus' coming. Have you borne "fruit that befits repentance"? What can you learn from the preaching of John the Baptist?

After the small-group discussion, watch Jeff Cavins' video presentation on *Session 4* – Matthew 3 – John: The Forerunner to the King.

Facilitators: *Read these responses to the questions ahead of time to help you prepare to lead the small-group discussion.*

Participants: *Reinforce what you have learned by reviewing these responses after the small-group discussion and before you go on to the next session.*

A. Review the Context

Facilitators: Take a moment to review the context and what was learned in the previous session. If you like, use the following questions to encourage discussion:

- *What did you learn about John the Baptist's message and Jesus' baptism? Did anything challenge you?*

B. Read the Story

Facilitators: If there is time, have someone read each passage aloud before it is discussed.

C. Take a Deeper Look

The Temptation of Jesus (Matthew 4:1-11)

1. *In Matthew 4:1-11, Jesus is tempted by the devil. What is the purpose of the devil's questioning?*

   At the end of Matthew 3, God says, "This is my beloved Son." Now, in Matthew 4, Satan says, "If you are the Son of God …" The devil is testing Jesus, tempting him to prove who he is. He is testing his relationship with the Father. He is tempting him to avoid suffering and death (and thereby fail at his mission), and he is tempting him to seek earthly kingdom and glory (something that is already his by right).

2. *What weapons does the devil employ against Jesus?*

   The devil employs a single weapon against Jesus—the Word of God.

3. *How does Jesus fight back? What is the result?*

   Jesus does not simply fight back; he prepares for action by prayer and fasting. Because he is intentionally hungry and thirsty, Satan's lures of refreshment lose their appeal. By fasting and standing up against the Serpent, Jesus puts his own physical desires on the back burner instead of allowing them to have more importance to him than the Word of God. When he does fight back, he uses the "Sword of the Spirit, the Word of God" (Ephesians 6:17)—rightly handled this time. As a result, the devil leaves, and angels minister to Jesus.

4. a. *Who leads Jesus into the desert in verse 1, and why?*

   The Holy Spirit leads Jesus into the desert so he can be tempted by the devil.

b. *Does this seem odd to you? Why is it important for Jesus to be tempted? Read what the Church has to say about Jesus' temptations in* ***CCC 538–540.*** *(See also* ***Hebrews 4:15-16.****)*

God became man so that we could have a high priest who sympathizes with our weaknesses. He has been tempted in the same ways we are tempted. In the desert, he fights the devil not with divine power or miracles but with powers that are available to all of us.

The Fall came about through the disobedience of one man: Adam. To undo that damage, it is necessary for another man—Jesus Christ—to be perfectly obedient. The Bible says Jesus has to learn obedience and be made perfect (Hebrews 5:8). In the desert, Jesus is called on to prove that even in extreme circumstances, he will obey. Where Adam failed and fell, Jesus resists and prevails. His humanity is therefore completed ("made perfect"), and on the basis of this perfection, he becomes "the source of eternal salvation" for us (Hebrews 5:9).

5. ***Think About It:*** *If even the devil can quote Scripture, how can we know when it is correctly used and when it is not? How can we avoid being misled? (Try to answer this from what you have learned in this session. (If you need additional help, see* ***CCC 85–86 and 109–119.****)*

To avoid being misled by those who use Scripture incorrectly, follow Jesus' example: Be prepared. You can prepare yourself by praying and by reading and studying the Bible. Know God's Word, and know it in context. Read it, meditate on it, and allow it to take root in your heart and mind. Follow the Church's teachings regarding Scripture interpretation and be obedient. If God's Word is being used in an attempt to convince you to disobey, something is wrong. Trust his way, even if it does not make sense in human terms.

Jesus Ministers in Galilee (Matthew 4:12-22)

Facilitators: These questions refer to Matthew 4:12-25. Have someone locate Galilee on the map on page 5 before you begin. The Hebrew tribes of Zebulun and Naphtali were in this region.

6. *The tribal areas of Zebulun and Naphtali were the first regions to be carried into exile by the Assyrians. During Jesus' day, there were some Jews (from Judah) living in Galilee, but the population was made up mostly of Gentiles and descendants of the Israelites (Northern tribes) who had returned from exile. Why do you think Jesus chooses to start his ministry there?*

It is fitting that Christ begins his ministry of restoration in the very area that went into exile first. While these people might no longer be exiled physically, they remain spiritually exiled and estranged from God due to their sin (of breaking the covenant). Jesus has come to restore them from this far greater exile.

7. *In verses 15-17, Matthew connects the start of Jesus' ministry with a prophecy from Isaiah. Read the original prophecy in* ***Isaiah 9:1-7.*** *What does Matthew want his readers to understand?*

Light is dawning on the people who have lived in the darkness of exile, the deep exile from God that is sin. The quote brings to mind the context of the whole: Light dawns in the coming of the "child," the "Son," who will reign forever on the throne of David. This light is Jesus, walking first in the land of Zebulun and Naphtali and spreading the light of the kingdom of heaven.

8. a. *Notice that Jesus' message in* ***Matthew 4:17*** *is identical to John the Baptist's message in* ***Matthew 3:2.*** *Why is this significant?*

   The fact that Jesus' message is identical to that of John the Baptist shows continuity. Jesus takes up where John the Baptist leaves off, starting "from that time" of John's imprisonment. This is all part of a single plan. Jesus withdraws into Galilee when he hears of John's arrest (verse 12)—not to hide, but because it is time for his ministry to begin.

   b. *Why is this message so important for Israel to hear?*

   Jesus' plea for repentance is important because returning to God and living in his kingdom will take more than simply returning to the Promised Land and defeating the Romans. The people have to return in their hearts as well and repent and live in a way that shows evidence of that repentance.

9. *How does Jesus call his first disciples (see verse 19), and how do they respond?*

   Jesus calls them in a personal way—in the context of their everyday work. Jesus sees them fishing and mending their nets and calls out to them to follow him, promising he will make them "fishers of men." He will elevate their profession and use it in an extraordinary manner. Simon, Andrew, James, and John respond by leaving their nets immediately and following him.

10. a. *How does Jesus minister to the people in Galilee (see verses 23-25)?*

   In Galilee, Jesus teaches the people about the kingdom of heaven and heals their diseases and infirmities.

   b. *How is he received?*

   Large crowds of people from the entire region (including the North and South beyond the Jordan) follow Jesus wherever he goes and bring their sick to him.

D. Application

Facilitators: If time allows, have group members share their responses to the following application questions.

How well do you know God's Word? The author of Psalm 119 says: "I have laid up thy word in my heart, that I might not sin against thee" (verse 11). How can you do this? How can you resist temptation as Jesus did? If you need courage, remember the words of Hebrews 2:18: "For because he himself has suffered and been tempted, he is able to help those who are tempted."

After the small-group discussion, watch Jeff Cavins' video presentation on *Session 5* – Matthew 4: The Tempting of the King.

Matthew 5 – The Bar Is Raised by the King

Facilitators: *Read these responses to the questions ahead of time to help you prepare to lead the small-group discussion.*

Participants: *Reinforce what you have learned by reviewing these responses after the small-group discussion and before you go on to the next session.*

A. Review the Context

Facilitators: Take a moment to review the context and what was learned in the previous session. If you like, use the following question to encourage discussion:

- *By the end of Matthew 4, Jesus is attracting crowds of people from all over Palestine. They are anxious for the restoration of the kingdom of Israel. They have gathered to hear him, and at the start of Matthew 5, he will sit down to teach them. Think about it for a moment: What might you expect him to say?*

B. Read the Story

Facilitators: If there is time, have someone read each passage aloud before it is discussed.

C. Take a Deeper Look

The Beatitudes (Matthew 5:1-11)

1. *Look up the definition of "blessed." What does it mean? What do you mean when you call someone "blessed"?*

   Answers will vary based on the dictionary participants use. Possible answers include: to be blessed is to be highly favored or fortunate; to have good fortune bestowed upon one; to be characterized by happiness and good fortune; to enjoy the bliss of heaven. The Hebrew is *ashrei*—"happy" or "blessed"—which denotes a deep satisfaction.

2. *Who does Jesus proclaim in the Beatitudes will be the "blessed" of the kingdom?*

   According to Jesus, the "blessed" of the kingdom are the poor in spirit; those who mourn; the meek; those who hunger and thirst for righteousness; the merciful; the pure in heart; the peacemakers; and those who are persecuted for righteousness' sake.

3. a. *In Jesus' day, "beatitude" (blessedness) would ordinarily have been determined by a person's good fortune. On what basis does Jesus determine blessedness?*

   The things Jesus is calling blessings here are things we would consider bad fortune: poverty, sorrow, hunger, thirst, and persecution. What a paradox. Understood properly, these "curses " can actually be blessings that help a person reach the kingdom of heaven.

   b. *What point is Jesus making about the kingdom of heaven and happiness (blessedness)?*

True happiness (or blessing) is found only in God's kingdom, not in such "blessings" of the world as pleasure, wealth, achievement, or acceptance. We may think these earthly things will satisfy us, but only God can fulfill the longings of our hearts and meet our desire for happiness. True happiness (blessing) is found not in selfish striving and grasping, but in giving ourselves away through the practice of such virtues as mercy, purity of heart, and peacemaking. The kingdom of heaven cannot be gained by birthright, force, or achievement—it belongs to those who are children of God at heart and who imitate him and long for righteousness.

4. *The first beatitude, "Blessed are the poor in spirit, for theirs is the kingdom of heaven," lays the groundwork for the rest. Who are the "poor in spirit"? (For help with this question, see* **CCC 544.***)*

   The "poor in spirit" are the humble—those who are aware of their spiritual poverty, who know they are nothing without God, and who are convinced of their need for his love and mercy.

Salt and Light (Matthew 5:13-16)

5. *Jesus calls his disciples "the salt of the earth" in verse 13. Discuss what it means to be "salt."*

   Salt has a number of properties and uses that might apply here:

   - Salt is pure. It can be used as an antiseptic to purify other things. Christ's followers should be pure in character and free from the contamination of sin.
   - Salt is a preservative. In this sense, being "salt" might mean preserving the Catholic Faith and passing it on, or it might mean preserving society or those around us from the corruption of sin.
   - Salt seasons food and enhances flavor. In a similar way, "salty" Christians can bring out the best in the community.
   - Salt produces thirst, and the lives of Christians should produce a thirst for God in those around them.
   - Salt is needed to stay alive. We should be like Jesus, transforming the world around us with his love and bringing new life to those around us.

6. a. *Read* **verses 14-16.** *This is not the first time the children of Israel have been called the light of the world. Read* **Isaiah 42:6-7 and 49:5-6.** *What is Israel's God-given mission, and how does Jesus expect his disciples to fulfill it?*

   In the Old Testament, God called Israel to fulfill a mission for him: to be a light to the nations and to open people's eyes and bring them out of darkness into the light of his salvation. Now, Jesus is calling on his disciples to fulfill the same function: to shine in their good works and to live lives that attract others to God.

   b. *How does the image of light enhance your understanding of what God calls his children to do?*

   Without light, we cannot see things as they are; without light, we cannot find our way; without light, we can become afraid, make mistakes, stumble, and fall. But light enables us to see clearly, to find our way, and to walk steadily and well. Light is also necessary for life and growth.

People who lack the light of God cannot see truth. By shining the light of God's Word into the world through our own attitudes, behaviors, and actions, we can do for the world what a light does for a dark room or path.

The Law and the Prophets (Matthew 5:17-48)

7. *Part of living out this new law involves being salt and light in the world. How do we put this into practice? Read* **Matthew 5:21-48,** *in which Jesus applies his New Covenant understanding to Old Covenant laws regarding murder, adultery, divorce, swearing falsely, retaliation, and enemies. How would you summarize his basic message?*

   Jesus is taking examples from the Old Covenant Law ("You have heard that it was said …") and adding new depth to their meaning. Each time he says, "But I say to you," he is indicating that his interpretation is the authoritative one. It is not simply the act of murder or adultery that is wrong: Entertaining the kind of thoughts that lead to those actions is wrong as well. Under the New Covenant law, people must be ready to go the extra mile, to give more than is demanded, to avoid retaliation, and to love their enemies and those who persecute them. Rather than using the Law as a ruler to measure out fair play, Jesus wants us to use God as our measure and to be merciful like he is.

8. *Choose one of these laws, and explain how Jesus deepens your understanding of the purpose or intent of the original Law.*

   Answers will vary and may be personal. Encourage discussion.

9. ***Think About It:*** *The* Catechism *tells us, "In Jesus, the same Word of God, that had resounded on Mount Sinai to give the written Law to Moses, made itself heard anew on the Mount of the Beatitudes" (CCC 581). What similarities and differences do you see between God's Word in the Ten Commandments (Exodus 20:1-17) and God's Word in the Beatitudes? In what sense do the Beatitudes "fulfill" the Ten Commandments or reveal what the earlier Law only pointed to?*

   The Ten Commandments (or Decalogue) are prohibitions, while the Beatitudes are promises and blessings. The Decalogue was given to the newly freed children of Israel to teach them how to live in freedom as redeemed people of God. It taught them how to avoid being drawn back into bondage to the false gods of this world. The Beatitudes go deeper and address the attitudes necessary to be God's children: poverty of spirit; mourning; meekness; spiritual hunger; and thirst for righteousness; mercy; purity; peacemaking; and a willingness to be persecuted for the sake of righteousness. The Beatitudes do not take the place of the Ten Commandments. Rather, a person who follows the Beatitudes will fulfill the commandments as a matter of course and will receive the kingdom of heaven.

10. ***Think About It:*** *What does Jesus' discussion of anger in verses 21-26 say about the connection between our worship of God and our relationships with one another? (See also* **Matthew 6:15.***)*

    Offering a gift at the altar is an act of repentance that seeks God's mercy. How can we properly worship and accept God's forgiveness if we do not pass that mercy on to others? Later in Matthew's Gospel, Jesus says, "If you do not forgive men their trespasses, neither will your Father forgive your trespasses" (Matthew 6:15). Before seeking God's forgiveness, we must forgive others.

11. *Love of neighbor is one of the two greatest commandments of the Old Testament Law.*

    a. *How does Jesus expand on the definition of "neighbor" in verses 43-48?*

    Jesus includes Gentiles and sinners—even our enemies—as neighbors we are called to love.

    b. *On what basis does Jesus say to love even our enemies?*

    Jesus says to love even our enemies on the basis of God's unconditional and impartial love. It is easy to love people who love us. As Christians, we must be different. We must imitate the love and mercy of our heavenly Father. "Be perfect, as your heavenly Father is perfect" (Matthew 5:48). This is how we show God's love to the world.

D. Application

Facilitators: If time allows, have group members share their responses to the following application question.

In his words regarding adultery and lust, Jesus calls us to a radical removal of anything in our lives that leads us to sin and keeps us from living as citizens of the kingdom of heaven. If you are struggling with a particular sin, consider what leads you into that sin and what you can do to "pluck it out"? (Matthew 5:29).

Optional: *Read CCC 1716–1724, "Our Vocation to Beatitude"; then meditate once more on Matthew 5:3-12. Ask God to speak to your heart. What truths come to mind? What changes do the Beatitudes invite you to make in yourself?*

After the small-group discussion, watch Jeff Cavins' video presentation on *Session 6* – Matthew 5: The Bar Is Raised by the King.

Facilitators: *Read these responses to the questions ahead of time to help you prepare to lead the small-group discussion.*

Participants: *Reinforce what you have learned by reviewing these responses after the small-group discussion and before you go on to the next session.*

A. Review the Context

Facilitators: Take a moment to review the context and what was learned in the previous session. If you like, use the following question to encourage discussion:

- *What did you learn in Matthew 5 about God's desire for you?*

B. Read the Story

Facilitators: If there is time, have someone read each passage aloud before it is discussed.

C. Take a Deeper Look

Personal Piety (Matthew 6:1-4)

1. *In this section of Jesus' Sermon on the Mount, he turns to matters of personal piety, or "acts of righteousness."*

    a. *What three practices are discussed in verses 1-18?*

    Jesus discusses three acts of piety, the traditional works of mercy: almsgiving, prayer, and fasting.

    b. *What is the gist of Jesus' message in these verses?*

    When you give alms, pray, and fast, do not perform these works to be seen and praised by others. Rather, do them in secret, "and your Father who sees in secret will reward you" (verse 4).

    c. *What is revealed about the nature of true piety?*

    Piety literally means "righteousness"—it is the same word Jesus used in Chapter 5 when he said, "Unless your righteousness exceeds that of the scribes and Pharisees, you will never enter the kingdom of heaven" (verse 20). Jesus makes it clear that piety is more than what a person *does*. True piety comes from the heart and has as much to do with motivation as action. Truly pious actions are done not to be noticed, but for God.

2. *Matthew uses the title "Father" or "heavenly Father" for God twelve times in Chapter 6.*

    a. *What fatherly traits of God are illustrated in this chapter?*

    Answers will vary; in Chapter 6, we are told that God's fatherly traits include that he rewards his children; he wants us to do things out of love for him; he knows our needs and provides for them; he forgives; he teaches us to follow him; and he wants us to trust him so we can be free from anxiety.

b. *What difference does it make to your personal piety, or acts of righteousness, when you relate to God as your Father instead of as a master or judge?*

Answers will vary; encourage discussion. Some possible responses include:

- When we relate to God as our Father instead of master or judge, our actions flow out of love and a longing to please him instead of from a sense of duty or a need to fulfill a law or avoid punishment.
- When we view God as our Father, we can approach him in confidence and intimacy rather than in fear.
- We will be more motivated to imitate God and be like him when we see him as our Father.

Prayer (Matthew 6:5-14)

3. *In verses 5-14, Jesus introduces prayer as a means of intimate communion with our heavenly Father. The Lord's Prayer gives us a framework so we will understand how to pray.*

a. *What is the primary focus of the Lord's Prayer (see verses 9-10)?*

Jesus tells us in the Lord's Prayer to focus first on God and his glory: on his Name, his kingdom, and his will.

b. *St. Thomas Aquinas once said: "The Lord's Prayer is the most perfect of prayers. … In it we ask, not only for all the things we can rightly desire, but also in the sequence that they should be desired" (CCC 2763).*[1] *Why do you think these initial requests precede the more personal ones of verses 11-13? (See also* ***CCC 2764.****)*

In the Lord's Prayer, Jesus teaches us to desire and pray for the new life he offers. The words of this prayer help us to order our thoughts appropriately and recognize our position relative to God. We first turn to God in love, recognize him as our Father, and worship his name as holy. We profess our desire for his will be done above all else. We then ask for his care and forgiveness. When pray this way—adoring him first—our petitions are put into perspective, and our thoughts and desires are more likely to be molded to his will.

4. *Read* ***verses 11-13.***

a. *What earthly concerns does Jesus direct us to pray about?*

Jesus directs us to pray for our daily physical and spiritual needs because everything we have comes from God. He instructs us to address any sin that is separating us from God and to forgive those who have sinned against us. Finally, Jesus tells us to pray we will escape the temptation to sin and will be delivered from evil.

b. *Which one of the petitions speaks most to you? The* Catechism *discusses them in detail in Article 3 (see* ***CCC 2803–2854****). Read the pertinent section for the petition you choose, and record what you learn from it.*

Responses will vary and will be personal. Use this question to draw out participants' insights.

---

[1] *Summa Theologica II-II*, 83, 9.

Forgiveness (Matthew 6:15-18)

5. *What does Jesus say people must do for their sins to be forgiven?*

   We must forgive other people for wrongs they have done to us.

6. ***Think About It:*** *Why do you think Jesus makes such a point of the need for forgiveness in his instructions on prayer?*

   When we harbor resentment and refuse to forgive others, our hearts become hardened to God's mercy toward us. We also fail to imitate Christ and to point others to God's grace. Failure to forgive others serves as a roadblock in our relationship with our heavenly Father.

God and Mammon (Matthew 6:19-24)

7. *What is Jesus saying in verses 19-24? (Note: The phrase "a sound eye" in verses 22-23 refers to an ancient Hebrew idiom for generosity.)*

   Jesus is talking about our attitude toward money and earthly things. When we focus on accumulating material "wealth"—whether it be money, land, possessions, or security—our energies will be on providing for ourselves, and our eyes will be turned away from our loving Father and his provision. Jesus is saying that we should give generously to others, rather than hoarding what we have for ourselves, and that we should trust that God will provide for our needs and give us everlasting treasure.

Anxiety Versus Trust in the Father's Care (Matthew 6:25-34)

8. a. *What reasons does Jesus give us in this passage not to worry about how we will be taken care of?*

   Jesus wants us to realize there is more to life than food and clothing, and that excessive worry about these things misplaces our focus, which should be on God. Next, he gives us proof of God's care with an example from nature: If God cares for even the birds and the grass, how much more will he care for his own children? He reminds us that worrying will not add a second to our lives, nor will it solve our present problems. Furthermore, he says that God already knows what we need and that he is in control. If we make seeking his kingdom and righteousness our top priority rather than focusing on temporal concerns, he will take care of these needs as well.

   b. *When Jesus tells us not to worry about what we will eat or wear, is he telling us not to work to provide for ourselves? Read* **CCC 2830.**

   Jesus is not saying we should stop working for these things; he is saying we should not be overly anxious about them. Jesus invites us to seek the Father's kingdom and righteousness first and to trust in the loving providence of God.

   c. *What related point does the apostle Paul make in* ***Philippians 4:6-7?***

   Paul says in Philippians that if we take our cares to God in prayer with thanksgiving, then his peace will hold us steady in Christ.

D. Application

Facilitators: If time allows, have group members share their responses to the following application questions.

When Jesus spoke of the traditional works of mercy—almsgiving, prayer, and fasting—he was attempting to combat the tendency of the people of his day to perform these works for the purpose of appearing holy to others. Today, we are more likely to hear a homily on why we should perform these works at all rather than on why we should not flaunt them. Are these acts of piety a regular or only an occasional part of your life? Do you perform these works out of a sense of duty or out of love? How can you make these works a regular part of your life coming from the heart?

After the small-group discussion, watch Jeff Cavins' video presentation on *Session 7* – Matthew 6: Personal Piety.

Matthew 7 – Choices in the Kingdom

Facilitators: *Read these responses to the questions ahead of time to help you prepare to lead the small-group discussion.*

Participants: *Reinforce what you have learned by reviewing these responses after the small-group discussion and before you go on to the next session.*

A. Review the Context

Facilitators: Take a moment to review the context and what was learned in the previous session. If you like, use the following questions to encourage discussion:

- *How do you approach God in prayer? What did you learn from Matthew 6 that can strengthen your relationship with the Father?*

B. Read the Story

Facilitators: If there is time, have someone read each passage aloud before it is discussed.

C. Take a Deeper Look

Judging Others (Matthew 7:1-6)

1. a. *In verse 1, Jesus says, "Judge not, that you be not judged." What kind of judgment is he talking about, and why does he speak against it? See also* ***James 4:11-12.***

   Jesus is teaching us not to judge others for their faults because we will be judged by the same measure we use for others. If we judge others unmercifully, we will bring that same judgment on ourselves. Jesus also tells us not to condemn others when we ourselves are guilty. Ultimately, this is about who we are (and what our place is) in relationship to God. As James says, "There is one lawgiver and judge, he who is able to save and to destroy." When we judge others for their moral failures, we are playing a role that belongs to God alone.

   b. *How do Jesus' instructions regarding judging others relate to his words in* ***6:14-15?*** *(See also* ***CCC 678.****)*

   Receiving God's mercy is directly related to showing mercy to others. Failure to show mercy can manifest itself in a refusal to forgive others or in condemnation of others for their faults. The way we treat others is the way we treat Christ and demonstrates whether we have accepted or refused his grace.

   c. *If we refrain from judging others, when will they be judged, and by whom? Read* ***1 Corinthians 4:1-5.***

   The authority to judge has been given to Jesus to carry out when he returns. St. Paul says that when he comes, he will "bring to light the things now hidden in darkness and will disclose the purposes of the heart."

d. *Does Jesus mean we should never make any judgments? Read **verses 6 and 15-19.** What kinds of judgments should Christians make?*

While we cannot know the motives of people's hearts and cannot pass judgment on them, we should exercise critical discernment and judge between right and wrong so that we can act prudently ourselves. In addition, if we examine our own faults first, we can help others to see clearly when moral failure is clouding their vision.

Prayer (Matthew 7:7-12)

2. *What promises does Jesus make in verses 7-12 about prayer?*

Boldness and perseverance in prayer will pay off. Jesus tells us to ask, seek, and knock, and that we will receive, find, and see the door opened to us because God is our Father. Earthly fathers know how to give good gifts to their children and to provide for their needs (and even for their wants). How much more does God—who created us and loves us—give us (his children) good things?

This does not mean God is like an ATM machine and prayer like a pre-paid debit card. If we ask for things that will not be good for us, God—like any father—will say, "No." James talks about the importance of asking "in faith, with no doubting" if we want to receive from God (James 1:6-8). The more our will is aligned with God's, the more his answer will be, "Yes."

3. *The "Golden Rule" in verse 12 is found in a negative form in rabbinic Judaism and other world religions: Do not do things to others you do not want them to do to you. How does Jesus change this? How does this change relate to true righteousness?*

Jesus turns the prohibition inside out, directing it toward doing good for others as opposed to merely refraining from doing evil. This relates to true righteousness because it stems from an attitude focused toward others instead of toward oneself (with the result of us judging others). As God's children, we imitate him and his righteousness. "This is the law and the prophets," Jesus says. It sums up the entire gospel as does his commandment "that you love one another as I have loved you" (John 15:12).

Entering the Kingdom – "The Two Ways" (Matthew 7:13-23)

4. *Jesus' admonitions in the Sermon on the Mount may seem hard to fulfill. What does Jesus say about the way to the kingdom in verses 13-14?*

Jesus says the the way to the kingdom is narrow and difficult and that few find it. There is another "way" that is wide and pleasant, and that is the way many people choose. If we are to enter eternal life in the kingdom of God, we must look for the narrow gate and make sure we enter it regardless of the direction those around us are taking and regardless of the difficulty of the way.

5. ***Think About It:*** *Is this a new message, or has Israel heard something like it before? Compare Jesus' words here about the two gates with God's message to Israel through Moses as the people prepared to enter Canaan (see **Deuteronomy 30:15-20**).*

There have always been two ways. Moses set before the people life and good on one hand and death and evil on the other. Following and obeying the Creator of life leads to life, while going one's own way and serving other gods leads to death. The paradox remains today, and Jesus makes this clear. Though one way might seem appealing and easy, it is fraught with peril. God's way might seem narrow and restrictive, but it alone leads to life and blessing.

6. *Read* ***verses 21-23.***

   a. *What are some examples of things people might mistakenly rely on to convince themselves they will enter God's kingdom?*

   Jesus warns of danger signs along the road, particularly people who may lead us off the right path. These people may call Jesus "Lord" and prophesy and do mighty works in God's name even though they are false prophets. How can we tell the difference? By their fruit. We should not just listen to what they say but watch what they do and see what results. We should also apply this to ourselves. Are our lives bearing fruit?

   b. *How can you be sure to follow the narrow way and enter the kingdom?*

   Following the narrow way entails obedience: doing the will of the Father. We must love God and imitate Christ; nurture our relationship with God through prayer; give from the heart; show mercy and leave judgment to God; and be humble—all the things Jesus teaches us in the Beatitudes.

Hearers Versus Doers (Matthew 7:24-29)

7. *Jesus compares those who hear and obey his words to a wise man who builds his house upon the rock. What is the "moral sense"—life instruction—of his teaching? (See* ***CCC 117.****)*

   Just as Solomon, the ultimate wise man, built the LORD's house on a great rock so that it would endure, if we are wise, we will build our spiritual houses on the rock of hearing and obeying God's Word. To tie this in with Jesus' other teaching in the Sermon on the Mount: The foolish man will build on his own strength and rely on the treasure he amasses on earth. These things can easily be swept away by the storms of life. His foundation will not be strong and will not hold. The wise man, who puts his trust in his heavenly father and follows him, praying as Christ has shown him and living according to his Word, will not be moved.

8. *How does the crowd respond to Jesus' teaching?*

   The crowd responds with astonishment at Jesus' teaching because "he taught them as one who had authority." In contrast, the scribes taught existing traditions. Jesus is a "new Moses," giving the people a "new law" that fulfills the old Law and surpasses it.

D. Application

Facilitators: If time allows, have group members share their responses to the following application questions.

Reflect for a moment on your own life and family. What kind of a spiritual foundation have you laid, and how are you fortifying it? If you think your house is "built on sand," what can you do to build a stronger foundation? Do you have a plan?

E. Wrap-Up – Book One: Announcement of the Kingdom

Facilitators: If there is time, ask if anyone can summarize Book One of Matthew's Gospel (Chapters 3–7). Answers will vary. The point is not to find a "correct" answer, but to explore the major points of the chapters. You might ask questions like:

- *How do the events depicted in Matthew 3–7 set the stage for Jesus' ministry?*
- *What is the gist of Jesus' first recorded words to the people?*

After the small-group discussion, watch Jeff Cavins' video presentation on *Session 8* – Matthew 7: Choices in the Kingdom.

The King and His Kingdom

Session 9 – Responses

Matthew 8 – The King's Power Demonstrated

Facilitators: *Read these responses to the questions ahead of time to help you prepare to lead the small-group discussion.*

Participants: *Reinforce what you have learned by reviewing these responses after the small-group discussion and before you go on to the next session.*

A. Establish the Context

Facilitators: Take a moment to review the material from the previous session and to establish the context of Book Two of Matthew's Gospel. If you like, use the following question to encourage discussion:

- *Based on the title of the second book of Matthew's Gospel—"Establishment of the Kingdom"—what might you expect to see in the coming chapters?*

B. Read the Story

Facilitators: If there is time, have someone read each passage aloud before it is discussed.

C. Take a Deeper Look

Jesus' Miracles (Matthew 8)

1. *In the New Testament, the miracles of Jesus are most often called* dynameis, *or "powers." The focus is not on Jesus as a miracle worker, but on Jesus as the power of God made manifest on earth. How—and over what—does Jesus demonstrate his divine power in Matthew 8?*

   Matthew shows Jesus healing diseases, forgiving sins, calming a storm, and casting out demons. Jesus is demonstrating power over the destructive forces of nature, the devil, sin, and disease: over all that separates us from God.

Jesus Cleanses the Leper (Matthew 8:1-4)

2. a. *Under the old Law, anyone with leprosy was isolated from the community. Not only were they forbidden from interacting with people who were "clean," they were denied access to the Temple for worship. They lived outside the camp, and if anyone came near, they had to call, "Unclean! Unclean!" so no one would touch them and become defiled themselves. Given this background, what is remarkable about the way Jesus cleanses the leper?*

   Jesus touches him. He does not have to touch him—remember, he healed the centurion's servant with a word. The significance of this touch cannot be overstated. No one in Jesus' day would purposely touch a leper, for fear of becoming leprous and because that touch would render a person ceremonially unclean. Jesus touches the leper, and something remarkable happens. Not only does Jesus not become unclean, the leper becomes clean. The power in Jesus is greater than the power of evil. He is doing something greater than being holy himself: He is imparting his holiness to others. What a contrast to the Pharisees, who put all their efforts into a negative sort of holiness by separating themselves from those who are defiled.

b. ***Think About It:*** *The Church distinguishes between the literal and spiritual "senses" of Scripture, which, taken together, add richness to our understanding of God's Word. The literal sense is the intended meaning of the text; the spiritual senses are based on the literal sense and represent the way in which the text points to or is a sign of a deeper reality. These spiritual senses can be "allegorical"—pointing to Christ; "moral"—pointing to the way we ought to act; or "anagogical"—pointing to our eternal destiny. Can you see a spiritual sense behind leprosy in general or something in the Church that Christ's healing of the leper points to?*

Here is a moral sense of the passage: Leprosy is a "living death" that slowly destroys the body while putting to death communion with others. As such, it is a sign of the deeper illness of mortal sin, which kills spiritual life in the soul, severs communion with God and the Church, and ultimately leads to death.

Leprosy also renders a person "unclean," or unfit for public worship. The passage does not say Jesus "heals" the leper; it says he "cleanses" him. Similarly, we speak of needing "cleansing" from sin before we can properly engage in worship. In Jesus' healing of the leper, we see a sign of the sacrament of reconciliation: Jesus reaches out to save us from sin's leprous touch and restores us to full membership in God's family. Notice that Jesus does not send the man on his way, but sends him first to the priest to be officially restored to the community. In the same way, we go to a priest for reconciliation.

The Centurion's Servant (Matthew 8:5-13)

3. a. *Jesus praises the Roman centurion for his faith. What qualities of faith do you see in the words and actions of the centurion?*

The Roman centurion recognizes the power and authority of Jesus over sickness as surely as he sees his own power and authority over his men. He believes in the power of Jesus' word without doubt. Even though he knows Jesus should have nothing to do with him—a Gentile—he approaches him and begs for healing. These are all outstanding qualities of faith.

b. *What quality, which is lacking in some "sons of the kingdom," does this Gentile have that makes him fit for heaven?*

The centurion's strong faith makes him fit for heaven, while some of the "sons of the kingdom"—the Jewish people—rely on their blood relationship to the patriarchs to save them.

4. *You may recognize the words of the centurion in the following words we say at Mass prior to receiving the Eucharist: "Lord, I am not worthy that you should enter under my roof, but only say the word and my soul shall be healed." What does the story of the centurion add to your understanding of these words?*

At Mass, we put ourselves in the humble shoes of the Gentile centurion, separated from God by sin yet believing in his power to cleanse us and trusting in the healing power of his Word.

The Cost of Discipleship (Matthew 8:18-22)

5. *In this passage, Matthew gives us a picture of two potential followers of Jesus. Based on Jesus' replies to their questions, what are they unwilling to let go?*

The apostles drop everything to follow Jesus (see Matthew 4). In contrast, these followers hesitate to give up their security and their family obligations. These things are important, but commitment to Jesus must come above all else.

6. ***Think About It:*** *Read* ***verses 18-22*** *along with* ***1 Kings 19:19-21.*** *Why do you think Jesus tells the disciple to "leave the dead to bury their own dead" even though Elijah permitted Elisha to take leave of his family?*

   When Elisha destroyed the means of his own livelihood in the process of saying goodbye to his previous life, he showed he was really leaving everything behind to follow Elijah. Jesus may see in these would-be disciples a desire to linger, to hold on to worldly concerns instead of following without reserve. Matthew's account indicates the higher demands of New Testament discipleship, which require a complete personal surrender to Jesus and an identification with the One who has left his heavenly home and Father, humbled himself, and lived among us with "nowhere to lay his head."

Jesus Calms the Storm (Matthew 8:23-27)

7. a. *Jesus calls the disciples who are with him in the boat "men of little faith." They have enough faith to go to him for help; what do they lack?*

   Their fear betrays their uncertainty. Can he help them, or not? Will they survive? It is the age-old question: Do you trust God even when circumstances make it appear he is ignoring you or that he is not in control?

   b. *How might the disciples act differently with stronger faith?*

   It is possible that even with stronger faith, the disciples still would wake Jesus but without panic, without that telling phrase: "We are perishing." Perhaps they would pray the prayer of the father of the boy convulsed by an evil spirit in Mark 9: "I believe; help my unbelief!" (verse 24). They might come to him with the calm certainty of the centurion who knows that with a word, Jesus can heal his servant.

The Gadarene Demoniacs (Matthew 8:28-34)

8. *What questions do the demon-possessed men address to Jesus? What do these questions reveal about their knowledge of Jesus?*

Question	What It Reveals
What do you want with us, Son of God?	The demon-possessed men immediately recognize Jesus for who he is, the Son of God.
Have you come here to torture us before the appointed time?	They recognize his authority over them and his role in the coming time of judgment.

9. ***Think About It:*** *What do the leper, the centurion, and the demoniacs have in common? Is there a reason these are among the first people Jesus reaches out to in Matthew's Gospel?*

   Each is a social or religious outcast who is considered "unclean," or outside the Jewish community. In establishing his kingdom, Jesus goes *first* to the outcasts and opens the door to them. He is not merely healing; he is restoring people who have been excluded. Sickness, demon possession, and separation from other people are all consequences of sin in the world. In returning to heal the rift between God and man and to heal the damage done by sin in the world, Jesus reaches out first to the most obvious casualties.

Why does Jesus not heal everyone? According to the *Catechism:* "By freeing some individuals from the earthly evils of hunger, injustice, illness, and death, Jesus performed messianic signs. Nevertheless he did not come to abolish all evils here on earth, but to free men from the gravest slavery, sin, which thwarts them in their vocation as God's sons and causes all forms of human bondage" (CCC 549).[1]

D. Application

Facilitators: If time allows, have group members share their responses to the following application questions.

Are you experiencing a storm in your life? If so, are you frantic, afraid you will drown? Or are your eyes on the One who can save you? Prayerfully re-read Matthew 8, asking God to give you greater insight into who Jesus is and the power and control he has over everything. Ask also for faith. Are there examples in the reading for this session that can give you strength?

After the small-group discussion, watch Jeff Cavins' video presentation on *Session 9* – Matthew 8: The King's Power Demonstrated.

[1] See John 6:5-15, 8:34-36, 18:36; Luke 19:8, 12:13-14; Matthew 11:5.

Matthew 9 – New Wine, New Wineskins

Facilitators: *Read these responses to the questions ahead of time to help you prepare to lead the small-group discussion.*

Participants: *Reinforce what you have learned by reviewing these responses after the small-group discussion and before you go on to the next session.*

A. Review the Context

Facilitators: Take a moment to review the context and what was learned in the previous session. If you like, use the following question to encourage discussion:

- *How have you seen the power of Jesus in action in your own life?*

B. Read the Story

Facilitators: If there is time, have someone read each passage aloud before it is discussed.

C. Take a Deeper Look

Jesus Heals a Paralytic (Matthew 9:1-8)

1. a. *Why do the scribes, who are experts in Mosaic Law, believe Jesus is blaspheming? (For help with this question, see* ***Isaiah 43:25; Mark 2:7;*** *and* ***Leviticus 17:11.****)*

   Only God can forgive sins. Under the Old Covenant, God gave his people a system of animal sacrifice through which they made atonement and obtained forgiveness. Here, in the New Covenant, Jesus claims God's power and authority for his own. Not only does he forgive the paralytic, he bypasses the sacrificial system. For a mere man to do that would be considered blasphemy.

   b. *What does Jesus demonstrate to the scribes, and how does he go about it?*

   Jesus demonstrates his God-given authority as the Son of Man to forgive sins. He does this by showing his authority over the man's physical illness. In healing the physical, Jesus shows he can also forgive sins. Jesus "has come to heal the whole man, soul and body" (CCC 1503).

   c. *Whose faith is responsible for the healing of the paralytic and the forgiveness of his sins?*

   The paralytic is healed because of the faith of the people who bring him to Jesus.

   d. *Can we bring the sick before God in faith today and ask him to heal them? Read* ***James 5:14-15.***

   Yes, we *can* bring the sick before God for healing. We can do the same thing the friends of the paralytic did. James makes it clear that the prayer of the elders—not just the faith of the sick person—is effectual. This is the basis for the sacrament of the anointing of the sick, which makes the same link between physical healing and forgiveness that James does. (In the words of the rite: "Through this holy anointing may the Lord in his love and mercy help you with the grace of the Holy

Spirit. May the Lord who frees you from sin save you and raise you up" (CCC 1513).[1] It is through the sacraments that Christ "touches" us today to heal us.

2. ***Think About It:*** *The* Catechism *tells us: "It is the experience of Israel that illness is mysteriously linked to sin and evil, and that faithfulness to God according to his law restores life" (CCC 1502). It is easy to see how the Jewish leaders, focused on attaining holiness, righteousness, and life through strict adherence to the Law and avoidance of everything unclean, might look upon people who are sick as sinners and outcasts. How does Jesus begin to change this thinking?*

   Jesus begins to change this way of thinking by healing people who have faith, not just those who follow the rules. The emphasis is changing from external conformity to internal transformation. Notice that the centurion's servant in Chapter 8 is healed because of his master's faith; the paralytic is cured because of the faith of his friends. Later in Matthew 9, Jesus will heal a woman who reaches out to him in faith. Others are healed simply because Jesus has compassion and mercy on them. No one is said to be healed because they have followed all the rules. (Obedience must be the "obedience of faith," obedience that rises from a heart turned toward God.)

Jesus Calls Matthew (Matthew 9:9-13)

3. *The Pharisees object when Jesus and his disciples eat with tax collectors and sinners. Explain what Jesus means when he makes the following three replies in Matthew 9:12-13.*

   a. *"Those who are well have no need of a physician, but those who are sick."*

      The Pharisees would never sit with such men because of fear of contaminating themselves. In contrast, Jesus recognizes that what is in him is stronger than illness and sin. He is not concerned at all about how such contact might affect him or his reputation. He is only concerned about healing.

   b. *"Go and learn what this means, 'I desire mercy, and not sacrifice.'" Jesus quotes from the prophet Hosea, who spoke to the Northern Kingdom about its arrogance, its worship of other gods, and its spiritual sickness. Hosea announced God's judgment, writing: "For I desire mercy and not sacrifice, the knowledge of God, rather than burnt offerings" (Hosea 6:6).*

      Jesus is saying that the Pharisees have not learned the lesson Hosea taught long before. Although sacrifice was necessary under the Old Covenant because of sin, it was not what God wanted from his people. He wanted their hearts and for them to carry out the role he had created them for: extending his love and mercy to others. The Pharisees are caught up in the sacrificial system and details of the Mosaic Law to the point that they are focused entirely on themselves and love neither God nor others.

   c. *"I came not to call the righteous, but sinners."*

      Again, Jesus turns upside down the Pharisaic expectation that the outwardly righteous will inherit the kingdom. Who are the righteous? Jesus has redefined this in the Beatitudes. Now, he is reaching out to the poor, the meek, the lowly, and the outcast—the "sinners" rejected by the religious authorities who consider themselves "righteous."

4. *In Matthew 4, we read how Jesus called his first four disciples. Why do you think Matthew highlighted his own calling in this chapter rather than in the beginning of his Gospel? Think about this in the context of the various accounts of Jesus' healings.*

[1] Cf. *Codex Iuris Canonici,* 847 § 1.

Matthew's occupation sets him apart from the rest of the Twelve. As a tax collector, he would have ties to the Gentile authorities. For this reason—and because tax collectors in Jesus' time made money by collecting more than required—they were despised. In this passage and others, tax collectors are lumped together with "sinners." The fact that Jesus eats with these "untouchable" people and even chooses one of them as a disciple, draws attention to the fact that he is reaching out to include outsiders in his kingdom.

A Question of Fasting (Matthew 9:14-17)

5. a. *A second criticism comes from the disciples of John in verse 14. They ask, "Why do we and the Pharisees fast, but your disciples do not fast?" How does Jesus answer?*

   Jesus portrays his disciples as wedding guests and himself as the Bridegroom. (This is similar to the image of God as Israel's husband in Isaiah 54:5.) Jesus says they should not mourn while he is still present and that there will be plenty of time to fast after he is taken away. Jesus treats fasting not as a ritual observance to be done out of duty, but as something that should come from the heart and that should be done at the appropriate time.

   b. *Jesus' words to his disciples in verses 16-17 about new wine and old wineskins can be applied equally to the Pharisees in verses 10-13. What is he teaching them?*

   The "old garment" represents the Old Covenant way of doing things. Just as new wine will burst old, dried-up wineskins as it ferments, so the grace of the New Covenant has so much power it cannot be contained in the framework of the Old Covenant. "Fresh wineskins" are required—fresh ways of looking at things in the new kingdom that can hold the outpouring of grace and mercy that Jesus brings.

More Healings (Matthew 9:18-34)

6. a. *What does the woman with the hemorrhage need to do to be healed?*

   The woman only has to touch the hem of his garment, and the healing power goes out from the Lord.

   b. *How do you account for the different reactions of the Pharisees and the crowd to Jesus healing the mute demoniac depicted in verses 32-34?*

   The crowds marvel at what they see; the Pharisees credit Jesus' miracle to the "prince of demons" (Matthew 9:34). They are set against him and unwilling to believe he is who he says he is or that God's power is at work in him, and so they fail to properly see or marvel at what God is doing.

   c. *How would you react if you heard about such a miracle occurring today?*

   There is no set answer to this question; encourage discussion. (To read what the *Catechism* has to say about the gift of miracles, see CCC 2003.)

7. ***Think About It:*** *Moses performed many miracles in his day; so did Elisha and others. Yet, the people marvel at Jesus' healings: "Never was anything like this seen in Israel," they say in verse 33. What sets Jesus' miracles apart from these other miracles?*

   Other prophets called upon the power of God. They were his agents, and God used them to display his power; but Jesus *is* God. His divine power and authority flow *from* him—not merely *through* him—of his own free will. Notice in the healing of the woman with the hemorrhage that Jesus is the source, not just the agent, of healing. All she has to do is touch his robe (she does not even ask permission first), and healing power flows out of him. In addition to that, he is master of even the wind and the ocean—of the destructive forces of nature. He touches the leper and is not defiled. He heals not just to heal, but so people will know he can forgive sins. God's power is made manifest in his Son.

The Harvest and Laborers (Matthew 9:35-38)

8. a. *After the Southern Kingdom of Judah went into exile, the prophet Ezekiel blasted the "shepherds of Israel" for failing to care for the sheep, God's people. "So they were scattered, because there was no shepherd; and they became food for all the wild beasts" (Ezekiel 34:5). Even though the people have returned physically from exile, how can you tell from this passage in Matthew's Gospel that Jesus sees them in the same situation in his day?*

   Jesus has compassion because the people are "harassed and helpless, like sheep without a shepherd" (verse 36). The Pharisees and scribes of his day take no better care of the people than the leaders of Ezekiel's day did.

   b. *God continues: "I myself will search for my sheep, and will seek them out" (Ezekiel 34:11). "And I will set up over them one shepherd, my servant David, and he shall feed them: he shall feed them and be their shepherd" (Ezekiel 34:23). Who is this "servant David" who will be their shepherd?*

   This "servant David" who will be their shepherd is Jesus, Son of David, heir to the Davidic throne, and shepherd of the New Israel—the Church.

9. *How does Jesus respond to the needs of these "harassed and helpless," shepherd-less sheep?*

   Jesus enlists his disciples in his mission of compassion and healing, asking them to pray that the Lord will send "laborers into his harvest." It is interesting that he responds to the problem of lost sheep by talking about a harvest, which is a gathering together and is a cause for celebration. It hints of an expected end, rather than aimless wandering. It brings to mind food for the hungry: fruit, blessing, and bounty.

D. Application

Facilitators: If time allows, have group members share their responses to the following application questions.

The laws forbidding contact with all that was "unclean" were meant to protect the people from their own weakness and tendency to sin. The Pharisees have turned the Law into a way of measuring their own strength. Are you tempted to make the same mistake? Do you avoid association with, or look down on, some people instead of offering healing or mercy? What can you do to be salt and light in the world?

After the small-group discussion, watch Jeff Cavins' video presentation on *Session 10* – Matthew 9: New Wine, New Wineskins.

Session 11 – Responses

Matthew 10 – Jesus Commissions the Twelve

Facilitators: *Read these responses to the questions ahead of time to help you prepare to lead the small-group discussion.*

Participants: *Reinforce what you have learned by reviewing these responses after the small-group discussion and before you go on to the next session.*

A. Review the Context

Facilitators: Take a moment to review the context and what was learned in the previous session. If you like, use the following question to encourage discussion:

- *Of all the things you learned about Jesus from Matthew 9, what was the most meaningful?*

B. Read the Story

Facilitators: If there is time, have someone read each passage aloud before it is discussed.

C. Take a Deeper Look

Jesus Gives His Disciples Authority (Matthew 10:1-4)

1. *What do you think is the significance of Jesus' selection of twelve apostles? (For help with this question, see* ***Luke 22:28-30*** *and* ***Revelation 21:10-14.****)*

   "Twelve" is significant because the nation of Israel was built from the twelve sons (tribes) of Jacob, (later renamed "Israel"). Ten of those tribes went into exile in 722 BC, and the others were taken into Babylonian captivity less than 150 years later. Jesus has come to restore the lost tribes and to reconstitute Israel around himself. By selecting twelve disciples, Jesus shows that even though he is not literally bringing back the same tribes that were lost, he is structuring them anew on these men. The twelve apostles are the foundation stones of the New Israel.

2. a. *Read the names of the twelve apostles. Whose is the first name on the list?*

   "Simon, who is called Peter" and who was the first disciple (along with his brother) that Jesus called, is given primacy over the others from the start.

   b. *Are any of the other apostles' names familiar to you from the preceding chapters of Matthew's Gospel? What kind of men are those described already? (See* ***Matthew 4:18-22 and 9:9.****)*

   Answers will vary. The disciples are men of faith who leave everything behind to follow Jesus. For the most part, they are men of low social standing. Peter, Andrew, James, and John are fishermen. Matthew is a tax collector. Tax collectors are outsiders that many Jews see as traitors because they work for Rome and collect more taxes than the people owe.

c. ***Think About It:** At the end of the list is "Judas Iscariot, who betrayed him." Surely, Jesus knows what kind of man Judas is and that he will betray him; yet, he chooses Judas to be an apostle. Do you sometimes see people in positions of authority in the Church who seem unworthy of those positions? What does Jesus' choice of Judas as an apostle suggest our attitude toward these people and their offices should be?*

People in positions of authority in the Church, whether priests, cardinals, or the pope, are sinners like the rest of us. We should still respect their offices and the Church Christ established. All authority comes from God.

The Mission of the Apostles (Matthew 10:5-15)

3. a. *What charge does Jesus give his apostles, and how does he empower them?*

Jesus charges his apostles with bringing the Good News of the kingdom to the lost sheep of Israel; healing the sick; raising the dead; cleansing lepers; and casting out demons. In other words, he instructs them to continue the work he has been doing. And he gives them a share in his own authority (power) over illness, death, and demons so they will be able to do this work.

b. *Who will be the initial recipients of their ministry? Is this significant? (Recall what you learned in **Matthew 4:12-16.**)*

Even though Jesus first heals those outside the kingdom, he instructs the disciples to go first not to the Gentiles or Samaritans, but rather "to the lost sheep of the house of Israel." These are the descendants of the scattered Northern tribes of Israel who have returned from exile and live among Gentiles in the region of Galilee. Jesus chooses this area to begin his ministry because he is going to restore Israel (God's people), which has been lost and scattered, and because he wants his disciples to continue his mission.

4. a. *What additional instructions does Jesus give the Twelve?*

Jesus instructs his disciples to spread the Good News and to "give without pay," just as they did not pay to receive the Good News (see Matthew 10:8). He also tells them not to depend on their own resources—not to bring money, extra clothing, or even a staff with them in their missionary travels. Rather, he tells them to depend on those to whom they minister for their needs and to stay with "worthy" people in each town they visit.

b. *When Jews left "unclean" Gentile territory for their own land, it was customary for them to shake the dust from their feet. What is the significance of Jesus' instructions in verses 13-15?*

"Shake off the dust from your feet" represents a warning of judgment on people who do not receive the apostles—they may not be ritually unclean in the eyes of the Law, but in their refusal to receive the Good News, they render themselves separate from God's kingdom.

The Cost of Discipleship (Matthew 10:16-39)

5. a. *Read **verses 16-24.** Jesus asks his apostles to deliver fantastic news, news that everyone has been longing to hear. Not only that, he gives them the ability to transform people's lives for the better, healing diseases, raising the dead, and casting out demons. In spite of all this, what kind of reception does he tell them to expect?*

Jesus tells his apostles to expect the kind of reception sheep would get from a pack of wolves. "They will deliver you up to councils, and flog you in their synagogues" (Matthew 10:17). They will even be hated and put to death.

b. *How does Jesus tell them to respond?*

Jesus tells them to be wary, but not to think all is lost if they end up in court. He says this is part of the plan, because it will allow them to bear testimony before governors, kings, and Gentiles. He also tells them not to be anxious about what to say, because the Holy Spirit will speak through them. He tells them that if they are persecuted in one town, they should flee to the next, and that they will not be able to cover the whole territory before the Son of Man returns.

c. *What hope and comfort does Jesus give the apostles in these verses?*

As ambassadors of Jesus, the Twelve should not expect to be treated differently than he has been treated. (The Pharisees have called him "Beelzebul"—"prince of demons.") They should follow in Jesus' footsteps, doing as he has done. If they endure to the end, they will be saved. He also tells them that the Son of Man will come before they get through all the towns of Israel. In a note on Matthew 10:23, the *Ignatius Catholic Study Bible* says: "As a prelude to his Second Coming, this initial 'coming' refers to his visitation of destruction upon unfaithful Jerusalem in AD 70, an event that destroyed his enemies and vindicated his words of judgment."[1]

6. a. *Following this assurance of persecution, Jesus says in verse 26, "So have no fear of them." How can he say this?*

Jesus' assurance is based on the character of God, which does not change. It is based on God's power and love. There is no need to fear what other people can do, because they cannot touch the soul. The worst thing they can do will have only a temporal effect. It is better to focus on a proper fear of God, who has the power to destroy both soul and body forever. All will be brought to light, and justice will prevail in the end. We can trust in the Father's love. Each of his children is of inestimable value to him. If you doubt that, consider the sparrows: They are worth very little in comparison to mankind, and God watches over even them (see Matthew 10:29-31). If we acknowledge Jesus as Lord and defend him to other people, he will acknowledge us before his Father in heaven. So, there is no need to fear those who persecute us for his sake.

b. ***Think About It:*** *Read* **Genesis 3:15** *to refresh your memory of the first announcement of the Good News in the Bible. In light of these words of God, why should we not be surprised by Jesus' insistence on the inevitability of persecution—and his admonition not to be afraid?*

God told the Serpent after the Fall in the Garden of Eden: "I will put enmity between you and the woman, and between your seed and her seed; he shall bruise your head, and you shall bruise his heel" (Genesis 3:15). Jesus is the "seed of the woman" who has come to bruise the head of the enemy. All who follow Christ are joined in the battle and will be bruised. But God and his Son will be victorious. There is no need to fear when you know you are on the side of the victor.

7. a. *Read* **Matthew 10:34-39.** *Are Jesus' words in verses 34-36, where he says he has come not to bring peace but a sword, a contradiction of his words in John 14:27: "Peace I leave with you; my peace I give to you; not as the world gives do I give to you. Let not your hearts be troubled, neither let them be afraid." Explain your answer.*

---

1 *Ignatius Catholic Study Bible* (San Francisco: Ignatius, 2001), 34.

Both are true. Jesus comes to bring peace between God and man and among men. He also promises peace to his followers—not the world's peace, which is the absence of discord, but an inner peace and assurance in the midst of whatever is happening in the world. As in the parable of the man who builds his house on the rock, the storm will not prevail. But in the process of establishing the New Covenant, there will inevitably be conflict with those who want to hang onto old ways. This conflict may even extend to members of the same family—but the spiritual family Jesus is founding is more important than blood ties.

b. *What does the cross—a cruel instrument of execution that all Jesus' followers would be familiar with—represent in verse 38?*

The cross represents the total commitment required of Jesus' disciples. They will be required to deny themselves—and even suffer and die. But as Jesus' death and resurrection will soon demonstrate, that death will lead to eternal life.

Rewards (Matthew 10:40-42)

8. *In verses 14-15, Jesus pronounced judgment greater than that on Sodom and Gomorrah on those who refuse to receive the apostles. In verses 40-42, what does he say is in store for those who do receive them? (Note: Jesus refers to the apostles here as "little ones.")*

Because they are carrying on Jesus' mission, those who receive the disciples also receive Jesus and God himself. For this, they will receive rewards like those due to the prophets and righteous men. Even simple acts of kindness, such as giving a drink of water to a disciple of Christ, will be rewarded.

D. Application

Facilitators: If time allows, have group members share their responses to the following application question.

Think about your daily interaction with the Lord. What changes might you make in your life in terms of study, prayer, and action so you can become a better disciple of Christ?

E. Wrap-Up – Book Two: Establishment of the Kingdom

Facilitators: If there is time, ask if anyone can summarize Book Two of Matthew's Gospel (Chapters 8–10). Answers will vary. The point is not to find a "correct" answer, but to explore the major points of the chapters. You might ask questions like:

- *How does Jesus establish the kingdom of God on earth?*
- *In what ways is God's power made manifest?*
- *What kind of foundation does Jesus lay for the kingdom?*

After the small-group discussion, watch Jeff Cavins' video presentation on *Session 11* – Matthew 10: Jesus Commissions the Twelve.

Session 12 – Responses

Matthew 11–12 – Jesus Confronts an Evil Generation

Facilitators: *Read these responses to the questions ahead of time to help you prepare to lead the small-group discussion.*

Participants: *Reinforce what you have learned by reviewing these responses after the small-group discussion and before you go on to the next session.*

A. Establish the Context

Facilitators: Take a moment to review the material from the previous session and to establish the context of "Book Three" of Matthew's Gospel. If you like, use the following question to encourage discussion:

- *What fears keep you from sharing the Good News of God's kingdom? Is there anything from the previous session that might help you face these fears?*

B. Read the Story

Facilitators: If there is time, have someone read each passage aloud before it is discussed.

C. Take a Deeper Look

John the Baptist (Matthew 11:1-19)

1. a. *Although Jesus' answer seems to merely reiterate what John already knows (that Jesus has been healing people and preaching the Good News), it actually says much more. How is Jesus elaborating on what John already knows? (Read* ***Isaiah 35:4-6 and 61:1-2.****)*

   Jesus quotes from the Old Testament to show that by his miracles, he is fulfilling prophecies about the Messiah. "Blessed is the man who does not fall away on account of me," he concludes. In other words: Do not be discouraged. Do not doubt me because I am not what you expected. See the signs for what they really are. I AM he who is to come.

   b. *Jesus tells the crowd that John the Baptist is more than a prophet—he is the Elijah who who is to come. He is the greatest of all the prophets, sent to prepare the way for Jesus and the kingdom. Yet, great as John is, Jesus says that even the least in the kingdom is greater than him. What do you think he means by this?*

   John is from the Old Covenant age. His mission is to announce and prepare the way for the New Covenant. He even baptizes the "one who is to come." Yet, he will die before Christ's work is completed. The least of those who enter the kingdom will be greater than John because they will be part of Jesus' bride (the Church). John knows this and tells the people, "I am not the Christ, but I have been sent before him. … He must increase, but I must decrease" (John 3:27-30).

c. *What does Jesus say about his generation in verses 16-19?*

Jesus rebukes those of his generation who have rejected him and John the Baptist. Jesus seems to imply that if people are spiritually wise, they will see that both have been sent from God for specific purposes.

Woe on Unrepentant Cities (Matthew 11:20-24)

2. *Read **verses 20-24;** then use the map on page 5 to locate the cities mentioned. Why does Jesus compare the first three cities unfavorably to Tyre and Sidon and pronounce such a harsh judgment on them?*

Chorazin, Bethsaida, and Capernaum are all in Galilee, "where most of his mighty works had been done" (verse 20). They have been privileged to witness his miracles firsthand. Yet, they have not repented of their sin. Tyre and Sidon, on the other hand, are Gentile cities that Jesus says would have repented if given the opportunity. Sodom was destroyed for its immorality and for refusing to properly receive God's messengers, yet Jesus says the Day of Judgment will be more tolerable for Sodom than for them. In spite of being favored with Jesus' presence, his teaching, and his miracles, his own people reject him and the mercy he offers. They fail to repent.

Jesus' Yoke (Matthew 11:25-30)

3. a. *In contrast to the unrepentant cities that reject Jesus' teaching and miracles, who are those that know the Father and "come" to Jesus?*

"Babes," or infants, with their simple trust, are more open to God's revelation. Those who turn to Christ with their burdens (take on his yoke and learn from him) are given rest.

b. *What is the "yoke" Jesus refers to in verse 29? (See also **Sirach 51:23-26** and **1 John 5:3.**)*

A yoke is not a burden but rather a shared way of carrying a burden. If the yoke that joins a pair of oxen is well-fitted, the burden will be light and "easy" to carry. This makes it easier to keep one's eyes on Jesus and follow him instead of concentrating on the burden itself. Submission to Christ and obedience to him is liberating and brings us peace and rest. If we take on his yoke—follow in his footsteps and learn from him—his commandments will not be burdensome in the way the Old Covenant Law was burdensome.

Challenges to Jesus' Authority (Matthew 12:1-21)

4. a. *What two charges do the Pharisees bring against Jesus and his disciples in verses 1-14? (See also **Exodus 20:10.**)*

The Pharisees bring charges of two violations of the Sabbath laws: working on the Sabbath and healing on the Sabbath.

b. *What is Jesus' defense? (Note: If you want to read about the incident Jesus refers to in verses 3-4, it can be found in **1 Samuel 21:1-6.** In verse 5 of this passage, it says that priests who do the work required to offer sacrifice on the Sabbath, do so without guilt.)*

Jesus cites precedent in Scripture to defend the actions of his disciples in collecting grain on the Sabbath. He reminds the Pharisees that David and his men ate the bread of the Presence on the Sabbath (see 1 Samuel 21:2) and that it is lawful for the priests to work on the Sabbath (see Matthew 12:3-5). In addressing the issue of his disciples healing on the Sabbath, Jesus points out that the

Pharisees allow the care of injured sheep on the Sabbath and states: "Of how much more value is a man than a sheep!" (Matthew 12:12).

c. *Read* ***CCC 2168–2172****. What was the original purpose of the Sabbath that the Pharisees have lost in their zeal to enforce the Law?*

The Sabbath is the seventh day of the week, the day God rested after creating the world. When God brought Israel out of Egypt, one of the first things he charged them with was keeping the Sabbath holy by resting—and allowing others to rest—from work on that day. The purpose of the Sabbath was to protect the people from servitude to work and the worship of money. It also gave them a way to imitate God by showing mercy to others. The Sabbath was to be a permanent memorial of their liberation from the bondage of Pharaoh, who would not allow them to rest from labor to worship God. Setting aside one day a week to praise God and remember his work of Creation and his saving acts on their behalf was to be a sign of the covenant between them. The Pharisees are so focused on the Law that they have forgotten the importance of showing mercy. They fail to enter God's rest, and they keep others from resting as well.

Challenges to the Source of Jesus' Power (Matthew 12:22-37)

5. a. *What serious charge do the Pharisees make against Jesus?*

The Pharisees charge Jesus with casting out demons by the power of Beelzebul, the prince of demons—the devil himself.

b. *How does Jesus reveal the fallacy in their charge?*

Jesus points out that Satan does not fight against himself. If he did, his kingdom would collapse.

c. *In verses 30-34, what grave risk does Jesus say the Pharisees are taking by making this charge? (****Optional:*** *Read* ***CCC 1864, 679.****)*

Jesus warns them that if he is, in fact, casting out demons by the power of God, then the kingdom has arrived, and they are in danger. By standing against Jesus, they are scattering the kingdom and working against God. And by attributing the work of God to Satan they are committing an unforgivable sin for which they will be held accountable for on the Day of Judgment.

Jesus Confronts His Generation (Matthew 12:38-45)

6. a. *Read* ***verses 38-45****. What does Jesus mean by "the sign of the prophet Jonah"? (For help with this question, see* ***CCC 994.****)*

The Old Testament prophet Jonah, who spent three days in the belly of a "great fish" (see Jonah 1:17), is a sign of Christ's death and resurrection. After being saved from the fish, Jonah took a call for repentance to Nineveh, a wicked Gentile city that repented and was saved from God's judgment. The Pharisees attribute Jesus' work to the devil and fail to repent. They will kill Jesus, and he will be placed in a tomb; yet, like Jonah, he will rise to new life on the third day to complete his mission of bringing the Good News to the Gentiles (who will completely destroy both Jerusalem and the Temple forty years later).

b. *Jesus gives two examples of Gentiles—one nation (Nineveh) and one person (the queen of the South, or Sheba)—who will arise and condemn his generation. Why would they do this?*

Nineveh repented; the Queen of Sheba marveled at Solomon's wisdom. Here, in Jesus, is someone greater than either Jonah or Solomon, and his own countrymen reject his wisdom and refuse to repent.

7. *Both Jesus and the Pharisees expel evil spirits. What will happen, though, if that generation ("the man" of Jesus' illustration in verses 43-45) fails to fill the resulting vacuum with acceptance of the kingdom Jesus offers and with the power of the Spirit of God?*

   Seven spirits more evil than the first will come in, and it will be worse than before.

Jesus' True Family (Matthew 12:46-50)

8. *Read* ***verses 46-50.*** *How does Jesus broaden the concept of family? (See also* ***John 1:11-13*** *and* ***1 John 3:10.****)*

   Jesus broadens the concept of family from the physical to the spiritual. In the new kingdom, the children of God are not those who are born into it (and can claim it by birthright), but those who receive Jesus, who believe, and who act as God's children by doing his will.

D. Application

Facilitators: If time allows, have group members share their responses to the following application question.

Are you carrying a burden that is too heavy for you? "Come to me, all who labor and are heavy laden, and I will give you rest," says the Lord. Pray and ask God to show you what it means to exchange this burden for his yoke that is easy.

After the small-group discussion, watch Jeff Cavins' video presentation on *Session 12* – Matthew 11–12: Jesus Confronts an Evil Generation.

Session 13 – Responses

Matthew 13 – Parables of the Kingdom

The King and His Kingdom

Facilitators: *Read these responses to the questions ahead of time to help you prepare to lead the small-group discussion.*

Participants: *Reinforce what you have learned by reviewing these responses after the small-group discussion and before you go on to the next session.*

A. Review the Context

Facilitators: Take a moment to review the context and what was learned in the previous session. If you like, use the following question to encourage discussion:

- *What did you learn about the difference between those who come to Jesus and those who reject him?*

B. Read the Story

Facilitators: If there is time, have someone read each passage aloud before it is discussed.

C. Take a Deeper Look

Parable of the Sower (Matthew 13:1-23)

1. *This chapter is filled with Jesus' parables about the kingdom of heaven. The Greek word for "parable" is* parabole*—literally, a "placing beside." In the Gospels, it is a comparison from everyday life that is used to illustrate a spiritual truth. What reason does Jesus give in verses 10-16 for using parables?*

   Some truths can be known only by revelation from God. Those who are unwilling to receive Jesus' message are unable to see the truth in the parables. In contrast, those who are sincerely interested in Jesus' message are challenged by the parables to make further inquiry. The purpose of the parables is not to confuse the people. Jesus speaks in parables because the hearts of the people have become "dull" (verse 15). Their eyes do not see the truth in front of them, and their ears do not hear it. His quote refers to Isaiah 6. Isaiah was called by God to pronounce judgment on Israel for its spiritual deterioration and infidelity. The people of Israel disregarded the signs because their hearts had become dull and calloused by sin. Jesus speaks in parables to reveal the ignorance of the people and to awaken them.

2. *What is given to the disciples but not to the crowd, and why? (See* ***verses 11-17*** *and* ***CCC 546.****)*

   Only the disciples receive knowledge of the secrets of the kingdom of heaven. This does not necessarily mean that they understand immediately, but they receive the spiritual understanding that makes them open and receptive to Jesus' teaching. They embrace Jesus and his life. The *Catechism* explains that the parables hold up a kind of mirror to those who listen. Their response reveals whether the soil of their hearts is receptive to the Word of God, or whether it is hard and stony and hostile to it. One must enter the kingdom to know its secrets. "For those who stay 'outside,' everything remains enigmatic" (CCC 546).

3. a. *Read the parable of the sower in* **verses 18-23.** *According to Jesus, what do each of the following things refer to?*

   The seed that falls along the path: refers to the hardened heart that hears the message and does not understand, so that the evil one snatches it away

   The seed that falls among rocks: refers to the shallow heart that receives the Word with joy but does not allow it to take root, so it quickly falls away under trouble or persecution

   The seed that falls among thorns: refers to the strangled heart that receives the Word but allows it to be choked away and rendered unfruitful by the worries of life or the deceitfulness of wealth

   The seed that falls on good soil: refers to the believing heart that hears and understands so that the seed takes root, grows, flourishes, and produces a bounteous crop

   b. *What is the main message of this parable?*

   The parable of the sower explains that when the message of the gospel does not take root, it is the fault of the hearers, not of the message. Just as seeds need well-prepared soil to grow successfully into plants, the kingdom will only grow in people whose hearts are prepared to receive it. Some seeds fall on hearts that are hard-packed and without understanding. These seeds make no impression on the soil at all, but are snatched up by the "birds" (the evil one). Other seeds fall on shallow soil on top of rock (on hearts capable of receiving the message with joy but that are too hard inside to allow it to take root). When the new plant faces trouble (persecution) because of its newfound faith, it is not strong enough to last. Other seed falls on hearts full of worry and care for material things (which eventually choke out the new life). Only the seed received by hearts that fully understand its import achieve full potential. In these hearts, it grows in the rich soil and produces a crop that multiplies.

   c. *Why is the Word of God not always effective in our lives? (Read also* **1 Thessalonians 2:13** *and* **Hebrews 4:2.***)*

   The seed of the Word is not a "magic bullet." God's grace requires our cooperation to take effect. The Word must be digested and pondered—as St. Paul hopes for the Colossians (3:16): "May the Word of God dwell in you richly." According to 1 Thessalonians, the Word must be accepted as the actual Word of God, which is at work in those who believe. The author of the book of Hebrews concurs, saying that the gospel is of no value to the hearer who does not have faith. Another reason the Word of God is not always effective in our lives is that sin can obscure our vision so that we cannot receive the Word. As St. Jerome said, "We, in the flesh of Christ, which is the word of divine doctrine, or the interpretation of the Sacred Scriptures, receive manna in accordance with and in proportion to our desire. If you are a saint, you will find refreshment; if a sinner, anguish."[1]

Parable of the Weeds (Matthew 13:24-30, 36-43)

4. *Read the parable of the weeds in* **verses 24-30** *and what Jesus says about it in* **verses 36-43.**

   a. *What do the following represent?*

   The sower of the good seed: the Son of Man

   The field: the world

   The sower of the bad seed: the devil

1 *Sermo* 1-59, on the Psalms.

The good seed: sons of the kingdom

The bad seed (weeds): sons of the evil one

The reapers: angels

The time of the harvest: the close of the age

b. *What will happen to those who cause sin and to all who do evil? What will happen to the righteous?*

Those that cause others to sin and do evil will be pulled up, weeded out, thrown in the fiery furnace, and left to "weep and gnash their teeth" (verse 42). In contrast, "the righteous will shine like the sun in the kingdom of their Father" (verse 43).

c. *Read* ***CCC 827 and 681–682.*** *What ramifications does this parable have for the Church today? (You might ask yourself: Who is responsible for pulling the "weeds"?)*

The children of the kingdom are not perfect. They are at the same time holy and in need of purification; and sin and good will be mixed in each until the end. Just as the weeds and good plants are left to mingle until harvest in the parable, there will always be sinners in the Church and even among its ministers. Some people ask, "Why not just 'clean house' of all the sinful people and imperfect ministers? Pull all the weeds now!'" But it is not our responsibility to do this. Like Jesus, the Church clasps sinners to her bosom until the end of time when Christ will return to judge the world according to each person's works and acceptance or refusal of God's grace.

Four More Parables (Matthew 13:31-35, 44-46)

5. *Jesus tells four more parables in verses 31-46.*

a. *What is the connection between the kingdom of heaven and the mustard seed and the way it grows?*

Although the kingdom of heaven starts out small like a tiny mustard seed with just Jesus and twelve disciples, it will grow to be very large like the mustard tree.

Facilitators: Jesus' description of the tree with birds resting in its branches may allude to passages like Daniel 4:21, which suggests the worldwide dominion of a kingdom that will provide rest for people from all nations.

b. *How does Jesus use the concept of yeast to expand our understanding of the kingdom?*

Just as a small amount of yeast will leaven a large amount of meal (three measures would provide bread for more than a hundred people), so the kingdom, though small when planted, will penetrate and expand to give life and spiritual food to many.

c. *What is the lesson of the two parables in verses 44-46?*

The kingdom of heaven is likened first to a treasure hidden in a field and then to a pearl of great price, both of which are purchased by someone who sells everything to buy them. Both parables teach that the kingdom is of such great value that people should be willing to give up everything they have to gain it. It is interesting that Jesus uses two parables to get the point across. Perhaps the focus is as much on the cost as the value: Jesus wants his disciples so convinced of the kingdom's value, that they will be willing to give up everything to gain it.

Parable of the Net: A Prophet Without Honor (Matthew 13:47-58)

6. *Read* ***verses 47-52.*** *What does the parable of the net tell us about the judgment to come?*

   The message in this parable is similar to the message of the parable of the weeds: It is not for us to separate the wicked from the righteous. On the Day of Judgment, the angels will gather everyone like a fisherman would gather a load in a fishing net, and they will separate the wicked from the righteous and throw the wicked into the furnace. This parable ties in with Jesus' earlier admonition to "judge not." It acknowledges that we are all sinners, that there is good and bad in all of us and that at any single point in our lives, it may be hard to tell whether we are weed or wheat. It is not for us—or even the Church—to judge anyone's final destination, which will not be known or revealed until the Day of Judgment.

7. a. *Why are the people of Jesus' hometown "amazed" at him (verse 54)?*

   These are the people Jesus has grown up with. They know his family as ordinary people like them. They cannot understand where he gets his wisdom and the power to perform miracles (or perhaps they are jealous).

   b. *How does their reaction differ from the "amazed" crowd in Matthew 7:28?*

   The crowd in Matthew 7:28 is amazed at his authority and listens to him; this hometown crowd takes offense and does not believe.

   c. *What is the consequence of their unbelief?*

   As a consequence of their unbelief, Jesus refrains from doing many miracles in his hometown.

D. Application

Facilitators: If time allows, have group members share their responses to the following application questions.

Is your heart like the "good soil" in which the seed of the Word can grow readily? You might look at different aspects of your life in light of the four types of soil described in Matthew 13. For example, consider the "soil" of your marriage or your moral life. Is it receptive to the Word, or is it rocky, unreceptive, or choked with care? How can you make sure you hear, understand, and bear fruit?

E. Wrap-Up – Book Three: The Kingdom Defined

Facilitators: If there is time, ask if anyone can summarize Book Three of Matthew's Gospel (Chapters 11–13). Answers will vary. The point is not to find a "correct" answer, but to explore the major points of the chapters. You might ask questions like:

- *What kind of opposition did Jesus face when he began to establish his kingdom?*
- *How did he confront the religious leaders?*
- *What was the purpose of the parables he used?*

After the small-group discussion, watch Jeff Cavins' video presentation on *Session 13* – Matthew 13: Parables of the Kingdom.

Matthew 14–15 – Instructions to the Twelve

Facilitators: *Read these responses to the questions ahead of time to help you prepare to lead the small-group discussion.*

Participants: *Reinforce what you have learned by reviewing these responses after the small-group discussion and before you go on to the next session.*

A. Establish the Context

Facilitators: Take a moment to review the material from the previous session and to establish the context of Book Four of Matthew's Gospel. If you like, use the following question to encourage discussion:

- *What in the parables was meaningful to you personally?*

B. Read the Story

Facilitators: If there is time, have someone read each passage aloud before it is discussed.

C. Take a Deeper Look

The Death of John the Baptist (Matthew 14:1-12)

1. *When Jesus hears that John the Baptist has been beheaded, he does not demand justice or confront Herod but withdraws to a lonely place. Why do you think he does this?*

   Answers will vary. It is possible that Jesus wants to be alone to mourn John's death. He also may want to stay out of Herod's sight. He needs time to prepare his disciples for his death and their coming task, and he cannot yet risk the kind of attention that led to John's execution.

Jesus Feeds the Five Thousand (Matthew 14:13-21)

2. a. *Contrast the disciples' reaction to the needs of the crowd with Jesus' response to their needs.*

   The disciples want to send the people away to fend for themselves; Jesus meets the need of the people. The disciples look at the situation and their own resources; Jesus looks with compassion at the need of the people. The disciples conclude the situation is hopeless; Jesus comes to a solution. The disciples see only limitations; Jesus shows them abundance.

   b. *Jesus asks his disciples to do something that is humanly impossible. What do you think the disciples learn from this experience?*

   Encourage discussion. The disciples may learn that the magnitude of the need or the paucity of their own resources should not discourage them; as long as they are willing to put what they have at Jesus' disposal, he will multiply their "loaves and fishes" to more than meet the need. It is a marvelous lesson demonstrating what he has just taught by parable: The kingdom of God may start small, but it contains tremendous power for growth.

c. *Notice that Jesus does not feed the people himself; he has his disciples pass around the bread and fish in his name; and by his power, they distribute abundance from their meager store. Do you see a parallel to this in the Church today? (For help with this question, see* ***CCC 1335.****)*

Jesus' miracle points to the Church, through which he will feed the spiritually hungry multitudes with his priests. What we bring to him in the natural (bread and wine), he takes, multiplies, and transforms into the supernatural (his Body and Blood) in the hands of his priests, who distribute this spiritual food to the Church.

Jesus Walks on Water (Matthew 14:22-33)

3. *It is not the storm that first frightens the disciples, but the sight of Jesus walking toward them. How does Jesus respond to their fear?*

Jesus responds immediately and with compassion, revealing his divine identity: "Take heart, it is I! Have no fear." "It is I" is literally, "I AM" or "Yahweh"—the name God revealed to Moses at the burning bush and Israel's covenant name for God.

4. a. *When Peter realizes it is Jesus, his immediate response is to ask Jesus to permit him to walk on the water. What causes Peter to doubt after his initial success?*

Peter begins to doubt when he sees the strong wind and starts to sink. He is afraid and cries out to Jesus for help.

b. *What significant confession do the disciples make after this event, and how does it contrast with their reaction the first time they saw Jesus' power over a storm? (For help with this question, see* ***Matthew 8:23-27.****)*

The disciples' fear turns to worship as they say, "Truly you are the son of God." This is much different than their earlier reaction, which was to wonder what sort of a man he was, that even the winds and the waves obeyed him. Their faith has grown even in the short time Jesus has been with them.

5. *What have you learned about faith from the two miracles Jesus performs in Chapter 14?*

Answers will vary; encourage discussion.

Clean and Unclean (Matthew 15:1-20)

6. a. *In verses 1-9, the scribes and Pharisees once again attempt to catch Jesus and his disciples in an infraction of the Law. What do they accuse the disciples of doing?*

This time, they accuse Jesus and his disciples of failing to wash their hands before eating, flaunting "the tradition of the elders." This washing is expected as a means of ritual purification, not for cleanliness in the sense that we expect hand washing today.

b. *How does Jesus reply?*

Jesus does not defend himself or his disciples but turns the question back on their accusers as he asks: Why do you break the command of God, then, for the sake of that tradition? Some of the religious leaders are using a tradition to set aside future earnings for the Temple as a reason not to support their parents.

c. *How does Jesus explain his parable in verses 17-20?*

Jesus explains that what one eats passes out again and therefore cannot make one unclean. It is immorality, rather ("things which come out of the mouth and that come from the heart"), that makes a person unclean. Defilement comes from an impure heart, not from violating external rules. Fellowship with God is not interrupted by ritual uncleanness but by sin.

The Faith of the Canaanite Woman (Matthew 15:21-28)

7. a. *How does the Canaanite woman obtain healing for her daughter despite Jesus' initial refusal to heal her?*

The Canaanite woman obtains healing for her daughter by virtue of her strong faith, which is evident in her persistence.

b. *How can this incident give us confidence as we approach the Father in prayer? (See* ***CCC 2609–2610.****)*

Like the Canaanite woman, we can approach God boldly in prayer, confident that all things are possible when we pray in faith.

Jesus Feeds the Four Thousand (Matthew 15:29-39)

8. a. *Before feeding the four thousand, Jesus performs many other miracles in this primarily Gentile region (see* ***verses 30-31****). List them, and describe how the crowd reacts to them.*

Jesus heals the lame, the blind, the crippled, the mute, and many others. Those who see these works glorify the God of Israel.

b. *Why do you think Matthew includes this list of miracles in his Gospel?*

These miracles give continuing evidence that Jesus is the expected Messiah. They show his ministry extending to the Gentiles and provide a contrast to the reception he receives in his hometown.

9. a. *Notice the verbs Matthew uses in* ***14:19 and 15:36.*** *Read* ***Matthew 26:26.*** *What do the miracles recorded here anticipate? (See also* ***CCC 1335.****)*

Matthew 14:19, which is part of the story of Jesus feeding the five thousand, says, "Taking the five loaves and the two fish he looked up to heaven, and blessed, and broke and gave the loaves to the disciples, and the disciples gave them to the crowds." In Matthew 15:36 (the feeding of the four thousand), we see the same words in the past tense: "He took the seven loaves and the fish, and having given thanks he broke them and gave them to the disciples, and the disciples gave them to the crowds."

The words Jesus uses in the two feeding miracles anticipate the words he will use when he institutes the Eucharist at the Last Supper (Matthew 26), when he will take a cup, give thanks, and give it to the disciples. These miracles do more than demonstrate Jesus' divinity. They foreshadow what he has come to do: to spiritually heal and feed a multitude of needy people. *He* is the healer. *He* is the feeder. *He alone* can satisfy the needs of everyone.

b. ***Think About It:*** *Matthew records not one but two feeding miracles. These miracles have the effect of brackets, focusing the reader's attention on what is between them: the offense the Jewish leaders take at the disciples. Contrast the roles Jesus assigns his disciples in these stories with the role the scribes and Pharisees play. How does this illuminate the difference between the Old and New Covenants?*

The New Covenant will focus on sacraments instead of sacrifice. The "source and summit" of life in the Church will be the Eucharist (CCC 1324).[1] The scribes and Pharisees have busied themselves with figuring out how to obey the Law; the disciples will live the law from the heart and mediate God's grace to his people through the sacraments. The scribes and Pharisees have been so wrapped up in external trappings and rituals that they have forgotten what it means to have mercy. They spend their time imposing laws and checking up on people, instead of shepherding the sheep. Jesus is showing them how to feed his sheep.

D. Application

Facilitators: If time allows, have group members share their responses to the following application questions.

Are you facing a problem that looks as impossible to solve as feeding five thousand people seemed to the disciples? Look for inspiration to Blessed Teresa of Calcutta (Mother Teresa), who started out with nothing more than a rosary, a few dollars, a Bible, and a change of clothes. What "little" do you have that you can turn over to Jesus so he can work through you?

After the small-group discussion, watch Jeff Cavins' video presentation on *Session 14* – Matthew 14–15: Instructions to the Twelve.

[1] *Lumen Gentium* 11.

***Facilitators:** Read these responses to the questions ahead of time to help you prepare to lead the small-group discussion.*

***Participants:** Reinforce what you have learned by reviewing these responses after the small-group discussion and before you go on to the next session.*

A. Review the Context

Facilitators: Take a moment to review the context and what was learned in the previous session. If you like, use the following question to encourage discussion:

- *What is there in the example Jesus set in Matthew 14–15 that you can follow in your life?*

B. Read the Story

Facilitators: If there is time, have someone read each passage aloud before it is discussed.

C. Take a Deeper Look

"A Wicked and Adulterous Generation" (Matthew 16:1-12)

1. *The Pharisees and Sadducees come to test Jesus in verse 1. In what way does their question reflect Satan's first temptation of Jesus in the desert in* ***Matthew 4:3?***

   Both are trying to force Jesus to give them solid proof of who he is: Satan tested Jesus, tempting him to prove his divine sonship by changing stones into loaves of bread. Now, the Pharisees and Sadducees test Jesus by demanding a sign that will prove that his authority comes from God.

2. a. *What "signs of the times" do you think Jesus is accusing the Pharisees and Sadducees of being unable to interpret?*

   The Pharisees and Sadducees may be able to forecast the weather by reading signs in the skies, but Jesus says they cannot interpret the changes that the signs of the times are predicting. They are blind to what is happening in the kingdom of God. They cannot read the true meaning of Jesus' miracles or see what he is trying to show them about the passing away of the Old Covenant, the coming of the kingdom, the inclusion of the Gentiles in that kingdom, and the true meaning of the Sabbath.

   b. *What kind of sign does Jesus offer them? Explain it. (**Optional:** Read the book of **Jonah,** which contains just four short chapters.)*

   Jesus offers them only "the sign of Jonah." God sent Jonah to Nineveh in Assyria to warn the people there of their impending judgment. They were given forty days to repent, and they repented. This "sign" is a warning to the Jewish leaders: If the nation does not repent, God's judgment will fall on them. The "sign of Jonah" is also interpreted to be a reference to Jesus' resurrection. (Just as Jonah was in the belly of the whale for three days, Jesus will be in the belly of the earth for three days before rising again.) This is the only sign (or proof) of Jesus' authority that will be given to that generation.

3. *In verses 5-12, Jesus warns the disciples to beware of the "yeast" (teaching) of the Pharisees and Sadducees. What do the uses and properties of yeast add to your understanding of his warning?*

   Yeast is a living organism that makes bread dough rise. A small amount of yeast will permeate the dough and affect all of it; in the same way, false teaching is insidious. It takes only a little to permeate the whole thing. Yeast changes the very nature of the dough. False teaching can have the same kind of permanent, life-changing effect and be equally difficult to eradicate.

Peter's Confession (Matthew 16:13-20)

4. a. *How does Peter's understanding of who Jesus is compare with the way the religious leaders and other men see Jesus?*

   The religious leaders do not believe Jesus and want proof of his identity. The people wonder: Is he John the Baptist? Elijah? Jeremiah? One of the prophets? In contrast to the others, Peter proclaims, "You are the Christ, the Son of the Living God" (verse 16). The contrast between Peter and the religious leaders is significant. The Pharisees and Sadducees represent the teaching authority of the Old Covenant, but they do not recognize the Son of God, who is the fulfillment of that covenant.

   b. *Why is it important to know who Jesus is?*

   Jesus' identity is central to his mission. He is the one we must believe in to be saved. Calling him by the wrong name causes one to miss him entirely.

   c. *Whom does Jesus say is the source of Peter's knowledge?*

   Jesus attributes Peter's knowledge to God, "my Father who is in heaven."

5. a. *After Simon acknowledges Jesus to be "the Christ, the Son of the living God," Jesus gives him a new name—Peter—meaning "Rock." Can you remember anyone else who was given a new name by God, and why? (See* ***Genesis 17 and 32.****)*

   Only Abraham, Sarah, and Jacob were given new names in the Old Testament. These three people were called by God and given important roles in the foundation of his covenant family. Abraham and Sarah were given their names when God established the covenant of circumcision with them and made them the "exalted father" and "mother of nations." A royal house that will bless the world will descend from this couple. God gave their grandson Jacob the new name "Israel" because he would be the father of twelve sons who would become the twelve tribes of Israel and eventually the kingdom of Israel through which God would bless all the nations. Now, Peter is given a name that marks him in a special way as God's servant and expresses the role he will play in his kingdom.

   b. *The word "rock" was not commonly used as a name in Old Testament times the way "Peter" is used today. It was used to describe God, however. (See* ***Isaiah 26:4*** *and* ***2 Samual 22:32.****) On one occasion, it was used to describe someone else. Who was it? Read* ***Isaiah 51:1-2.***

   God called Abraham "the rock from which you were cut, the father of Israel."

   c. *Why is it significant that Jesus gives Simon the new name Peter?*

   Peter's new name signifies that he is to be a "rock"—the foundation stone of the new Church—just as Abraham and Sarah were the founding "stones" of the old kingdom. Abraham's faith formed the bedrock of the old kingdom; Peter's faith, along with the truth God reveals to him, form the foundation of the new kingdom. The fact that Jesus calls Simon Peter "rock" does not diminish the status of God as the "Rock of Israel." In the ancient world, naming something implied you had ownership or dominion over it. God is naming Peter "rock" here; therefore, he has dominion, power, and authority over Peter.

6. a. *What does Jesus promise Peter in verse 18, and what does this promise mean for the Church? (See also* ***CCC 552.****)*

   Jesus says he will build his Church on Peter and promises that the powers of death will not prevail against it. Peter (and his successors, the popes) will be "the unshakable rock of the Church" (CCC 552), victorious even over the powers of death. God establishes the Church, and he promises to uphold it. This is why the Church has been able to withstand centuries of attacks from outside (and even corruption from within). It provides a sure foundation for God's family on earth until Jesus comes again.

   b. *In verse 19, Jesus gives Peter "the keys of the kingdom of heaven" and tells him, "Whatever you bind on earth shall be bound in heaven, and whatever you loose on earth shall be loosed in heaven." Read* ***Isaiah 22:15-25*** *and* ***Revelation 3:7.*** *What insight do these passages give you into the meaning of the keys? Read also* ***CCC 553.***

   The "key of the house of David" represents the authority of the steward who was placed over the household or kingdom by the king in Old Testament times. This was a permanent position. Appointed by God, this man is responsible for his entire kingdom, "the whole weight of his father's house," as Isaiah says. The keys are a symbol of his power to open the gates of heaven to men: "to absolve sins, to pronounce doctrinal judgments, and to make disciplinary decisions in the Church" (CCC 553). Before Jesus leaves his apostles, he entrusts Peter with the power of the keys to the kingdom of heaven on earth. The keys denote the office, not the person, and they have been handed down to Peter's successors, the popes, for nearly two thousand years.

Jesus Prophesies His Death (Matthew 16:21-28)

7. *Verse 21 marks a turning point in Matthew's Gospel. God has revealed Jesus' identity to Peter and made him the foundation stone of the Church. "From that time," Jesus begins to tell his disciples what the establishment of this new kingdom will require.*

   a. *Why are Jesus' words so hard for Peter to take?*

   Jesus tells them he must go to Jerusalem to suffer and die and then rise on the third day. Peter's rebuke of what Jesus says must happen reveals that he is not seeing from God's viewpoint, but from man's. He cannot yet imagine a kingdom that would require the suffering and death of its leader.

   b. *Why does Jesus reply with such force? (Do you see any parallel between Peter's remark and the words of the Serpent in Genesis 3 or of Satan in Matthew 4 when he tempts Jesus in the desert?)*

   The very thing that makes Peter "rock"—his recognition of the Messiah—is in jeopardy because he misunderstands the importance to Christ's mission of his suffering. Peter's words are reminiscent of those of Satan to Adam and Eve in the Garden of Eden ("You will not die" if you refuse to do God's will), and to Jesus in the desert (where he tempts him to avoid suffering and to worship him instead of God). This is why Jesus responds to Peter with, "Get behind me, Satan!"

   c. ***Think About It:*** *How should we see Peter's error in light of the special revelation he has just received and the fact that he will be the foundation of the Church? For that matter, how do we understand the mistakes of any of the later popes in light of their infallibility?*

God has chosen Peter—a fallible human—to head his Church. Peter replied to Jesus' question—"Who do you say that I am?"—with a divinely inspired declaration of truth about Jesus' identity. Peter's later resistance to the need for Jesus to suffer and die is a human reaction Satan uses to tempt Jesus not to fulfill his mission. Peter is as susceptible to Satan as any man, and this is also true of his successors, the popes. The pope is infalliable—protected from error by the Holy Spirit—in the declaration of dogma. This infallibility is necessary because if the truth could be corrupted, the gates of Hades could prevail against the Church, which Christ has assured them will not happen. This promise for protection does not depend on the holiness of a particular pope, but rather on the faithfulness of God. However, the pope's infallibility does not mean he is "impeccable" (without sin).

8. a. *It is not only Jesus who will suffer. What does Jesus say will be required of anyone who follows him? (Read also **Romans 8:15-18** and **John 12:24.**)*

Jesus says: "Unless a grain of wheat falls into the earth and dies, it remains alone; but if it dies, it bears much fruit" (John 12:24). Without death, there can be no resurrection. This is the hard truth that the followers of Jesus Christ must come to grips with, because what was true for Jesus is true for us as well. To follow him to glory we, too, must take up our crosses.

b. *How can we do this today?*

Encourage discussion. Answers will vary. The important point is that total commitment—even to death—is required to be a follower of Jesus. Disciples of Jesus must follow his example, put aside their own agendas and ideas of how things "should be," and suffer with him in order to be glorified with him as fellow heirs and children of God. Jesus intends for his disciples to dwell on the reward, not the price. Those who take up their crosses will find life. Jesus will save their souls. The suffering of the Cross is always paired with eternal glory.

D. Application

Facilitators: If time allows, have group members share their responses to the following application questions.

St. Rose of Lima said: "Apart from the cross, there is no other ladder by which we may get to heaven" (CCC 618).[1] *Is it difficult for you to suffer and die to yourself—to take up your cross in your daily life and carry it willingly as a share in Christ's burden? Read Colossians 1:24-26 and CCC 618. How can the examples of Jesus' early followers give you encouragement?*

After the small-group discussion, watch Jeff Cavins' video presentation on *Session 15* – Matthew 16: Jesus Establishes the Church.

1 St. Rose of Lima, cf. P. Hansen, Vita mirabilis (Louvain, 1668).

Matthew 17 – The Transfiguration

Facilitators: *Read these responses to the questions ahead of time to help you prepare to lead the small-group discussion.*

Participants: *Reinforce what you have learned by reviewing these responses after the small-group discussion and before you go on to the next session.*

A. Review the Context

Facilitators: Take a moment to review the context and what was learned in the previous session. If you like, use the following question to encourage discussion:

- *What is the most important thing you learned about God's kingdom on earth?*

B. Read the Story

Facilitators: If there is time, have someone read each passage aloud before it is discussed.

C. Take a Deeper Look

The Transfiguration (Matthew 17:1-13)

1. *The Transfiguration takes place in the context of the events of Matthew 16, in which Peter declares Jesus to be the Christ, Son of the living God, and in which Jesus foretells his passion and speaks of the cost of discipleship.*

   a. *Six days later, who does Jesus take up a mountain, and what is revealed to them there?*

   Jesus takes his "inner circle" of disciples—Peter, James, and John—up on a mountain where he is revealed in all his kingly glory and majesty. They see him "transfigured": His face shines like the sun, and his clothes become white as light in a way that recalls Moses on Mount Sinai, whose face shone so brightly after being with God that he had to cover it with a veil. Jesus' identity is further revealed as God himself identifies him in a voice from a cloud: "This is my beloved Son, with whom I am well pleased; listen to him" (verse 5).

   b. *In what way will this experience prove significant for the apostles later on? (See* ***2 Peter 1:17-18*** *and* ***CCC 555.****)*

   Because they are eyewitnesses of his majesty and hear the voice of God, their message of the Lord's power and coming is trustworthy. They use this as proof in their preaching, and it gives them divine authority. It also strengthens them. After this experience, they may grieve over what Jesus will have to suffer, but there is no longer room for any doubt. As the Byzantine Liturgy proclaims: "You were transfigured on the mountain, and your disciples, as much as they were capable of it, beheld your glory, O Christ our God, so that when they should see you crucified they would understand that your Passion was voluntary, and proclaim to the world that you truly are the splendor of the Father" (CCC 555).[1]

---

[1] Byzantine Liturgy, Feast of the Transfiguration, *Kontakion.*

2. a. *Moses and Elijah represent the Law and the Prophets. Why do you think these two "greats" appear on the mountain for this occasion? (A brief ode to Elijah can be found in the first part of* ***Sirach 48.****)*

   The names of Moses and Elijah are heavy with significance. Moses was used by God to deliver his people from slavery in Egypt and then received the Old Covenant Law from God on Mount Sinai. He is the acknowledged author of the Pentateuch, the first five books of the Bible. Elijah was one of the greatest Old Testament prophets. He did not die, but was taken up to heaven in a fiery chariot. There are many parallels between the lives of Elijah and Moses, and Elijah appears here as the one who is to be "ready at the appointed time, it is written, to calm the wrath of God before it breaks out in fury, to turn the heart of the father to the son, and to restore the tribes of Jacob" (Sirach 48:10). Just imagine: Moses and Elijah represent all the Law and the Prophets, and they are present to bear witness to Jesus, which the Law and the Prophets all pointed toward.

   b. *From Luke's Gospel, we know that on this occasion, Moses and Elijah speak with Jesus about his "departure, which he was to accomplish at Jerusalem" (Luke 9:30-31). The literal meaning of "departure" here is "exodus." What would calling it an "exodus" add to the disciples' understanding of Jesus' mission?*

   This exchange with Moses about an "exodus" can only refer to a new delivery for God's people. Their first delivery was from slavery in Egypt. This new "exodus" will be from the bondage of sin. The reference here to this new exodus being from Jerusalem—taken together with Jesus' earlier announcement that he will go to Jerusalem to die—indicates that Jesus' death will bring about this new exodus. Death itself will be conquered. Christ's suffering and death are not an accident—they are a fulfillment. Christ's suffering and death purchase for us release from the bondage of earthly life into the liberty of eternal life.

3. *Peter wants to extend Moses' and Elijah's stay by building tents for them. What do we learn by the fact that they do not stay?*

   Answers will vary. This may indicate that Peter wants the New Covenant along with the Old Covenant but that the old must pass away. He may want to focus on the representatives of the Old Covenant, when he needs to turn to God's beloved Son and listen to him. They are left with "Jesus only" (verse 8) after this. The "new wine" cannot be held in the "old wine skins."

4. *How does the Transfiguration relate to our own hopes for the future? (See* ***2 Corinthians 3:18.****)*

   We who behold his glory are being transformed into it. We also will be transfigured one day.

The Healing of a Boy with a Demon (Matthew 17:14-23)

5. a. *Why are the disciples unable to drive the demon from the man's son?*

   Jesus says the disciples do not have enough faith. Some manuscripts add—and Mark includes part of this in his Gospel—"but this kind does not go out except by prayer and fasting." Perhaps the disciples are taking their power for granted or have forgotten that it is not their own power but the Lord's power working through them. By praying and fasting, they will acknowledge that the source of all power against evil is Christ.

   b. *What does Jesus say they need?*

   According to Jesus, they need "faith as a grain of mustard seed." Because a mustard seed is very small, and their faith is "little," the problem must not be the amount of their faith. Genuine faith may start small, but it takes root and grows. This faith involves accepting Jesus as who he says he is and having confidence in God and his promises and power. Perhaps their faith is misplaced in themselves. In contrast, when the boy's father comes to Jesus, he comes begging for Jesus' help because he recognizes the source of his power. He has faith in Jesus, and his son is healed.

c. *What do you make of the disciples' failure?*

Answers will vary. The disciples' weakness should be a source of encouragement for us. They are earnest but fallible people who have to learn through trial and error and repeated instruction what it means to believe in and follow Christ. Before his resurrection and the coming of his Spirit at Pentecost, the disciples are often confused and lacking in faith; yet, they know *who* to follow, and he works with them until they learn the lessons he has for them. In the same way, he works with us over time while we learn to follow him.

6. a. *In verses 22-23, Jesus again says he will be betrayed, killed, and raised to life on the third day. The first time he said this in Matthew 16:21-22, Peter was shocked, and the disciples misunderstood him. Do they understand him this time? How do you know?*

The disciples are beginning to understand what must happen. Matthew says they are "greatly distressed" (verse 23) by the knowledge.

b. ***Think About It:*** *By the time Peter wrote his epistles, his view of Christ's suffering—and of suffering in general—had changed markedly. Read* **1 Peter 1:6-8, 4:12-13, and 5:10.** *Do you think witnessing the Transfiguration had an impact on his change of view? Explain your answer.*

Following the Transfiguration, Peter knows without a doubt that Jesus is the Son of God. He has seen Christ's glory with his own eyes; he has heard the voice of God and seen Moses and Elijah bear witness to him. Peter also knows now that suffering and death are the way to resurrection and eternal life and glory that will far exceed this suffering. He knows that Christ's glory will be shared with us one day. We are called to his glory, and Christ himself will restore and strengthen us. Christ's resurrection glory, which on the Mount of Transfiguration was only hinted at, offers us the glorious hope of "the salvation of [our] souls" (1 Peter 1:9).

The Temple Tax (Matthew 17:24-27)

7. *The half-shekel tax (literally,* didrachma*—"two-drachma tax") represented about two days' wages; it was an annual tax on adult males for the Temple upkeep and was a symbol of the people's redemption, or purchase, from Egypt.*

a. *Who does Jesus say is exempt from the tax, and why?*

"The sons" are exempt from the tax. Just as in any kingdom, kings collect money from others, not from their own sons.

b. *By implication, of whom is he speaking specifically?*

Jesus, who identifies himself in Matthew 12:6 as one "greater than the temple," is the Son of God and, therefore, is exempt from the Temple tax. Likewise, Peter is also exempt because Jesus has made him the foundation of the Church, which will replace the Temple in Jerusalem.

8. *If they are exempt, why does Jesus ask Peter to pay the tax for the two of them?*

   Jesus shows solidarity between himself and his vicar by paying the tax for the two of them. They are exempt, but he pays the tax to avoid offending those who are collecting it.

9. *Do you think Jesus accomplishes more by submitting to the authorities in this way than he would by insisting on his rights?*

   Jesus accomplishes far more by submitting to the tax. In the act of paying the tax, he displays far more power than if he refused. It is ironic that in the very act of submitting to the authority of the religious leaders, he displays his authority and power over nature and the folly of being considered "just another taxpayer." This is just a microcosm of the way Jesus will reveal his power with finality later in the ultimate submission he makes in his death on the Cross.

D. Application

Facilitators: If time allows, have group members share their responses to the following application question.

We often speak about "mountaintop" and "valley" experiences. What can you take from the mountaintop experience of the Transfiguration that will help you walk through the "valleys" in your own life?

After the small-group discussion, watch Jeff Cavins' video presentation on *Session 16* – Matthew 17: The Transfiguration.

Session 17 – Responses

The King and His Kingdom

Matthew 18 – Characteristics of the Christian Community

Facilitators: *Read these responses to the questions ahead of time to help you prepare to lead the small-group discussion.*

Participants: *Reinforce what you have learned by reviewing these responses after the small-group discussion and before you go on to the next session.*

A. Review the Context

Facilitators: Take a moment to review the context and what was learned in the previous session. If you like, use the following question to encourage discussion:

- *What spoke especially to you in Matthew 17?*

B. Read the Story

Facilitators: If there is time, have someone read each passage aloud before it is discussed.

C. Take a Deeper Look

Humility (Matthew 18:1-4)

1. a. *In verse 1, the disciples ask Jesus, "Who is the greatest in the kingdom of heaven?" How does Jesus answer their question?*

   Jesus does not answer directly, but presents them with a child and tells them that to enter the kingdom of heaven, a person must be humble and become like a child. Humility is necessary to enter the new kingdom and is a distinguishing feature of those who are great in that kingdom.

   b. *What do you think Jesus has in mind when he says to "turn and become like children"?*

   Jesus is challenging the disciples not to think in terms of social hierarchy, but to be like children—humble and unpretentious. People will be born into the new kingdom and will be children of the Father, completely dependent on him, trusting him to supply every need and growing up to be like him.

2. *What must we do to enter the kingdom of heaven? (See also **John 1:12-13** and **CCC 526.**)*

   To enter the kingdom of heaven, we must humble ourselves and become small. There is no room for pride in the kingdom. We must become children of God by being born spiritually from above. Christ—God's own Son—must be born in us.

Purity (Matthew 18:5-9)

3. *What warning does Jesus issue to those who would cause "one such child" to sin?*

   Jesus says: "It would be better for him to have a great millstone fastened round his neck and to be drowned in the depth of the sea." Causing others to sin is such a serious offense, that it would be better to be drowned or to cut off whatever part of the body is causing the temptation than to continue in the sin. The implication is that leaders who mislead the flock will be cast into the eternal punishment of hell.

4. a. *In Matthew 5, Jesus said to take drastic measures if necessary (figuratively, to cut off or pluck out the offending member) to combat personal temptation and avoid sin. In this illustration in Matthew 18, how does he extend this concern to the community as a whole?*

   Jesus is using a literary device in which a human body and its parts refer figuratively to a corporate body or community and its members. Here, Jesus recommends that the Church use the same extreme action prescribed in Matthew 5 against someone who is causing others in the body of Christ to sin. All sin affects the entire body and must be dealt with. If a member of the body of Christ is causing others to sin, it is better for the member to be "cut off" than for it to drag the whole body down with it.

   b. *What is the goal of these drastic measures?*

   The goal is remedial, not ultimately destructive or vindictive. Think of the "cutting off of limbs" as life-saving surgery.

5. ***Think About It:*** *When the* Catechism *discusses "Life in Christ," it includes a section called "Respect for the souls of others: scandal." Read it in* **CCC 2284–2287.** *What does this add to your understanding of Jesus' words in Matthew 18:5-9?*

   Answers will vary; encourage discussion. One aspect of "scandal" that has not been covered in these questions is the responsibility people have for the effects their sins have on others.

Family (Matthew 18:10-14)

6. *What does the parable of the lost sheep tell you about God?*

   The Father looks after each of "these little ones" (his children) with the tender care of a shepherd. Like a shepherd, he cares for each member of his flock individually. He is persistent in trying to win each and rejoices greatly when a lost one returns to the fold. This brings to mind what God said about himself through the prophet Ezekiel (Chapter 34): That unlike the unfaithful leadership of Israel, he himself would be their Shepherd; he would search them out and rescue them and restore, feed, and heal them.

Justice ... (Matthew 18:15-20)

7. a. *As the earthly shepherds of God's flock on earth, the disciples will need to know how to deal with lost sheep and problems in the sheepfold. What are Jesus' instructions for dealing with sin in the Christian community?*

   Jesus outlines a three-step process designed to restore sinners to the community when possible or exclude them if necessary. (Sometimes exclusion is necessary for the health of the whole, as explained in verses 7-9.)

- There should be an attempt at private reconciliation.
- If the offender will not listen, the offended person should return with two or three others to bear witness. (This supports the offended person and protects the offender from a false accusation.)
- If the offender still will not listen, he should be brought before the Church.

b. *In verse 17, Jesus says that if the offender refuses correction by the Church, "Let him be to you as a Gentile and a tax collector." What does this mean?*

Gentiles and tax collectors were despised and excluded from the Jewish community. To treat someone like a Gentile or a tax collector meant not to associate with the one who refused correction. It also meant they would be excluded from worship. This is not so much punishment as it is a physical demonstration of a spiritual reality: That person stepped outside the walls of the family when he or she insisted on living outside the guidelines set for members of the Church.

c. *What is the ultimate goal of this process? (See also **Galatians 6:1-2.**)*

The ultimate goal of correction is always restoration to fellowship. It is never vindictive. Even excommunication is levied in the hope that the person will repent so his soul will be saved.

8. a. *How does Jesus' assurance that what the apostles bind or loose on earth will be bound or loosed in heaven relate to this? (See also **CCC 1443–1445.**)*

When Jesus says that what the apostles bind or loose on earth will be bound or loosed in heaven, he means that those they include in the earthly community (or exclude from it) will be welcomed into (or excluded from) communion with God. Notice that the emphasis is on restoring sinners to communion. It is the person who continues in sin who chooses to step out of the community. Jesus forgives and restores sinners and gives his apostles the same power. "Reconciliation with the Church is inseparable from reconciliation with God" (CCC 1445).

b. *Who has this authority today, and how is it practiced? (See **CCC 1461–1463.**)*

The successors of the apostles, the bishops (and priests in collaboration with them), have the authority to carry on the apostolic ministry of reconciliation. Through the sacrament of reconciliation, sinners obtain God's pardon and are reconciled to him and to the Church.

. . . and Mercy (Matthew 18:21-35)

9. *What does Jesus mean by saying that even seven times is not enough, but "seventy times seven"?*

The rabbis of Jesus' time taught that a person should forgive another three times, so Peter is being magnanimous. Jesus' answer renders the whole question absurd. It reveals the very foundation of dealing with sin in the Christian community—mercy. As God has forgiven us, so we must forgive others. If we set limits on forgiveness, we miss the point. When Jesus says, "seventy times seven," he is saying something like, "times without end." Peter asks for a just measuring rod, and Jesus tells him just to forgive—and to forget the measuring rod.

10. a. *How does Jesus illustrate the foolishness of putting limits on forgiveness? (Note: One "talent" would represent about twenty years' wages for a laborer; one "denarius" could be earned in a day.)*

Jesus tells a parable about a servant who is forgiven an enormous debt and then turns around and refuses to forgive another person's small debt. Consequently, he is turned over to the jailers until he can repay his own debt. The implication is that we have been forgiven a tremendous debt by

God, an impossible amount to pay by ourselves. God freely offers his forgiveness to all who humble themselves to receive it, but to receive this forgiveness, we must forgive others the comparatively tiny debts they owe us.

b. *What does this parable teach about justice in the kingdom of heaven? (Read also* **CCC 2832–2843.***)*

In God's kingdom, justice is measured against the measuring rod of the boundless mercy God has shown to each one of us. By forgiving us and paying our debt, God has set the pattern we must follow in our individual relationships and within the Church.

c. ***Think About It:*** *Forgiving others sounds good on paper, but it can be the hardest thing we have to do. How is it possible to carry this out in our lives?*

In Luke 6:36, Jesus tells us to "be merciful, even as your Father is merciful." Humanly speaking, it is impossible to be merciful by simply imitating God. The *Catechism* tells us that we must participate from the depths of our hearts in the love and mercy of God. Only the Spirit can give us the mind of Christ and enable us to forgive one another as God in Christ forgave us (CCC 2842). The key to showing mercy to others can be found in the final words of the parable: "from your heart." In the final analysis, everything is bound and loosed in the heart. On our own, we may not be able to forgive. We need the help of the Holy Spirit to turn our pain into compassion and the transforming power of forgiveness.

D. Application

Facilitators: If time allows, have group members share their responses to the following application question.

Forgiveness is not so much a matter of feelings as it is an act of the will. Jesus has released us from our sin and asks us to release others who have sinned against us. Is there someone in your life you have not forgiven? If so, release them today, and say a prayer for them.

E. Wrap-Up – Book Four: Transfer of the Kingdom's Authority

Facilitators: If there is time, ask if anyone can summarize Book Four of Matthew's Gospel (Chapters 14–18). Answers will vary. The point is not to find a "correct" answer, but to explore the major points of the chapters. You might ask questions like:

- *What incidents in Jesus' life does Matthew use to show him transferring his authority to his disciples?*
- *What do these events reveal about the characteristics of the kingdom?*
- *What makes someone great in the kingdom of God?*

After the small-group discussion, watch Jeff Cavins' video presentation on *Session 17* – Matthew 18: Characteristics of the Christian Community.

Session 18 – Responses

Matthew 19 – Marriage: A Demonstration of God's Love

Facilitators: *Read these responses to the questions ahead of time to help you prepare to lead the small-group discussion.*

Participants: *Reinforce what you have learned by reviewing these responses after the small-group discussion and before you go on to the next session.*

A. Establish the Context

Facilitators: Take a moment to review the material from the previous session and to establish the context of Book Five of Matthew's Gospel. If you like, use the following questions to encourage discussion:

- *Which characteristic of the kingdom is most important to you? Why?*

B. Read the Story

Facilitators: If there is time, have someone read each passage aloud before it is discussed.

C. Take a Deeper Look

Marriage and Divorce (Matthew 19:1-12)

1. *The action shifts from Galilee in the north to "Judah beyond the Jordan." Locate this area on the map on page 5. Do you remember what this region is associated with? (See* ***Matthew 3:1-6.****)*

   Judea is in the southern end of Palestine, where the Southern Kingdom of Judah is located. The kingdom of Judah is ruled by the Davidic line of kings, and the Jerusalem Temple (the national place of worship) is located within its borders. "Judea beyond the Jordan" points to the area east of the Jordan River and approximately opposite Jerusalem, Bethlehem, and Bethany. This is where John the Baptist ministers.

2. *We have seen the Pharisees plotting to kill Jesus since Matthew 12. Forbidden under their own law from carrying out a death sentence, they will need to find him guilty of breaking Roman law or get him to provoke the secular authorities. In 19:3, they test Jesus by asking, "Is it lawful to divorce one's wife for any cause?" What do you think is behind this question? Can you think of any way in which it represents a potentially lethal trap for Jesus? (Hint: Remember the fate of John the Baptist.)*

   Beyond the Jordan, in the very area where John the Baptist had his ministry and presumably in the very area where he called Herod Antipas on the carpet for divorcing his wife in order to marry his brother's wife, the Pharisees ask: "Is it lawful to divorce one's wife for any cause?" If he answers "yes," Jesus can be accused and discredited before the people for taking too liberal a stance on the Mosaic Law. If he answers "No," he runs the risk of inflaming Herod and being imprisoned and even beheaded like John the Baptist.

3. a. *How does Jesus avoid the trap?*

The Pharisees expect Jesus to take sides and get into trouble, but he sidesteps those options and turns the trap back on them, asking: "Have you not read that he who made them from the beginning made them male and female, and said, 'For this reason a man shall leave his father and mother and be joined to his wife, and the two shall become one'" (verses 4-5). Of course they have read it. But they have become so fixated on interpreting and following the Mosaic Law, that they have forgotten God's law that existed before this covenant. Jesus takes them back to the beginning and restores marriage to its original integrity.

b. *What is the next objection of the Pharisees, and how does Jesus handle it?*

The Pharisees ask Jesus to explain why Moses commanded divorce. Jesus replies that it was never a command. Jesus tells them that Moses "allowed you to divorce your wives" because of the "hardness of heart" of the people in order to regulate a situation that had gotten out of control. After forty years of wandering the desert, the Israelites were not following God as they should. They had forgotten their promises.[1]

4. a. *According to the following Bible and* Catechism *references, what does marriage represent? (**Optional:** Read **CCC 1602–1617.**)*

Ephesians 5:31-32: Marriage represents the union between Christ and the Church.

CCC 1604: Marital love is an image of the absolute and unfailing love with which God loves mankind.

CCC 1611: Exclusive and faithful married love images God's covenant with Israel.

CCC 1613: Marriage is an efficacious sign of Christ's presence.

CCC 1617: Marriage signifies and communicates grace as the sacrament of the covenant of Christ and the Church. Marriage between baptized persons is a true sacrament of the New Covenant.

b. *In Matthew 19:5, Jesus quotes from **Genesis 2:20-24.** Read this passage. What was God's original plan for marriage?*

God's original plan was an inseparable union between the two—that the husband and wife would be "one flesh."

c. *Read **Malachi 2:13-16.** What do these verses say about God in regard to divorce?*

God hates divorce. It means the breaking of a covenant, which should be inviolable. God "made and sustained for us the spirit of life." And he desires the "godly offspring" that proceed in that spirit of life from that union. He hates both divorce and violence, which tear apart the fabric of life.

d. *How does the reaction of the disciples in verse 10 support the Catholic teaching that the marriage bond is created by God and cannot be broken except by death?*

The disciples are incredulous. They think that a lifetime of celibacy would be preferable to Jesus' teaching on the indissolubility of marriage.

---

[1] For a concise view of the conflict, see the essay, "Jesus on Marriage and Divorce," on page 51 in the *Ignatius Catholic Study Bible.*

5. *Is the Church's teaching on the indissolubility of marriage impossible to bear? (See* ***CCC 1615.****)*

   The law regarding marriage set forth by Moses may seem kinder to us than Jesus' words regarding the indissolubility of the marriage bond. But the *Catechism* states: "By coming to restore the original order of creation disturbed by sin, he himself gives the strength and grace to live marriage in the new dimension of the Reign of God. It is by following Christ, renouncing themselves, and taking up their crosses that spouses will be able to 'receive' the original meaning of marriage and live it with the help of Christ" (CCC 1615; cf. Matthew 19:11). We are all called to take up our crosses and follow Christ. We are called to love and even suffer, if necessary, as Christ did. In doing so, we show Christ's love to the world. The sacrament of matrimony illustrates and gives us participation in the eternal and indissoluble love of Christ for his bride, the Church.

The Rich Young Man (Matthew 19:16-30)

6. *Why do you think Jesus responds the way he does when the rich young man asks what good thing he can do to attain eternal life?*

   Jesus changes the man's focus with his question. The young man is thinking only of external obedience. Jesus reminds him that goodness has to do as much with who we are and our attitudes as with what we do.

7. a. *Jesus says the young man has to obey the commandments to "enter life." For a list of the Ten Commandments, read* ***Exodus 20:1-17.*** *Which of the commandments does Jesus omit in the list he gives the young man in verses 18-19 that pertain to the young man's situation?*

   Jesus leaves out two related commands: (1) You shall have no other gods before me, and (2) you shall not covet.

   b. *Why do you think he omits those at first?*

   Jesus may leave these off the list to draw attention to them and emphasize what is lacking in the young man. The young man's heart is fixed on his possessions, and he cannot bring himself to part with them—even for eternal life. Wealth is his god and is holding him back.

8. a. *Why do you think the disciples are astonished at what Jesus says in verses 23-24?*

   The disciples think wealth is a sign of God's favor and probably wonder who can get into heaven if the rich man cannot.

   b. *Can you explain Jesus' reply in verse 26?*

   We may think some things are impossible (like attaining salvation), but with God, all things are possible. We need to remember that it is God's power that saves us, not our own. The rich, in their lack of need, may be under more temptation than the poor to rely on their own resources instead of on God.

9. ***Think About It:*** *In reviewing Matthew 19, what is the cost of commitment to the kingdom?*

   The kingdom has been portrayed as a pearl of great price worth selling all one owns to gain. Here, the cost of commitment is spelled out. It means keeping one's promises—no matter what. It means loving one's spouse as Christ loves the Church. For some, it means giving up a spouse and family to be celibate for the kingdom. For others, it means giving up things they value more than God. It is costly.

10. *Peter is quick to note that he and the others have left everything to follow Christ. What will be their reward?*

    Jesus gives a marvelous promise of rewards: Not only will the apostles sit on thrones judging the twelve tribes of Israel, but whatever they have given up for his sake will be returned a hundredfold, and they will inherit eternal life. In other words, they are not sacrificing but investing. If the cost of following Jesus ever seems too hard to bear, remember this promise. Jesus assures us that God will make good on our investment. In fact, he will pay it back many times over. Above all, remember Christ's words to the astonished disciples, who seem to think Jesus is making things far too difficult: "Jesus looked at them and said to them, 'With men this is impossible, but with God all things are possible.'"

D. Application

Facilitators: If time allows, have group members share their responses to the following application question.

All Christians find themselves in a marriage relationship. If you are single, you are married to the Lord. If married, you are also married to the Lord. In your state of life what three things might you do to improve your marriage so that the covenant you have may be stronger?

After the small-group discussion, watch Jeff Cavins' video presentation on *Session 18* – Matthew 19: Marriage – A Demonstration of God's Love.

Facilitators: *Read these responses to the questions ahead of time to help you prepare to lead the small-group discussion.*

Participants: *Reinforce what you have learned by reviewing these responses after the small-group discussion and before you go on to the next session.*

A. Review the Context

Facilitators: Take a moment to review the context and what was learned in the previous session. If you like, use the following question to encourage discussion:

- *What challenged you about Jesus' words to the rich young man?*

B. Read the Story

Facilitators: If there is time, have someone read each passage aloud before it is discussed.

C. Take a Deeper Look

"The Last Shall Be First" (Matthew 20:1-16)

1. *This parable continues and further clarifies Jesus' reply to the disciples' question in Matthew 18—"Who then can be saved?"—Jesus' replies: "Many that are first will be last, and the last first." Keep in mind when reading verses 1-16 that this is a parable. It is not something that actually happened, nor is it proposed as a model for labor relations today. Jesus is telling this story to help his disciples understand who will be part of the kingdom of God.*

   a. *What or who do the following represent?*

   The vineyard (see Jeremiah 12:10 and Isaiah 5:1-7): Israel

   Harvest time: the Last Judgment

   The employer: God

   The first group: those God reached out to first: Israel, and in particular in this parable, its religious leaders

   The later groups: the tax collectors and sinners (outcasts among the Jews); the Samaritans (half-breeds); and the Gentiles, who come in at "the eleventh hour"

   b. *How does this parable illustrate God's justice and mercy?*

   The householder (God) acts justly in giving the first workers the wage they contracted for. His mercy is evident as he gives the others what they need to live on even though they arrive late. In the same way, God acts justly to those who are his from the beginning, and he shows great mercy in allowing others to enter his family later. The kingdom is God's to give, Jesus says, and we must not begrudge his generosity. The same message of God's mercy comes across in the parable of the Prodigal Son; and we will see it again in the story about the thief crucified next to Christ who believes just before he dies and is promised a place with Jesus in paradise.

c. *What is the parable's message to Israel?*

God does not limit the kingdom to Israel, even though Israel was called first. Anyone who trusts in God's mercy and forgiveness will be welcome—even "at the eleventh hour"—like the later workers in the parable, the tax collectors and sinners, the thief on the cross, and even the Gentiles. This does not mean the thief on the cross will have a position or reward equal to someone who has given a lifetime of service to God. Jesus has just told Peter that self-sacrifice for his sake will be greatly rewarded and that the disciples themselves will sit on thrones judging the twelve tribes. Some of those who appear great in this life—the Jewish leaders, for example, or the rich young ruler of Jesus' time—may be least in the kingdom of heaven or may not enter it at all. In contrast, those who pour out their lives for God, who are "fools for Christ" on earth, will be great in his kingdom.

The "Cup" of Christ (Matthew 20:17-28)

2. a. *Twice already in Matthew's Gospel we have heard Jesus prophesy his passion. Review* ***Matthew 16:21 and 17:22-23.*** *What new information does Jesus give the disciples in 20:17-19?*

This time, Jesus' prediction contains more detail. He tells the disciples he will be mocked and flogged and that the Jewish authorities will condemn him and hand him over to the Gentiles to be crucified. The purpose of this prophecy is to prepare the disciples for what is to come and to let them know that the manner of Jesus' death is not a surprise to him, but is planned and deliberate.

b. *What "cup" is Jesus talking about in verse 22? (See also* ***Matthew 26:39, 42.****)*

Jesus is speaking of the cup of suffering and death, a share in his passion. In fact, James and John end up sharing this cup: James is martyred (see Acts 12:2) and John is exiled to Patmos. We also share in this cup in baptism when we die to our old selves and rise again with Christ.

c. *How is greatness achieved in God's kingdom?*

Greatness in God's kingdom is achieved by following Christ's example. Christ comes to serve and to give his life for us. The leaders of the new kingdom will be servants of the people and will pour themselves out for others. The secret of greatness in the kingdom of God is in living a life of self-donating love.

The Triumphal Entry into Jerusalem (Matthew 20:29–21:17)

3. *To better understand the significance of the way Jesus enters Jerusalem, read* ***Zechariah 9:9-10; 1 Kings 1:32-46;*** *and* ***2 Kings 9:13.*** *With these verses as the background, what does* ***Matthew 21:4-5*** *say is being fulfilled, and how do you know?*

Prophecies about the coming Messiah are fulfilled in the person of Jesus. Zechariah 9:9-10 is the source of the quote in Matthew 21:4-5. In this passage, Zechariah portrays the coming Messiah riding humbly on an ass, yet triumphant and victorious: "He shall command peace to the nations; his dominion shall be from sea to sea." 1 Kings 1 describes the coronation of King Solomon. He rode in on David's mule to the acclamation of the people ("long live King Solomon!"), which caused an "uproar in the city" so that "the earth was split by their noise." In Matthew's Gospel, Jesus rides into Jerusalem on a mule to the acclamation of the people ("Hosanna to the son of David!"), and "all the city was stirred." Here, the word *eseisthe* means "shook"—a word used to describe the effects of an earthquake. In both cases, it is metaphoric language describing a momentous occasion. In 2 Kings 9, people are shown throwing their garments on the ground before the newly proclaimed king, Jehu. When the people spread their garments and branches on the road in front of Jesus, it shows they are honoring the new King.

4. *In verse 13, Jesus says to those who are changing money and selling pigeons in the Temple: "It is written, 'My house shall be called a house of prayer'; but you make it a den of robbers." Jesus does not want the Temple profaned by being turned into a marketplace. Read that verse from its original context in* ***Isaiah 56:6-12.*** *What else does Jesus indict the Jewish leaders for when he quotes this verse?*

   In Isaiah 56:6-12, God said he would bring "the foreigners who join themselves to the LORD" and "the outcasts of Israel" into the Temple. There, they would be joyful and he would accept their offerings. God intends his house to be "a house of prayer for all peoples." In Matthew 21:12-13, money changing and selling activities are blocking the Gentiles—the very people God wants to welcome—from entering the Temple. The religious leaders, like the shepherds of Isaiah 21:12-13, are interested only in their own gain.

Jesus Curses the Fig Tree (Matthew 21:18-22)

5. a. *How is what Jesus does to the fig tree in this passage prophetic? (For help with this question, read* ***Jeremiah 8:5-9, 13*** *and* ***Hosea 9:10-17.****)*

   Jesus' action here prophesies God's judgment, as did the prophecies of Jeremiah and Hosea. The barren fig tree represents the Israel that has borne no fruit. The withering of the fig tree represents the time of judgment. Jesus' act of withering the fig tree prefigures the destruction of Jerusalem and the Temple in AD 70.

   b. *What is the message of this incident for us?*

   Answers will vary. Try to draw out individual responses. Some participants might say we should be careful not to be "all leaves and no fruit." This is a message of Chapter 7. God wants obedience and good deeds that spring from a living love for him, not a series of actions hung out for everyone to see. Others might say this illustrates the tremendous power of prayer. Jesus' words are more than a promise that requests will be answered; they are an assurance that great faith, expressed in prayer, is very powerful.

Jesus Is Challenged by the Religious Authorities (Matthew 21:23-45)

6. a. *What challenge does Jesus face from the chief priests and elders?*

   For three years, Jesus has been challenging the authority of the chief priests and elders, and they want to know who has given Jesus the authority to do the things he does. They want to know where his authority comes from.

   b. *How does Jesus handle their question?*

   Jesus turns the question back on them by asking them where John the Baptist's authority came from. (John declared Jesus to be the Lamb of God, and if John's own authority is from God, then Jesus' authority must be from God as well. But the leaders can neither confirm nor deny what Jesus says without getting into trouble. By claiming ignorance of the origin of John's baptism, they show themselves incapable of speaking with authority.

7. *Jesus tells the leaders two parables. Summarize the message behind the parable of the two sons in verses 28-32.*

   A father asks two sons to work in the vineyard. One son initially refuses, but then does the work; the other son initially says, "yes" but then does not do the work. The first son represents the outcasts of Jesus' day—such as the tax collectors and prostitutes—who believe John the Baptist's message and do the Father's will (and thus will enter the kingdom first). The second son represents the Jewish leaders who give "lip service" to John's message but do not obey (repent and believe) even after seeing the others do so.

8. *In the parable of the tenants in verses 33-41, the servants represent the Old Testament prophets, many of whom were killed. The son represents Christ, condemned by the religious leaders. The other tenants are the "outcast" Jews and the Gentiles.*

   a. *In verse 40, Jesus asks what the owner will do to the unfaithful tenants. How do the religious leaders respond?*

   They say the owner will get rid of the first tenants ("put those wretches to a miserable death") and rent it out to someone who will give him his share of the harvest.

   b. *Do the Pharisees understand the meaning behind the parable? Who is the parable directed to?*

   The Pharisees realize Jesus is referring to them: God will take the kingdom from them and give it to people who will produce fruit.

   c. *How do the Pharisees react to this, and what keeps them from overt action against Jesus?*

   The Pharisees are furious. They look for a way to arrest him but are afraid of the crowd, who believe Jesus is a prophet.

9. *What message is Jesus trying to send when he refers to* ***Psalm 118:22-23*** *(in* ***Matthew 21:42****)?*

   The religious leaders are rejecting the One who will become the cornerstone of the new kingdom. Jesus is reminding them that the Scriptures themselves have foretold that the cornerstone's rejection, but that it will stand strong. Jesus asks them: "Have you never read in the Scriptures: 'The very stone which the builders rejected has become the head of the corner; this was the Lord's doing and it is marvelous in our eyes'?" (Psalm 118:22-23).

D. Application

Facilitators: If time allows, have group members share their responses to the following application question.

The secret of true greatness lies in a life of self-donating love. Think about someone in your life you consider great. What attributes does this person exhibit that you might incorporate into your own life?

After the small-group discussion, watch Jeff Cavins' video presentation on *Session 19* – Matthew 20–21: Stepping Down into Greatness.

Facilitators: *Read these responses to the questions ahead of time to help you prepare to lead the small-group discussion.*

Participants: *Reinforce what you have learned by reviewing these responses after the small-group discussion and before you go on to the next session.*

A. Review the Context

Facilitators: Take a moment to review the context and what was learned in the previous session. If you like, use the following question to encourage discussion:

- *Why did announcing the advent of the new kingdom so often lead Jesus into clashes with the religious authorities?*

B. Read the Story

Facilitators: If there is time, have someone read each passage aloud before it is discussed.

C. Take a Deeper Look

Parable of the Wedding Banquet (Matthew 22:1-14)

1. *a.* *To what does Jesus compare the kingdom of God in this parable?*

Jesus compares the kingdom of God to a royal wedding banquet. The invited guests ignore the invitation and kill the messengers, so the king invites people off the street.

b. *In what way does this parable tell the story of salvation history?*

The banquet is the kingdom to which God calls us. He first invites his Chosen People (Israel), but many of them ignore him and refuse to come. They even kill his prophets. He then extends his invitation to others (the Gentiles) after destroying their city—an ending that alludes to the Exile and presages the destruction of Jerusalem in AD 70.

c. *What is the significance of the man without wedding clothes who is thrown outside? (See **Revelation 19:7-9.**)*

An invitation is not a guarantee. Our response and preparation are important, too. We cannot simply show up and demand entry. We must be prepared to enter as a full participant, clothed in the righteous deeds that grow from true faith.

Three Challenges (Matthew 22:15-40)

2. *a.* *What trap is laid for Jesus in verses 16-17, and how does he escape it?*

Flattering Jesus for teaching the truth regardless of others' opinions, the Pharisees ask him whether it is right to pay taxes to Caesar. This is a loaded question. If he answers, "Yes," the Pharisees will denounce him as disloyal to Israel. If he answers, "No," the Herodians will report him to the governor for treason. Seeing the trap, Jesus asks whose picture is on the coin, then says to give to God what is God's and to Caesar what is Caesar's. He thus avoids either repercussion.

b. *How do the Sadducees try to trick Jesus in verses 23-28? (For help with this, see* ***Deuteronomy 25:5-10.****)*

The Sadducees try to discredit Jesus' authority by throwing him a tricky doctrinal question meant to disprove the possibility of life after death. They refer to a Jewish law of the time that required a man whose brother died without leaving an heir to marry his widow and raise a family for the dead man. The Sadducees present Jesus with the example of a family of seven brothers, each of whom takes the same wife in turn. In the resurrection, they ask, whose wife will the woman be?

c. *How does Jesus answer them, and what does his answer reveal about their knowledge?*

Jesus' answer is twofold and demonstrates that the Sadducees know neither "the Scriptures nor the power of God." First, he says their question is irrelevant because there will be no marriage in heaven. Second, he addresses their disbelief in the resurrection by quoting from the Pentateuch (of which the Sadducees have expert knowledge). He reminds them that God told Moses in Exodus 3:6: "I am the God of Abraham, the God of Isaac, and the God of Jacob." God did not say, "I was," but, "I am." Jesus is pointing out to them that God himself referred to these biblical men as still having life even though they had experienced earthly death. This silences the Sadducees so completely that Matthew describes them as "muzzled" (this word is translated to "silenced" in verse 34).

3. *Jesus' reply to the ethical question posed in verse 36 pairs the familiar* shema *of Deuteronomy 6:4-8—"Hear, O Israel: The Lord our God is one Lord; and you shall love the Lord your God with all your heart, and with all your soul, and with all your might"—with a second law: Love your neighbor as yourself (Leviticus 19:18). What point is Jesus making by joining these laws and saying they are the greatest commandments?*

Love of God cannot be separated from love of others. God does not desire rote obedience. He is looking for goodness that springs from the heart. Jesus is not doing away with the other commandments; he is saying that if we love God and neighbor, we will fulfill the commandments as well. This is where the Pharisees fall short. They concentrate on the individual laws but forget the basic command from which the laws are derived. Jesus not only answers their question, he draws attention to the flaw in their position. Love—not trying to follow a list of rules perfectly—is the secret of true obedience to God and of right behavior toward others.

Jesus Silences the Opposition (Matthew 22:41-46)

4. a. *What question does Jesus ask that finally silences the Pharisees, and why does it have this effect on them? (****Think About It:*** *If the Messiah is not David's son, whose son is he?)*

The Pharisees are finally silenced when Jesus asks them whose Son the Christ is. As experts in the Law, they give the standard answer: He is the Son of David. Jesus asks them how it can be that "the Lord said unto my Lord 'sit at my right hand, until I put your enemies under your foot?'" If the Messiah is David's son, why does he call him "Lord?" There is only one answer: As man, he is David's son. As God, he is David's Lord. The Messiah is both man and God. He is both "the root and the offspring of David (Revelation 22:16). Psalm 110:1 teaches the deity and the humanity of the Messiah. Jesus is both Son of David and Son of God. This is his identity and explains the source of his authority.

b. *Why do they not answer him or dare to ask him any more questions?*

Unless they are willing to admit that the Messiah is also God's Son, they cannot answer the question. Jesus has demonstrated his authority and said its source is in God; he has exposed their inadequacy and lack of authority. They are afraid to face the truth. Luke 20:40 says, "They did not have the courage to question him any longer about anything."

5. ***Think About It (optional):*** *Why do the Pharisees not "get it"? Why do they fail to recognize Jesus for who he is? (For help with this question, read* ***John 7:15-19.****)*

The Pharisees know the words of the Law, but they do not understand its meaning because they do not act on it. They use the Law as a goal rather than as a light. If their own wills were in line with God's, they would not question the source of Jesus' authority, let alone seek to kill him.

Jesus Denounces the Scribes and Pharisees (Matthew 23:1-12)

6. a. *"That the scribes and the Pharisees sit in Moses' seat" is a metaphor for their teaching and ruling authority as successors of Moses. According to Jesus, what practical implications does this have for the people regarding their teaching?*

The people should obey the religious leaders' teaching, but they should not follow their actions. This is because the leaders do not practice what they preach. They have a false concept of righteousness, ministry, and greatness. They put heavy demands on others but are not willing to help move them. Everything they do is for show and honor.

b. *What do you think Jesus means when he instructs them not to call anyone "rabbi," "father," or "master"? How literally should we take this? (To see how literally the disciples took this instruction in the early Church, read one or more of the following:* ***Luke 16:24; Romans 4:12; Acts 7:1-2; 1 Corinthians 4:14-16;*** *and* ***Philemon 10.****)*

Jesus is warning them not to seek titles of honor or set any person in authority over Christ. If he meant for them to never call anyone "father" in a literal way, it is unlikely that we would find this word in the New Testament or in the early Church. But "father" is used in the New Testament to refer to natural fathers and to Abraham in Luke 16 and Romans 4. Stephen uses the word "father" in addressing the elders in Acts 7; and Paul refers to himself as a spiritual father in 1 Corinthians 4 and Philemon.

The "Seven Woes" (Matthew 23:13-32)

7. a. *Jesus calls the scribes and Pharisees "hypocrites" six times in these verses. Look up the definition of "hypocrisy." What does it mean?*

Hypocrites are those who pretend to be something they are not. For these people, virtues such as piety are merely a pretense with no purpose other than to enhance their reputations. In hypocrisy, there is "a gap between appearance and reality, between saying and doing, caused by a misplaced hierarchy of values and excessive emphasis on external matters to the neglect of the interior."[1]

b. *What other words and images does Jesus use when talking about the scribes and Pharisees? What do these say about the leaders?*

Jesus calls the scribes and Pharisees "[children] of hell," "blind guides," "blind fools," "blind men," "whitewashed tombs," "full of hypocrisy and iniquity," "sons of those who murdered the prophets," "serpents," and a "brood of vipers." The religious leaders do not see the truth. They look good on

1 *Sacra Pagina: The Gospel of Matthew.* Edited by Daniel J. Harrington, S.J. Collegeville, MN: The Liturgical Press, 1991, p. 326.

the outside but are corrupt inside. They fail at their job of leading and teaching. They are as guilty as those who murdered the prophets.

c. *How does Jesus illustrate the hypocrisy of the scribes and Pharisees in the following verses?*

Matthew 23:13-14: They have an authoritative teaching position, yet hinder the spread of the gospel and close the doors of the kingdom.

Matthew 23:15: Their proselytizing gains members for their own sect, "[children] of hell!" They convert people to a false sense of pride and security, not to salvation.

Matthew 23:16-22: They set up a system of swearing oaths to avoid using God's name. Some oaths are said to be less binding because the thing sworn by is of less "value"—thus making it possible for some oaths to be taken lightly. Jesus argues that any real oath demands the intention of the one swearing it to appeal to God and, therefore, must be taken seriously.

Matthew 23:23-24: They carry tithing to an extreme and forget the important matters of justice, mercy, and faithfulness.

Matthew 23:25-28: They follow the cleanliness laws so that their outward appearance is clean, but inside, they are greedy and self-indulgent. Their righteous appearance belies the wickedness inside them.

Matthew 23:29-36: They claim to revere the Old Testament prophets and say they would never treat them like their forefathers did—yet they kill John the Baptist and then Jesus. The way they later treat the disciples will be further proof against them.

Jesus' Final Curse and Lamentation Over Jerusalem (Matthew 23:33-39)

8. *What judgment does Jesus say will fall on the leaders, and when will it come?*

   Jesus says the Pharisees (who honor the dead prophets) will "kill and crucify" the prophets, wise men, and scribes he sends to them. As a result, all the righteous blood that has been shed on the earth will come upon them. Jesus says this will happen in "this generation."

9. *What is Jesus' attitude in this rebuke of Jerusalem's false shepherds? Is there any hope? (See also* ***CCC 558.****)*

   Even as he denounces them, Jesus longs for their restoration. He says he longs to gather them as a hen gathers her chicks under her wings—but they are not willing. God will not force his love or salvation on people. And he will not change the consequences of their stubborn rejection. But the destruction of the Temple (the desolation of their house) will not be the end of the story. "For I tell you, you will not see me again, until you say, 'Blessed is he who comes in the name of the Lord'" (verse 39). A day will come when they will see and recognize him.

D. Application

Facilitators: If time allows, have group members share their responses to the following application question.

Spend some time in prayer, and ask God to show you if there are areas in which you are hypocritical. Think about your relationships. Are you genuine? Ask the Lord to help you be true to who he created you to be.

After the small-group discussion, watch Jeff Cavins' video presentation on *Session 20* – Matthew 22–23: "Let's Get Real."

Session 21 Responses

Matthew 24–25 – Jesus Predicts the End of an Era

Facilitators: *Read these responses to the questions ahead of time to help you prepare to lead the small-group discussion.*

Participants: *Reinforce what you have learned by reviewing these responses after the small-group discussion and before you go on to the next session.*

A. Review the Context

Facilitators: Take a moment to review the context and what was learned in the previous session. If you like, use the following question to encourage discussion:

- *What do the "woes" Jesus pronounced on the scribes and Pharisees tell you about the heart of God?*

B. Read the Story

Facilitators: If there is time, have someone read each passage aloud before it is discussed.

C. Take a Deeper Look

Signs of the End of the Age (Matthew 24:1-35)

1. *The Jews saw the Temple as a microcosm of the world and an image of the universe in miniature. God met his people there; his presence filled the Holy of Holies and from there, spread out to the world. Read* ***Matthew 24:1-2,*** *and review* ***21:13 and 23:38.*** *If the Temple is God's house and the center of worship, why does Jesus condemn it?*

   The house of God has "become forsaken and desolate" (Matthew 23:38). It houses wicked leaders and has become a center for sin and rebellion. The Temple also represents the Old Covenant, in which God's presence is focused in an earthly place. It is now time for that which the earthly Temple has been a sign to replace it. God is now present in his Son and will be present after the coming of the Holy Spirit in the Church, which is the spiritual temple built from "living stones"—Christ's followers.

2. *The disciples respond to Jesus' prophecy of the destruction of the Temple with the question: "When will this happen, and what will be the sign of your coming and the end of the age?" (See* ***verse 3.****) Thus, the destruction of the Temple is the context for Jesus' reply, which equates it with his coming and the end of the age. Summarize the signs Jesus gives in verses 4-31.*

   There will be many signs of the coming of Jesus, signs that also will presage the destruction of the Temple. False messiahs and prophets will deceive many people. There will be wars, famine, and earthquakes, and the disciples will be persecuted and killed. There will be a great increase of wickedness and distress. The sun and the moon will be darkened, and stars will fall from the sky. The Temple will be desecrated. Finally, the sign of the "Son of Man" will be seen in the sky, and God will gather his elect.

3. a. *Notice how Isaiah and Ezekiel use apocalyptic imagery in the following passages, and record the historic events they describe.*

   Isaiah 13:1, 9-10, 13: Isaiah says that the stars, sun, and moon will be darkened and the earth and heavens will shake to punish Babylon for its evil. This is a symbolic prediction of the destruction of Babylon, not a description of something that will occur in the sky.

   Isaiah 14:4, 12: Here, the fall of Babylon is compared to the fall of the morning star.

   Ezekiel 32:1-2, 7-8: Ezekiel says that when God overthrows Egypt, he will darken the heavens. The sun, moon, and stars will all be dark. This describes the end of Egyptian rule figuratively and is especially appropriate language since the Egyptians looked to those heavenly bodies as gods to rule and guide them.

   b. *In light of this literary tradition, how should we interpret the apocalyptic imagery found in Matthew 24?*

   In traditional Jewish apocalyptic writing, God's intervention in world affairs (particularly when kingdoms were raised up or overthrown) was described with the imagery of cataclysmic, earth-shaking events. Rather than looking at these passages as literal descriptions of things that will happen in nature, the literary tradition suggests viewing them as foretelling the end of a nation, a ruling power, or an age. In the Old Testament, the prophets foretold the ends of the great world powers of Babylon and Egypt.

   In Matthew 24, Jesus is prophesying the end of the Old Covenant. Jerusalem and the Temple will be destroyed by Rome in AD 70. To the Jews of the time, the end of the Temple is the end of their world—the Old Covenant world. Jesus' prophecy points not just to events that will occur in history, but to events that will occur at the end of time. Jesus' earthly "coming" to Jerusalem and the destruction of the Temple are woven together in references to the future coming of the Son of Man at the end of the age and to the Last Judgment, when this world will be destroyed and replaced by the eternal dwelling place of God's heavenly kingdom. The literal (historical) meaning points to a future, more perfect fulfillment, which is the anagogical sense of the passage.

Be Watchful and Faithful (Matthew 24:36-51)

4. *Whether we are looking at the immediate or future fulfillment of these events, people commonly respond to apocalyptic messages by trying to determine the exact date on which the events will occur.*

   a. *Does Jesus intend for his followers to do this? How do you know?*

   No. In fact, he says that he will come when he is not expected. Only the Father (not even the angels or the Son) knows the time.

   b. *How does Jesus advise people to occupy themselves while they wait for his return?*

   Jesus says they should keep watch and be ready so they will be found doing what God wants them to do. Luke 21:34 uses similar language: "But take heed to yourselves lest your hearts be weighed down with dissipation and drunkenness and cares of this life, and that day come upon you suddenly like a snare." This is as true for the disciples who await the destruction that will befall Jerusalem as it is for us who await his coming in glory.

Two Parables (Matthew 25:1-30)

5. *The parable of the ten virgins reflects a Jewish custom in which the bridegroom brings his bride home at the head of a procession that ends with a weeklong celebratory banquet.*

   a. *Why are some of the bridesmaids in Jesus' story admitted while others are not?*

   The wise bridesmaids anticipate a delay and stock up on oil for their lamps. The foolish ones come unprepared and do not have lamps for the journey. When they finally arrive at the banquet, they are not recognized at the door and are not allowed to enter.

   b. *A wedding banquet often represents the wedding of Christ and the Church, when he will come to establish his kingdom in glory. What is the message of this parable?*

   Answers will vary. We must prepare for Jesus' return and be watchful in anticipation because the time of his coming will be unexpected. Notice that a general preparedness is required, not one that takes us away from necessary daily activity (such as sleeping). All the bridesmaids are asleep in the parable, but some are still ready.

6. a. *This parable is about the kingdom of heaven. Who do the people in this story represent?*

   The man in the parable represents God, and his servants represent us.

   b. *Why are the servants treated differently when the man returns?*

   They are rewarded in relation to the care they have taken to be good stewards of what their master has entrusted to them. Those who are faithful with the little he has given them are given much and are given a share in the master's joy. The servant who does nothing but bury his talent loses even what he has and is cast "into the outer darkness."

   c. *What does this teach us about the kingdom of God?*

   There are several levels of meaning to this parable. On the surface, it is about stewardship and sloth. This is also a story of a *Parousia:* A master is "coming" home from a journey and holding his servants accountable. Here, the "master" is Christ coming back and seeing which of his people have been faithful to his covenant. Those who have acted on their faith and allowed it to grow—who have been good stewards of the blessings God has given them—will enter into the joy of the Master. Those who fail to make use of the talents God has given them will lose them.

The Last Judgment (Matthew 25:31-46)

7. a. *When the Son of Man comes and sits on his throne in glory and gathers the nations before him, on what basis will he separate the "sheep" from the "goats," and what will be the destination of each group?*

   The King will separate the sheep from the goats on the basis of their care for those in need—and, therefore, their care for Christ in those others. The sheep will receive eternal life in the kingdom prepared for them since the creation of the world; the "goats" will go to punishment in the eternal fire prepared for the devil and his angels.

   b. *What do the people fail to understand in verses 37-39 and 44?*

   They do not understand that when Jesus says he was hungry, thirsty, or sick, he is referring to the needy in the world. The people have not seen Christ in these needy people and, as a result, have failed to reach out to them.

8. *What does this parable say about how we should live while we wait for Christ's return?*

    We should take care of others in need—see Christ in them and treat them accordingly.

D. Application

Facilitators: If time allows, have group members share their responses to the following application question.

What are some practical things you can do to prepare for Christ's return? Think about both the physical and spiritual aspects of preparedness.

E. Wrap-Up – Book Five: Announcement of the End of the Old Kingdom

Facilitators: If there is time, ask if anyone can summarize Book Five of Matthew's Gospel (Chapters 19–25). Answers will vary. The point is not to find a "correct" answer, but to explore the major points of the chapters. You might ask questions like:

- *How does Jesus go about announcing the end of the old kingdom?*
- *What is the reaction of the religious establishment?*
- *What kinds of signs does he say will accompany his second coming, and what do they mean?*

After the small-group discussion, watch Jeff Cavins' video presentation on *Session 21* – Matthew 24–25: Jesus Predicts the End of an Era.

Matthew 26 – The Trial of the Christ

Facilitators: *Read these responses to the questions ahead of time to help you prepare to lead the small-group discussion.*

Participants: *Reinforce what you have learned by reviewing these responses after the small-group discussion and before you go on to the next session.*

A. Establish the Context

Facilitators: Take a moment to review the material from the previous session and to establish the context of the "Conclusion" of Matthew's Gospel. If you like, use the following question to encourage discussion:

- *What is the most important thing to you of all you have learned about Jesus' coming?*

B. Read the Story

Facilitators: If there is time, have someone read each passage aloud before it is discussed.

C. Take a Deeper Look

Plan or Plot? (Matthew 26:1-5)

1. *When Jesus tells his disciples that the time is near for his crucifixion, he links it to an important event in Israel's history and ongoing tradition: the Passover. What is the Passover? (See* ***Exodus 12*** *for help with this question.)*

   The Passover is part of a weeklong celebration that includes the Feast of Unleavened Bread and the Feast of the First Fruits. It is a memorial of God's deliverance of Israel from Egyptian bondage, and its central theme is liberation. In Jesus' time, all Jews traveled to Jerusalem to celebrate the Passover, which began on the fourteenth day of the month of Abib (Canaanite name) or Nisan (Babylonian name) and marks the beginning of the Jewish religious calendar.

2. *Jesus says he will be crucified at Passover. In spite of the Jewish leaders' determination not to crucify Jesus during the feast, that is exactly what they do. What does this suggest about Jesus' death?*

   Jesus teaches that he must be crucified during Passover. The leaders do not want his crucifixion to occur during the feast. There is a mysterious connection between God's plan and our free will and actions. God does not force the Jews to kill his Son during the Passover. Yet, in spite of their determination not to do this, it is exactly what they do. This all takes place according to God's divine plan. There is a purpose behind everything.

Anointing and Betrayal (Matthew 26:6-16)

3. *Why do you think Matthew includes the story of the woman anointing Jesus with expensive ointment at the start of his Passion narrative?*

   The woman is preparing Jesus for burial. Juxtaposed between the leaders' plotting and Judas' betrayal, this anointing highlights Jesus' true worth. Judas will give Jesus up for thirty pieces of silver, but what Jesus will give up for all of mankind is priceless.

4. *Compare the price of the ointment "wasted" on Jesus with the price the priests place on his head. (For purposes of comparison, note that the owner of a slain slave was reimbursed thirty shekels of silver in Exodus 21:32.) What does this say about Judas and about the woman?*

   The fact that she lavishes "a very expensive ointment" on Jesus shows her understanding of his worth; Judas is more interested in personal gain than in Jesus' worth. He does not think Jesus is worth more than a slave.

The True Passover Lamb (Matthew 26:17-29)

5. a. *When the time comes during the Passover meal for the disciples to eat the lamb, what does Jesus ask them to eat instead? What is he doing?*

   It is interesting that at no time during any description of the Last Supper is there mention of a lamb. Jesus asks them to eat bread (presumably the unleavened bread of the meal), which he identifies as his Body. Jesus is substituting himself for the lamb. He is the Lamb of God who takes away the sins of the world, who dies so others might live. Do they know what he is doing? Perhaps the words he spoke after feeding the multitudes still ring in their ears:

   > "I am the living bread which came down from heaven; if any one eats of this bread, he will live for ever; and the bread which I shall give for the life of the world is my flesh." The Jews then disputed among themselves, saying, "How can this man give us his flesh to eat?" So Jesus said to them, "Truly, truly, I say to you, unless you eat the flesh of the Son of man and drink his blood, you have no life in you; he who eats my flesh and drinks my blood has eternal life, and I will raise him up at the last day. For my flesh is food indeed, and my blood is drink indeed. He who eats my flesh and drinks my blood abides in me, and I in him" (John 6:51-56).

   Now, Jesus is not only telling them that eating his flesh and drinking his blood will bring life, he is also giving them a context for this: the Passover meal.

   b. *Explain how you know Jesus is the Passover Lamb the other lambs only pointed to. (For help with this question, read **Exodus 12** and **1 Peter 1:18-19.**)*

   The Passover lamb was an unblemished lamb that was killed and eaten. Its blood spared God's people the death of their firstborn sons, and by it, they were "ransomed" from Egyptian bondage. This prefigures the way Christ's precious Blood will ransom people from bondage to sin.

   c. *In Exodus 24, the blood of the covenant was splashed on the altar and on the people to seal Israel in a family relationship with God. What does Jesus mean when he says, "For this is my blood of the covenant, which is poured out for many for the forgiveness of sins"? (See **verse 28** and **CCC 610, 613–614.**)*

   Jesus is inaugurating the New Covenant. Under the Old Covenant, redemption was obtained in a provisional way by the killing of lambs. Under the New Covenant, only one sacrifice is required: that of Jesus Christ. Mankind will be restored to God's family by Jesus' blood.

Prayer in the Garden (Matthew 26:30-46)

6. *What does Jesus' prayer in Gethsemane teach us about how and why to pray when we are in difficult circumstances?*

    Jesus' prayer in Gethsemane teaches us to pray persistently and not for our own will to be done, but for God's will to be done. It also tells us that we should pray in difficult circumstances because, in prayer, our will can be conformed to the will of the Father. This will give us the strength to obey, even to death.

Betrayal and Arrest (Matthew 26:47-56)

7. *In the garden, Jesus is faced by an angry crowd of armed men. Who is in control of the situation, and how do you know?*

    Jesus is in control. He knows when they are coming and rises to meet them. He is not afraid. He rebukes his disciples for using force and fighting back. He reminds them that everything is happening to fulfill prophecy.

8. a. *The picture Matthew paints is one of Jesus walking deliberately toward the crucifixion. Because he is God's Son, it would be a small matter to get rid of his enemies and avoid capture. What does he do instead? Read also **CCC 612.***

    Jesus is "obedient unto death," saying, "Nevertheless, not as I will, but as you will" (26:39). Although Jesus does not want to suffer, he willingly accepts suffering from God's hand because of what it will accomplish for us.

   b. *What does this suggest about the role of the betrayal of Jesus in God's plan?*

    The betrayal of Jesus, along with his trial, suffering, and crucifixion, are all part of God's plan and are necessary to it.

Trial and Denial (Matthew 26:57-75)

9. *What charges are brought against Jesus, and how does he answer them?*

    He gives no answer to the first charge—that he has said he could destroy God's Temple and rebuild it in three days. In answering the second charge, which is given under oath ("tell us if you are the Christ, the Son of God"), he says, "You have said so." This may sound ambiguous, but when he says, "Hereafter you will see the Son of man seated at the right hand of Power, and coming on the clouds of heaven," there is no question that he is claiming to be the Messiah.

10. a. *Jesus takes his answer from **Psalm 110:1** and **Daniel 7:1-18.** Read these passages. Who do the beasts represent in Daniel's vision?*

    The beasts are four Gentile kingdoms that wage war on the Jewish people: the neo-Babylonian empire, the Medo-Persians, Greece, and Rome.

    b. *What happens to the Son of Man in those verses, and who is defeated when he appears?*

The Son of Man comes with the clouds of heaven, is led into God's presence, and is given authority, glory, and sovereign power. The beasts are defeated. All people, nations, and men worship him, and his kingdom and dominion are everlasting.

11. *In light of this background, what is Jesus saying about himself—and about his accusers—when he claims to be the Son of Man that evokes their immediate condemnation?*

    Jesus claims to be the victorious Son of Man enthroned at the right hand of God in heaven. This is a greatness above that of the high priest, who is the only one permitted to enter the Holy of Holies (and then only once a year). Jesus is equating his detractors with the beasts who defy God's will and who will be defeated. They are like Gentile monsters that oppress God's people. By inference, they become the real enemies of the Jews because they are opposing the one God has sent to free his people.

12. *How does Peter fulfill the prediction Jesus makes in verse 34?*

    Peter denies knowing Jesus three times, including to a servant girl and to the crowd. The third time, he calls down curses on himself for emphasis. When the cock crows, he remembers Jesus' words and goes out and weaps bitterly.

D. Application

Facilitators: If time allows, have group members share their responses to the following application questions.

Have you ever denied knowing Jesus? Have you fallen asleep rather than waiting with him hidden in someone else? Do you feel your own suffering is too great for you to help bear the suffering of another person? Using Jesus' suffering as the model, how should you proceed in your own ordeal?

After the small-group discussion, watch Jeff Cavins' video presentation on *Session 22* – Matthew 26: The Trial of Christ.

Matthew 27 – The Passion of the King

Facilitators: *Read these responses to the questions ahead of time to help you prepare to lead the small-group discussion.*

Participants: *Reinforce what you have learned by reviewing these responses after the small-group discussion and before you go on to the next session.*

A. Review the Context

Facilitators: Take a moment to review the context and what was learned in the previous session. If you like, use the following question to encourage discussion:

- *How does Jesus' anointing set the stage for the rest of the Passion?*

B. Read the Story

Facilitators: If there is time, have someone read each passage aloud before it is discussed.

C. Take a Deeper Look

Judas Hangs Himself (Matthew 27:1-10)

1. a. *Compare Judas' remorse in verse 4 over his sin of "betraying innocent blood" with Peter's bitter sadness in* ***Matthew 26:75.*** *How do they differ?*

   Peter repents and is restored to a right relationship with God. Judas does not believe God's power to save him is greater than his own sin. His remorse leads to despair (instead of repentance), and he kills himself.

   b. *Read* ***CCC 1430–1431.*** *Would you say Judas experiences true repentance? Why, or why not?*

   Judas seems sorry, but not repentant. True repentance is a sorrow for sin that leads to a change of mind and action, a "turning around." Judas experiences a remorse that leads to despair. The *Catechism* says that repentance "entails the desire and resolution to change one's life, with hope in God's mercy and trust in the help of his grace" (CCC 1431). Judas displays no such hope. Distressed and remorseful, he makes the only kind of amends he knows how: He returns the money and then takes his fate into his own hands and kills himself.

2. ***Think About It:*** *Matthew says Jeremiah's prophecy is fulfilled in the purchase of the potter's field with the thirty pieces of silver. Similar images are found in both the books of Jeremiah and Zechariah.* ***Optional:*** *Read* ***Jeremiah 18 and 19; Zechariah 11:12-13;*** *and* ***Jeremiah 32–33.*** *What insights do these passages provide into the wider meaning of Judas' betrayal of Jesus, his death, and the purchase of the potter's field?*

   These Old Testament passages show God judging his people for breaking their covenant with him and then promising to establish a new, everlasting covenant with them. In light of them, Judas' betrayal of Jesus mirrors the people's betrayal of God by going after false gods and who have become stiff-necked and brittle like hard-baked clay pots. Judas' death even reflects the smashing of the clay pots. (See Acts 1:18, which says of Judas that "falling headlong he burst open in the middle and all his bowels gushed out.") But there also is hope. The fact that the potter's field is purchased with thirty pieces of silver suggests that Christ's death, the object of Judas' betrayal and the price for mankind's sin, has purchased a new field (like Jeremiah's field), making a New Covenant and the restoration of humanity to God possible.

Jesus Before Pilate (Matthew 27:11-26)

3. a. *Why does Pilate decide to offer the crowd Barabbas in Jesus' place?*

   Pilate is not convinced of the charge against Jesus. Jesus has done no evil. The crowd has no evidence against him, and Pilate knows they have delivered him up out of envy. He also receives a divine warning in a dream sent to his wife. He seems to expect that when given a choice between an innocent man and a notorious prisoner deserving of death, the crowd will free Jesus.

   b. *Read John's account of this trial in* ***John 19:1-22.*** *What is behind Pilate's final decision? Does he believe in it?*

   Pilate finally condemns Jesus because of the crowd's insinuation that if he does not do so, he will be seen as opposing Caesar (because Jesus has said he is King). Pilate himself does not find Jesus guilty. Pilate has a placard with "King of the Jews" written on it because Jesus' enemies have given him that title.

4. *Barabbas is a "notorious prisoner," guilty of insurrection and murder. He is possibly one of the Zealots, a group of Jews who seek to change Israel's fortunes by political rebellion and force. What does the crowd's choice to spare Barabbas over Jesus say about their understanding of God's way of accomplishing things? What are they really choosing?*

   By choosing Barabbas, the crowd shows they want salvation by military victory. They want revolutionary violence instead of mercy and forgiveness. They want the restoration of earthly rule, not the internal salvation and heavenly kingdom God offers. They want the Romans put down, not everyone else lifted up.

5. *In verse 25, the crowd cries, "His blood be on us and on our children!" Some people have interpreted that to mean that all Jews are cursed as a result. What does the Church have to say about this? Are the Jews as a people responsible for the crucifixion of Christ? Why, or why not? (See* ***CCC 597–598.****)*

   The *Catechism* states unequivocally that, "Jews are not collectively responsible for Jesus' death." Not only can we not lay responsibility for Jesus' death on the Jews in Jerusalem who called for his death (God alone knows the responsibility of the individuals involved), "still less can we extend responsibility to other Jews of different times and places, based merely on the crowd's cry: 'His blood be on us and on our children!' a formula for ratifying a judicial sentence" (CCC 597; Matthew 27:25; Acts 5:28; 18:6). The Church holds that all sinners are responsible for Christ's suffering and death.

The Death of the King (Matthew 27:27-56)

6. ***Think About It:*** *Jesus' passion should be seen in light of the curse that resulted from mankind's original sin, which Jesus has come to set right (see* ***Genesis 3:14-24****). Now read* ***1 Corinthians 15:45,*** *where Paul calls Jesus "the last Adam." What elements of the curse do you see reflected in Jesus' ordeal or redeemed by him?*

   This is the ultimate battle between the seed of the woman and the seed of the Serpent. Once again, it takes place in a garden and pits the "last Adam" against Satan himself. Jesus takes God's curse on mankind upon himself. The sweat is there in the drops of blood on Jesus' brow. The thorns appear again but have become his crown. There are also contrasting elements: Jesus is raised onto a tree and becomes the new fruit of the tree of life, once again accessible to humanity. And although he will die and be buried, as will all descendants of Adam, he will conquer death and be raised in newness of life. "Thus it is written, 'The first man Adam became a living being'; the last Adam became a life-giving spirit" (1 Corinthians 15:45). Jesus also takes onto himself the curses of the broken covenant. By doing this and by dying, he frees Israel from the Old Covenant so it will be free to enter into the New Covenant in his Blood.

7. ***Think About It:** Jesus' final words on the Cross are,* Eli, Eli, lama sabachthani?*—or, "My God, my God, why hast thou forsaken me?" (verse 46). To anyone familiar with the psalms, this should immediately bring to mind Psalm 22, which begins with the same line. Jesus could quote another psalm; there are many with similar sentiments. Why do you think he chooses this particular verse? Is he simply crying out in loss, or is there more in his cry?*

   If I said to you, "Fourscore and seven years ago," you would immediately think of Abraham Lincoln's great speech. Similarly, anyone familiar with the Old Testament would hear the first line of Psalm 22 and be struck with the full weight of a psalm that begins as the anguished prayer of a godly sufferer but ends in a torrent of praise and the confidence that God will ultimately vindicate him. It declares: "All the ends of the earth shall remember and turn to the LORD; and all the families of the nations shall worship before him. For dominion belongs to the LORD, and he rules over the nations" (verses 27-28). In this psalm, an innocent sufferer proclaims God's greatness, dominion, and rule over the nations. In the light of Christ, God's dominion and rule comes through the suffering of the innocent one. Surely, Christ experienced the depths of humiliation in his agony. Yet, he did not succumb to despair. In the very words that seem to cry out that God has abandoned him, are hidden the certainty that God is in control and will overcome his enemies.

8. a. *Review **Matthew 27:51-54.** What do you think is the significance of these events? Read also **Hebrews 10:19-22 and 12:18, 21-24, 28.***

   The curtain in the Temple separated the Holy of Holies (the Ark of the Covenant) from the Holy Place. The high priest was the only person permitted to enter the Holy of Holies, and even he could enter only once a year on the Day of Atonement to make a blood sacrifice in atonement for his sins and the sins of the people. This physical separation symbolized the separation between God and man caused by sin. The tearing of the curtain from top to bottom at the moment of Jesus' death, signifies the transition from the Old Covenant to the New Covenant, which will not require blood sacrifices. The earthquake signifies the momentous nature of the death of Jesus, the Son of God.

   These events echo the events that accompanied the establishment of the Mosaic covenant on Mount Sinai and provide a fitting close to the Old Covenant. In Hebrews 12, St. Paul says, "We are receiving a kingdom that cannot be shaken." He is referring to the kingdom announced by John the Baptist and inaugurated by Jesus Christ: the kingdom of heaven. The opening of the tombs and raising of the saints illustrate that Christ has conquered death. This anticipates the resurrection to new life that Christ's resurrection makes possible for all.

   b. *Of what do these signs convince the centurion and those who are with him?*

   These signs convince them that Jesus is truly the Son of God.

The Burial of the King (Matthew 27:57-66)

9. *What precautions are taken in sealing Jesus' tomb, and why?*

   Jesus' tomb is sealed with a large stone. Once the seal is placed, a guard of soldiers is posted so the disciples will not be able to steal the body and make it appear that Christ has risen.

D. Application

Facilitators: If time allows, have group members share their responses to the following application questions.

Matthew 27 ends with what appears to be the end of all the hopes and dreams of Jesus' followers. Have you ever felt the crushing impossibility of circumstance? Have you felt that God has abandoned you or that hope is dead and lying in a sealed and guarded tomb? What have you learned in this session that can help you avoid despair?

After the small-group discussion, watch Jeff Cavins' video presentation on *Session 23* – Matthew 27: The Passion of the King.

Session 24 – Responses

Matthew 28 and Conclusion – The Triumph of the King

The King and His Kingdom

Facilitators: *Read these responses to the questions ahead of time to help you prepare to lead the small-group discussion.*

Participants: *Reinforce what you have learned by reviewing these responses after the small-group discussion.*

A. Review the Context

Facilitators: Take a moment to review the context and what was learned in the previous session. If you like, use the following question to encourage discussion:

- *Of all that Jesus suffered in his passion, what means the most to you?*

B. Read the Story

Facilitators: If there is time, have someone read each passage aloud before it is discussed.

C. Take a Deeper Look

The Resurrection (Matthew 28:1-15)

1. a. *Compare the reaction of the women to the news of Jesus' resurrection with the reaction of the guards.*

   The women hurry away "with fear and great joy" to tell the disciples, while the guards are so afraid, they "became like dead men."

   b. *Why do you think these two groups react in different ways to their fear?*

   The women believe Jesus is the Son of God, but the guards do not. The guards are afraid of getting into trouble for failing at their post, while the women's love and longing override their fear.

2. *Read* ***CCC 2174–2176.***

   a. *What is the significance of Jesus rising on the dawn of the first day of the week after the Sabbath?*

   The "first day of the week" recalls Creation; as the "eighth day" (or "second first day"), it symbolizes a new creation through Christ's resurrection.

   b. *What is the difference between the Jewish Sabbath and the Christian Sunday?*

   The Christian celebration of the Lord's Day on Sunday replaces the Jewish Sabbath observance and fulfils the truths it pointed to. At the same time, it fulfills the obligation to worship and celebrate God, our Creator and Redeemer. The Sabbath rest the people looked forward to in the Old Covenant is announced in the New Covenant. As St. Ignatius of Antioch wrote, "Those who lived according to the old order of things have come to a new hope, no longer keeping the Sabbath, but the Lord's Day, in which our life is blessed by him and by his death" (CCC 2175).[1]

3. a. *The elders bribe the guards to lie and say the disciples have stolen Jesus' body. Is this lie convincing? Why, or why not?*

   The lie is not convincing. It is clearly a reaction to unwelcome news. They have to pay the soldiers and promise to keep them out of trouble with the authorities, who have put them on watch to prevent this from happening.

   b. *What are the religious leaders afraid of that prompts them to spread this story?*

   The leaders are afraid of the truth. They are afraid the empty tomb will result in people believing Jesus has risen.

4. a. *Read St. Paul's reflections on Jesus' resurrection in* ***1 Corinthians 15:12-24.*** *Why is it so important for Jesus to be raised from the dead?*

   By rising from the dead, Jesus defeats death and the curse that has plagued mankind since the Fall. Our eventual resurrection depends on the fact that Jesus has been raised first. It is because of his resurrection that we, too, can live forever. If he has not been raised, our faith is in vain. Christ's resurrection is the necessary precursor to the end of this world and his reign over God's kingdom.

   b. *Read* ***CCC 651–655.*** *What does this add to your understanding of the significance of the Resurrection?*

   Answers will vary; encourage discussion. Apart from the fact that the Resurrection is the chief supporting evidence for Christ's divinity, all the Old Testament promises and Jesus' teachings come together and are fulfilled in it. It is here that death is conquered and new life is opened to believers. It is by dying to ourselves and rising again with him that we are born as children into God's kingdom and share in the life of Christ. It is through resurrection to new life in him that we are able to keep his commands and carry out his mission.

The "Great Commission" (Matthew 28:16-20)

5. *Jesus instructs the women to send the disciples to Galilee where they will see him for themselves, and it is there that he appears to the disciples to give them the instructions that are often called "the Great Commission" (verses 16-20). On the map on page 4, note the relationship of Galilee to Jerusalem. Why would Jesus call his disciples to this particular location to see him and hear these important instructions?*

   Once again, this is a reminder that Jesus has not come only for the Jews, but for all people. By telling his own disciples in this place to reach out and make disciples of all nations, he brings particular emphasis to this fact. He has come to restore all people who have been exiled from God's grace by sin. Launching his public ministry from Galilee, the area from which the first Israelites were exiled, is one way to highlight this aspect of his mission.

6. a. *List the things Jesus tells the disciples to "go therefore" and do.*

   Jesus tells them to make disciples of all nations, to baptize them in the name of the Father and of the Son and of the Holy Spirit, and to teach them to observe all he has commanded.

[1] *Ad Magn.* 9,1:SCh 10, 88.

b. *Why does Jesus tell them to do this? Read also* **Daniel 7:14.** *Do you see a connection?*

Jesus' command to make disciples of all nations echoes Daniel's vision of the Son of Man to whom "was given dominion and glory and kingdom, that all peoples, nations, and languages should serve him" (Daniel 7:14). The unity of peoples in the kingdom of God is founded on the universal authority of Christ in heaven and on earth made possible through his death and resurrection. Jesus has everlasting, worldwide dominion over the earth. His charge to his disciples is to go out and spread the gospel, to incorporate others into the family of God, and to teach them to live as citizens of the kingdom of heaven.

7. ***Think About It:*** *The* Catechism *says: "Missionary endeavor requires* patience. *It begins with the proclamation of the Gospel to peoples and groups who do not yet believe in Christ, continues with the establishment of Christian communities that are 'a sign of God's presence in the world,' and leads to the foundation of local churches" (CCC 854).*[2] *How can you help your Christian community be "a sign of God's presence in the world"?*

Answers will vary. Encourage discussion about what churches and individuals can do to be signs of God's presence in the world.

8. a. *What comforting promise does Jesus leave with his disciples, and why do they need it?*

Jesus' parting words are, "I am with you always, to the close of the age" (verse 20). Because the disciples have a hard road ahead of them and because Jesus will not be with them physically, they need reassurance of his continued presence. His real presence in the Eucharist, along with the abiding presence of the Holy Spirit, will enable them to follow Jesus and exercise the authority they have received from him.

b. *What name of Jesus (a name that Matthew emphasizes in Chapter 1) are these words a reminder of?*

"I am with you always, to the close of the age" harkens back to Jesus' name, Emmanuel, which means, "God with us." In the Holy Spirit, God is with us.

c. *What does this name mean to you today?*

Answers may include such words as "comfort," "peace," "assurance," and "strength." God is with us in the Holy Spirit, in his Word, and in the Eucharist. Encourage discussion.

D. Application

Facilitators: If time allows, have group members share their responses to the following application question.

Jesus' resurrection is evidence that we can trust our heavenly Father even if it means we will suffer and die. How does Christ's resurrection change the way you will face hardship in the future?

[2] Cf. *Redemptoris Missio* 42-47; *Ad Gentes* 15 § 1; Cf. *Redemptoris Missio* 48-49.

E. Wrap-Up – Conclusion: Victory of the King

Facilitators: If there is time, ask if anyone can summarize the "Conclusion" of Matthew's Gospel (Chapters 26–28). Answers will vary. The point is not to find a "correct" answer, but to explore the major points of the chapters. You might ask questions like:

- *Is Jesus the long-awaited Messiah?*
- *How do you know?*
- *What did his death accomplish?*
- *What is so important about his resurrection?*

After the small-group discussion, watch Jeff Cavins' video presentation on *Session 24* – Matthew 28 and Conclusion: The Triumph of the King.

F. Review

Facilitators: If there is time, have participants share their responses to the following review questions after the video presentation.

- *What did you learn about Jesus?*
- *What did you learn about the kingdom of heaven?*
- *Which parables and teachings of Jesus' made a particularly strong impression on you?*
- *Did any of the sessions hit home, minister to you, or stand out?*
- *Have any of your thoughts, attitudes, or behavior changed?*
- *Review the prayers you wrote in response to the application questions at the end of each session. Were there any instances where you decided to make a change in your life? How can you continue to apply what you learned in this study during the coming weeks and months?*

Then …
Dive into Scripture with
The Great Adventure Foundational Series

Step 1
The Bible Timeline*: *The Story of Salvation

Step 2
Matthew*: *The King and His Kingdom

Step 3
Acts*: *The Spread of the Kingdom

Continue the Journey

Ephesians

Exodus

Psalms

The Prophets

First Corinthians

Galatians

James

Revelation

Wisdom

Follow Me

The Mass

Life Application